C000240689

My idea for this book is to combine a critical evaluation of a famous work of art with some art history in the thin guise of fiction.

I have had a lifelong love affair and fascination with *The Arnolfini Marriage* by Jan van Eyck in The National Gallery. I have done an enormous amount of research over the course of my life, read innumerable books and articles on the subject of Van Eyck in particular and Flemish art in general, as well as attending seminars at The National Gallery. I have lectured to local art societies on the subject and to the Summer School at Marlborough College.

The Arnolfini Marriage is a picture which becomes more fascinating and enigmatic the more one studies it. I have tried in my book to convey the curiosity and excitement that I feel whenever I encounter it. I believe that my book will be of equal interest to the informed art historian and to the casual visitor to The National Gallery who knows little about art.

ARNOLFINI

—

REFLECTIONS
IN A MIRROR

Jack Thomas

Arnolfini

—

Reflections
in a Mirror

Vanguard Press

A CIP catalogue record for this title is
available from the British Library
ISBN 1 843860 85 6

*Vanguard Press is an imprint of
Pegasus Elliot MacKenzie Publishers Ltd.*
www.pegasuspublishers.com

First Published in 2004

**Vanguard Press
Sheraton House Castle Park
Cambridge England**

Printed & Bound in Great Britain

Dedication

TO MY WIFE

IMOGEN

ACKNOWLEDGMENTS

My thanks are due to Mr Graham Hall for stopping me from wasting my time on Axe Cliff golf course by giving me two new hips and the recuperative and convalescent time to write this book; to Gerald Gosling for obtaining a map of Bruges; to Mary Kingsley for her research at the National Gallery; to Susan Jones, Assistant Curator of the National Gallery, for providing research on the mirror; to Neil MacGregor, Director of the National Gallery, for encouragement; to Jennifer Johnston for her lovely Irish enthusiasm and professional advice; to Molly Matthews for some invaluable help on matters mediaeval; to A.L.Kennedy for advice; to Barbara Ackermann for transatlantic good sense; to the Arvon Centre at Totleigh Barton in North Devon for giving me a loose excuse for calling myself a writer; to Major-General James Hay who purchased the Arnolfini picture for the nation after the battle of Waterloo; and to my wife, Imogen, for unstinting and loving encouragement, endless patience and impeccable judgment.

FOREWORD

This book has no pretensions to art criticism; it is a work of fiction. It is true that I explore many facets of the Arnolfini Wedding picture and put forward ideas. Some of my theories may be taken seriously; others are mere clay pigeons for the reader to shout 'poule' and to fire at.

For most of my life I have been obsessed with and admired the paintings of Jan van Eyck in general and the Arnolfini Wedding picture in particular. Now that it is magnificently displayed in the splendid Sainsbury wing, it is quite rightly one of the stars of the National Gallery. Visitor after visitor is attracted by this riveting picture and held by its magnetic properties.

The painting seems to pose so many fascinating problems. Why are two people standing in a bedroom with a dog at their feet? Why is Arnolfini looking so solemn? Why is he wearing his hat indoors? Is she pregnant? Why are the couple not wearing shoes? What is going on in the mirror? Who are the two men reflected in the doorway? What has happened? What is happening? What will happen? Why is the floor not tiled? Where do you get oranges in mediaeval Flanders? These and many other problems confront the intelligent and perceptive onlooker.

I have noticed that when a film or novel carries a disclaimer that all the characters are fictitious and bear no resemblance to any living persons, the characters always seem to bear an uncanny and suspicious resemblance to living persons. Nevertheless, I must here solemnly affirm that none of the characters portrayed in the twentieth century portion of this book is based on any living character.

If any of the historical persons from the 15th century portrayed in this book feel aggrieved and wish to sue me from the grave for defamation of character, I would feel both honoured and fascinated to find myself in the dock, facing them. I would welcome their resurrection.

For the officers and members of NADFAS at Beaminster, wherever that is, whose meetings I may have attended with enjoyment and cultural enlightenment, I have nothing but respect. Let none of them imagine for one moment that I have been lampooning them. The NADFAS section in the book is the stuff of Feydeau farce; their concern which I respect and applaud is with serious culture.

So is mine.

CONTENTS

For, don't you mark, we're made so that we love
   First when we see them painted, things we have passed
Perhaps a hundred times nor cared to see;
And so they are better, painted – better to us,
Which is the same thing. Art was given for that –
God uses us to help each other so,
Lending our minds out.
from Fra Lippo Lippi

ROBERT BROWNING

If circumstances lead me, I will find
   Where truth is hid, though it were hid indeed
Within the Centre.
from Hamlet

WILLIAM SHAKESPEARE

On a huge hill
   Cragged, and steep, Truth stands, and he that will
Reach her, about must, and about must goe;
And what the hills suddenes resists, winne so.
from Satyre: Of religion

JOHN DONNE

Chapter 1

20th July, 1434

For more than an hour we have been preparing the room. First the light. Always the light comes first. If you cannot paint light, you cannot paint.

So I tell Pieter to open all the shutters. There are twelve in all, six on each window. The twelve apostles! If I also have the door behind us open, that will give even more light. In this dark corner of Flanders, we shall need all the light we can get.

Pieter has finished.

"Now I want one shutter half closed, Pieter. That one."

I point imperiously.

"Why, Master?"

"Just do as I tell you."

By the way he does it, I can tell he is sulking. His mood will change. He is mercurial in temperament.

"Good. Now put two apples on the window sill. No, make it one."

"Like that?"

"A little further left. More. Stop. Good."

I pause and consider.

"Now I want five oranges on this end of the chest. There."

The oranges are placed.

"Give the floor a good sweep. It looks filthy."

"But, Master, it cannot be dirty. I swept it yesterday."

"Pieter!"

The peremptory tone of my voice is enough to frighten him. With short, lithe strokes of his besom, Pieter sweeps the floor and collects the dirt.

"Has Father Nicholas blessed the water?"

"Yes, Master, it is here."

"Very well, take the aspergillum and sprinkle the floor."

Pieter does so.

"Now unfold that Anatolian carpet and place it on the floor. By the bed."

Pieter is amazed.

"On the floor, Master? Surely it should hang on the wall!"

"Pieter!"

The carpet is carefully arranged by the bed.

"Now draw the curtains back around the bed and fold them up into swathes. Like this."

I show him how. Pieter is quick with his hands. When he grinds my paints, he always makes a good job of it.

"Yes, that is perfect. Now polish the mirror."

Out comes the chamois.

"Careful now. I don't want you to touch the little rondels around the edge."

The mirror is unique, hand-crafted for me by a Bruges craftsman.

"Good, now before you move the prie-dieu back, hang this set of glass beads on that nail. That one, left of the mirror. There! Yes, that's it. No, too symmetrical. I want thirteen beads on the left, sixteen on the right."

I know that Pieter does not know what 'symmetrical' means. Nor can he differentiate between his left and right hand. But a wave of my hand starts him in the right direction.

Pieter looks as if he wants to ask me why I want the beads arranged thus but my glance forbids it. He does as he is told and then replaces the prie-dieu in front of the mirror. The red cloth is slightly wrinkled. I leave it like that. It seems to give the impression of having been knelt on recently. I like that. Always I strive to suggest in my paintings that a room is lived in, that real people inhabit space.

We are nearly ready. The great bell of St. Donatian's chimes the three-quarter hour. They will be here at noon.

"Have you dusted the chandelier, Pieter?"

"Oh yes, Master, I gave it an extra special polish."

I examine it critically. It passes muster. The cold northern light of Bruges reflects off it. It gleams and glistens. At its base the head of a lion with a ring through his nose seems to wink at me.

"What shall I do with the duster, Master?"

He is a good lad and thinks of details I might otherwise have forgotten or overlooked.

"Hang it beside the bed. There! Next to St. Margaret and her dragon. Go on, he won't eat you. Good. That casts a nice shadow."

I give the room another critical look. Using my hands as a masking frame, I try to envisage the finished picture. Everything in front of me will be visible, even when the couple are standing there.

I point all this out to Pieter who has never ever looked in a mirror or seen his reflection.

"You see, Pieter, the mirror is what men of science call convex. It curves outwards."

Pieter looks puzzled. I make a gesture.

"Like the Blessed Virgin Mary, when she is great with child. It will reflect all those parts of the room which will be blocked by the standing couple. Do you see? The rest of the chest, the second window, that one there, the back of the bed, part of the ceiling, even the door will all be shown in the mirror. The mirror cannot lie. It will reveal all."

Pieter half understands what I have been saying and gives me half a smile, sufficient to show the gaping gaps in his teeth.

Pity! For a lad of eighteen, he is otherwise not bad-looking.

St. Donatian's starts to toll the hour.

"One last thing, Pieter – when I tell you, get a ladder and place one candle in the chandelier. Just the one. In the first bracket on the left, there!"

I point.

"Then light it."

"Yes, Master, and shall I…"

But what he was going to say we shall never know.

At that moment, there is a heavy knocking at the front door. When Pieter opens it, two people come into the room. They start to remove their shoes.

Oh, I nearly forgot. There is also a dog.

21

Chapter 2

May, 1942

The white page stared reproachfully up at him. John gazed back resentfully. In his hand his new blue Waterman fountain pen, freshly charged with Quink (washable) ink. In his mind a blank. He looked at Mr Price on his rostrum. Inspiration seemed a million miles away.

The pen had been a present from his mother on his thirteenth birthday. "To darling John with much love from Mummy, in the confident hope that this pen will make you a great writer."

He smiled wanly to himself. Fat chance! Mind you, he rather fancied his writing skills. This year he had already picked up three Golds for essays set by old 'Cut' Price. *How Do You Spend Christmas.* One boy had misheard the title and had written a fascinating but irrelevant essay on *How Do You Spell Christmas.* "Well, one variation is to use X instead of Christ as the prefix." Old Price had not been amused and had been forced to quell a near riot amongst the class who suffered from a paroxysm of the giggles. The boy in question, Digby Peel-Yates, had got nought for his essay and been sent with it to the Headmaster. He got four strokes with the slipper which had made quite impressive scars on his bum. The rumour that went the rounds of the dorms was that Common Room and the Old Man had all found it very funny but had not dared show their amusement publicly. The other two prize-winning essays had been on *What I Would Do If I Were Prime Minister* and *Pleasant Dreams.* What boring subjects!

But he knew how to churn out good essays. Interesting, even controversial ideas, good grammar, rock solid spelling, wide vocabulary, passable style based on bits of Dickens, Robert

Louis Stevenson and the Old Man's uncle, Rider Haggard. Then he always threw in for good luck bags of metaphors and similes, a bit of alliteration for effect and one startling personification. Pity about his ghastly handwriting. Still, there was nothing he could do about that. Why oh why was he born left-handed?

With a bit of luck those three Golds he had acquired plus the Cricket Cup which they were sure to win later that term would tip the scales in favour of the good old Vikings. Yes, they would win the Points Cup over the Pompous Pirates, the Smelly Sea Kings and the Revolting Rovers. The Vikings were quite simply the best!

And of course winning would mean a cream tea with the Headmaster's divine wife. That would be nice. For a moment he pictured Hilary with her golden hair and boyish figure striding down towards the Dancing Ledge with Jumbo, her retriever, racing joyously ahead, determined as always to be first into the pool.

His eye went round the classroom. Nothing much happening there. Medley was scratching away at the next desk. Really old fashioned he was too, still using a dip pen. Covering his fingers with ink. Twerp! "Carrots" Kelsey was slumped in his seat, apparently asleep. Brilliant at cricket, useless at everything else.

Younghusband caught his eye and winked.

John smiled and winked back, first with his left eye, then with his right. He was rather proud of that accomplishment. Not many people could do that.

He sighed and stared out of the window.

Across the courtyard, past the sundial dreaming in the sunshine where the two paths crossed, he could see the Dining Hall and above it his dorm, the Granary. Banks of flowers filled the herbaceous borders in front of the ivy-clad grey walls of the school.

He didn't know the names of many flowers. But he could do iris, pansy, lily and snapdragon, not to mention gladioli and forget-me-not. What's more he was rather proud of the fact that he knew that snapdragons were actually called antirrhinums. He wasn't absolutely certain whether antirrhinum had one or two

R's. Intuitively he thought it had two. But he knew about the hidden h, because he did Greek with old 'Wooders' ("Watch your accents, Arnold!").

Smashing day out there. The sun was blazing down, the ivy glistened, there wasn't a cloud in the sky and it looked really hot.

Half an hour more and he would be running, running, running down to the Dancing Ledge. There he would throw off his clothes and plunge into that icy pool of sparkling, fresh and oh-so-salty sea water. This time he was jolly well going to swim a length of the pool. He was sure he could do it. That would mean another Gold for the Vikings.

And provided Bullock and Willis-Fleming did not accumulate too many Blacks by the end of term, victory would go to the Vikings. The good old Vikings! He could hear the Division's victory finger salute – flick, flick, flick. Like the cracking of a whip. It took a bit of practice.

What you did was to clamp your thumb and middle finger together, then you allowed your forefinger to hang loose. A flick of the wrist would produce a sharp cracking sound if done properly, especially if the forefinger had been wetted first. All those fingers flicking! Absolute bliss!

Meanwhile he had this boring essay to write – *A Mystery*. He was feeling far from mysterious on this glorious summer's day. Mundane might be nearer the mark, or mischievous.

Mr Price with his receding hairline stirred on his rostrum where he was correcting blue exercise books and glanced round the classroom. John stared solemnly back at him as though seeking inspiration.

Maybe he overdid it but he rather prided himself on his acting. He had been a startling success the term before as Madam Gliserinski in *The Crimson Coconut*, an Absurdity in One Act by Ian Hay. Miss Cartwright had laughed herself silly at his acting. "I thought I was going to do myself an injury," she had chortled to him next day. He had taken that as a compliment.

"Any problems, Arnold?"

"No, sir,"

"Well, get on with it. You have exactly twenty-five minutes left."

John bent his head over his book and pretended to write. A few moments later, he risked glancing up. Old Pricey seemed to have been deceived by his display of industry and had returned to his marking.

Oh dear, he must start soon. In a panic he looked around the room for inspiration. Upper Classroom Two was not exactly a thrilling place. Twenty old desks, a bookcase, a rostrum for the beak, green walls.

Hang on! What about the pictures?

To his right, *The Hay Wain*. He liked that. The Old Man had given them a talk about it. He was doing a series of lessons on Great Painters. Constable, yes, that was the painter's name. Although John thought it was a good picture, somehow he didn't feel at home with the countryside. It didn't look at all like the Dorset that he knew and loved so well.

He was used to great green rolling downs, stone walls around neat fields, narrow lanes plunging down impossibly steep hills, houses built of Purbeck marble and a bare, heaving landscape. This picture was all trees and a pond and an old cottage. No wonder that stupid dog was looking at the hay wain stuck in the pond. No, it was not mysterious at all; it simply wouldn't do. So what?

Behind him *The Laughing Cavalier* smirked inanely. John couldn't see the joke at all. What was so funny? No, he couldn't write on that subject.

He turned his head casually to the left and there it was. Hanging on the wall, framed in gold, a good reproduction. What's more, he could read the artist's name under the picture with the date when it was painted. Somehow this picture had fascinated him ever since he first saw it. Two people standing in a room, the man wearing a curious brown tunic, the woman in a huge green dress with a dog in front. What was it all about? His fertile imagination started racing.

He unscrewed the cap of his fountain pen, wiped the nib carefully with a piece of blotch and started to write.

Feverishly.

***

The bell sounded.

"Stop writing. Burrows, would you please collect the books. Wait, Stobart, I have not said you can go yet. Hutton, sit down. Hancock, if you don't stop writing immediately, you will get a Black. If you don't all behave (this to the whole class), I shall keep you here a whole hour. Then you'll miss your bathe."

The air was rent with pitiful cries of "Sir! Sir! You wouldn't, Sir!"

"Oh yes, I would. Keep still all of you. Wait, I said. Be patient. Hurry up, Ascherson. You're keeping the whole class waiting. Thank you, Burrows. Miss Thomas has asked me to remind you that it is clean sheets tomorrow. That means top to bottom when you make your beds. Bottom sheet in the middle of the dormitory. Oh and Matron says you are all to go for your Virol tomorrow morning in the break."

Long pause. Then very slowly, just to tease them, "Enjoy – your – swim; you may go."

Up to the Granary dormitory, rip off all one's clothes, throw them on the floor, on with games kit and gym shoes, grab a towel and run, run, run down to the Dancing Ledge.

***

John had always been a good runner. He ran everywhere. Indeed his mother complained that he never stopped running.

"Oo, John, you are awful! Why do you run all the time? You're just like your father. He used to run all over the parish."

The implied criticism was his mother's coded method of praising him. The fact was that she idolised him; in her eyes he could do no wrong. It worried him that she spoiled him so. If only he had a father to keep him on the right track.

The right track! Keep left, through the gate at Spyway and on to the luscious, springy turf. Whoops! Mind that cowpat. Now he could really stretch his legs, leave all those weeds behind and run across those green, green fields, sloping down to the Ledge.

As he ran, intoxicated by the sheer physical pleasure of his effortless exercise and the splendour of his surroundings, his whirring mind conjured up a face. Where had he seen it before? Strange, penetrative eyes which seemed to brood inwards yet stare outwards with a hint of menace at one and the same time. A long nose with a curious tip to it. Those unusual ears and, above all, the cleft chin, just like his own. And if he took his hat off, the head would have a large forehead with an absence of hair.

Of course! Arnolfini was a bit like his father. Or was it Daddy dressed up to look like Arnolfini? What an extraordinary coincidence! How could his father whom he hadn't seen for four long years have got himself into a picture painted four or five hundred years earlier? And what was going on in that painting? Mummy and Daddy had separated four years ago, when he was nine years old. Now he found living alone with his mother a strain. She gave him too much adulation, was far too uncritical, allowed him too much rope and waited on him hand and foot. It was a strain having to set one's own standards.

The face swam into his consciousness again as he swerved to avoid a cow. Whose face was it? Arnolfini's or his father's? He knew they were different. His father had a rounder, gentler face; Arnolfini's was longer, more pointed. And yet, and yet, how similar! Then he remembered that Daddy wore glasses. If you put spectacles on Arnolfini, he would look quite like Daddy! He resolved to buy a post card of the Arnolfini portrait from the National Gallery at the earliest opportunity and paint spectacles onto Arnolfini's face. Yes, he might well look like Daddy.

So what was really going on in that painting? The Old Man in his talk had said something about a wedding. A wedding? Surely not. No one got married in a bedroom with a little dog at their feet. And Arnolfini wasn't holding her hand; he was taking his hand away from hers and holding his up. Of course! It was a private divorce ceremony. He was divorcing her in the presence of two witnesses. Lawyers, solicitors, whatever they were called, just as Mummy and Daddy had done all those years ago in some dingy office.

Blast! He wished he hadn't written such awful rubbish about the picture. He felt bad, it had deserved better than he had given it. Still, it was probably good enough to fool old Pricey.

As he stood at the top of the final steep incline down to the Ledge, he got his breath and his composure back. Around him, the sweeping curve of the landscape embraced two hikers along the coastal footpath and a deer running across a field to the right, startling two horses. It was all right. He had solved one of life's little mysteries. Now he had to swim that length.

Plunging down the hill, he dug his heels in, revelling in the conflict with gravity and his mastery of his environment. Daddy would come home one day, of that he was pretty confident. As for Arnolfini, from the expression on his face, he looked as though he was divorcing Mrs Arnolfini for good.

Bastard!

***

September, 1942

Four months later at his public school, John received from his prep school his copy of *The Chronicle* with all its news of the past year. In his Houseroom, sitting at his horsebox, he devoured it eagerly.

Yes, the Vikings had won the Points Cup and had their cream tea with Hilary. In swimming everyone except Bullock had passed their test. He looked at the sports, noted his name in the cricket XI and Matty's comments on each player ("Kelsey became a proficient bat and a fine captain; Arnold knew how to catch and could bowl a decent length, getting the odd one to swing"), skimmed through the Old Man's Editorial (all about setting 'new standards') noticed that Price had been called up and read the reviews.

"Arnold gave an excruciatingly funny performance as Madam Gliserinski. The audience and I were convulsed." The article was signed Joan Cartwright.

He came to the section marked Boys' Contributions, There was a note in italics – *These essays are completely original and have been written during ordinary work.*

And there it was. His essay.

A Mystery

by John Arnold, aged 13.4

'Two people are standing in a room full of mysterious objects. The air seems redolent with riddle, suffused with suspense, pungent with perplexity.

The man on the left is a policeman, wearing his official uniform of fur-lined gown and hat, a splendid affair with a huge brim. It has been designed thus to protect the cranium from the vicious attacks by footpads, so prevalent at this period in history. He looks like the Statue of Liberty redesigned by a Puritan sculptor.

The policeman has just arrested the woman on the right for stealing. She has been caught red-handed by him and his sniffer dog which stands proudly in the foreground. She has been purloining oranges. We can see three on the left which have just been taken off her. She has many other stolen objects about her person and concealed in the voluminous folds of that capacious dress which she is holding up. It is obvious that she has been shop-lifting.

Whilst holding the suspect, the policeman is giving evidence. To signify that it is a solemn moment, the artist, Jan van Eyck, has placed a single lit candle in the chandelier. It shines out like the blue lamp over a police station. The guardian of the law raises his right hand and swears to tell the truth, the whole truth and nothing but the truth, so help him God. We can see the Magistrate and his clerk reflected in the mirror at the back of the room.

The mystery is what will happen to the woman. Will she be hanged for her crime? The omens do not look good; notice all that blood red in the painting.

Oh, by the way, we know the name of the policeman. He has signed the picture on the back wall, above the mirror. **Johannes de Eyck fuit hic**. In other words Jan van Eyck was this man.

How did a humble policeman come to be an artist? Scotland Yard and the National Gallery do not normally have much in common. That is the real mystery.'

***

John passed the magazine to his neighbour without comment. He was pretty sure that Fergie wouldn't like it.

He waited anxiously for Ferguson's opinion, who sat there reading the essay rapidly and biting his nails. John respected Ferguson's judgment, just as he admired his ability to make excellent scrambled egg from dried eggs and his skill on the trombone. Fergie knew a thing or two about art. It was he who had introduced John to one or two famous pictures whose merits they had discussed. Ferguson owned a book called *100 Art Masterpieces*. Van Eyck's picture was in there.

The verdict when it came was not favourable.

"I don't think this is much good, Arnie. In fact, I'll go further and I'll be blunt with you. I think it's absolute toffee, fudge, slop." He made a long face expressive of bad smells in the vicinity as he groped for a phrase which would adequately convey his feelings. "Yes, it's copper-bottomed bunk."

A quick fight followed. But as they wrestled on the Houseroom floor, John knew that Ferguson was right. He let him win. As Ferguson bestrode him like a colossus (they were studying *Julius Caesar* in English that term), he felt glad that his fraudulence had been exposed. What he had written was rubbish, he now acknowledged, undeserving of the Gold it had won.

In the dust of the Houseroom floor, he resolved there and then to solve the mystery of that picture, to find out why the Arnolfinis were divorcing. Maybe not that term, probably not the next holidays, but some time. In the future.

He stood up, gave Ferguson a conciliatory grin, put the magazine back in his horsebox and went up to his dorm to change for Lowers rugger.

Chapter 3

March 1395

The river Meuse rises in the Champagne district of France, hesitates which direction to take before making up its mind to head north. It ambles through the Ardennes Forest, just missing Luxembourg. When it leaves France, something dramatic happens. It changes its name to the Maas and heads for Maastricht.

Just north of Maastricht and west of the Ruhr on the German border lies the small neat town of Maaseyk. Obviously it takes its name from the river which flows through it.

Here in March, 1395, picture if you will a small boy, aged five, with an alert face and tidy appearance, learning his alphabet in school. He has a slate and a piece of chalk. With care and precision, as he has been taught, he inscribes the 22 letters of the alphabet on his slate.

a b c d e f g h i k l m n o p q r ſ t v x y

He has been taught to write his s like a long lamp post with a curve at the top, something like this ſ. Twenty-two letters and then his name – in Latin – Johannes de Eyck.

He is a bright boy. So is his elder brother, Hubert, the famous painter, now aged thirty. Johannes, or Jan as he prefers to be known, is planning to follow in his brother's footsteps and become a painter. Already he shows promise. On the other side of the slate, he has drawn a picture of his teacher. A few deft strokes of the chalk and the likeness is unmistakable. The other two boys with whom he shares a desk are much slower than Jan. Their alphabets have taken an inordinate amount of time. Eventually, however, they have finished as much as their limited brains can remember and time allows.

Under the cover of his desk, Jan van Eyck surreptitiously wipes away with his sleeve the drawing which he has done as the schoolmaster, a huge, menacing brute of a man with piercing pig-like eyes under his velvet cap, approaches and scrutinises Jan's slate. He ruffles Jan's hair. It is an accolade, seldom bestowed. The work is so good that even this cavilling and pernickety pedagogue can find no fault with it. Not so the other two. Both arouse his wrath. Frans has left out the letter n, written two t's and made a hash of several other letters. Willem has got no further than the letter f. For both it is the paddle. Six sharp strokes on the palm of the hand and much repressed snivelling and whimpering.

Jan watches the administration of punishment with dispassionate interest. For him the human face is infinitely variable, endlessly interesting. Willem's squashed and vulgar physiognomy with the tears coursing down the runnels of his cheeks like the open sewer in the street outside is meticulously filed away in his memory for future reference. It might come in handy for a figure on the periphery of an Adoration. Fran's stoicism is also noted. Could be useful in a Martyrdom.

Jan's real education is in walking the narrow streets of Maaseyk and memorising the faces of its citizens; of going home and drawing their physiognomies from memory. He learns quickly, he draws divinely.

As soon as he is old enough, he will be joining a Guild of Artists as an apprentice.

The Maas eventually flows west. Like the river, Jan van Eyck will ultimately move on, due west in fact, past Ghent where his brother Hubert is working, to settle finally in Bruges, the scene of all his triumphs.

***

"Thank you, Heather. First of all, ladies and gentlemen, can you all hear me?"

Murmurs of assent.

"Good. Before we have the first slide, a few brief remarks about the artist.

Nothing is known about the life of Jan van Eyck before 1422. We may conjecture from various clues that he was probably born about 1390. He would have received a formal training as an artist. From 1415 to 1417 he was almost certainly working at The Hague for William VI, Count of Holland, Zeeland and Hainault.

Perhaps he is the author of one of the miniatures in *The Turin Book of Hours* which depicts William VI on horseback. Possibly he painted another miniature called *The Kiss of Judas*. He may even have painted a drawing of this period, tinted with watercolour, entitled *Fishing Party at the Court of William VI*. But all of this is conjecture.

What is certain is that by 22nd October, 1422, he had become attached to the Palace at The Hague of Count John of Bavaria, brother of William VI, as the official painter and 'varlet de chambre', whatever that may mean. He had been commissioned to decorate the palace. It is a task which will occupy him until 11th September, 1424. He was paid, incidentally, at the rate of eight lions a day, while his assistants each received two lions a day.

By the time he has finished his formal education, still only in his twenties, Jan van Eyck has arrived. His enormous talent is about to blossom. When Count John dies on 5th January, 1425, and civil war erupts, Jan seeks refuge in Flanders.

He moves to Bruges where all his masterpieces will be painted. That is where our story of Arnolfini takes place and that is where I hope to solve *A Mystery*.

Can we have the lights out, please? Thank you."

Click!

The first slide appears.

"Let's start with the simple facts.

33

Chapter 4

January, 1420

Fourteen miles from the sea, in the heart of 'il gentile' Tuscany, there is an old city. Surrounded by ramparts crowned with trees, Lucca lies in a fertile plain to the west of the river Serchio.

It was here in 56 BC that Julius Caesar formed a triumvirate with Crassus and Pompey and agreed to rule Rome. Lucca used to be the capital of Tuscany. Now under its Governor, Paolo Guinigi, it is a powerful Republic, independent and in constant strife with its neighbours, Pisa and Florence. Its bankers rival those of Siena in power and authority, it produces the finest olive oil in Italy, if not the world, and it was the first town in Tuscany to accept Christianity.

Ever since Marco Polo opened up the silk routes to the far east a hundred years earlier, Lucca has been rich, trading in silk and wool with the rest of Europe, especially with Flanders.

One Tuesday in January, 1420, a bitter west wind from the Mare Ligure is dusting the pink city with a thin carpet of snow. Nobody in their right senses would be out on the streets of Lucca on such a day.

Inside the Casa Michele, an ostentatiously grand house on the via San Giorgio, another triumvirate is in conference. Or rather, three generations have met. Around a blazing log fire in the Great Hall are assembled six members of the same family. It is a council of war. Opinions must be aired, minds made up, decisions taken.

The family's fortune depends largely upon the silk trade. Hangchow and Xian may be the source of silk; Samarkand may be the silk staging post, Champagne the clearing-house, Bruges its destination, but Lucca is the linchpin. From here its talented citizens are ready and avid to conquer the business world of

Europe whose capital lies in Flanders.

The family name is Arnolfini. Its coat of arms is emblazoned proudly upon the mantelpiece. In front of the fire, feet braced, arms thrust deep inside his red-quilted coat, stands Arrigo Arnolfini. Like all Arnolfinis he has high cheek bones, a tall forehead, hooded eyes which deceive one into thinking that he is half asleep, a long hooked nose, large flat ears and a cleft chin. A huge fur hat gives him a spurious air of authority. The real power in this family lies not with the patriarch, not even with Arrigo, but with the next generation, the up-and-coming, ambitious and enormously talented sons, Michele and Giovanni. Especially Giovanni Arrigo Arnolfini.

Giovanni listens attentively to his father's peroration. The speech carries passion, substance, even style. But Giovanni realises almost imperceptibly that it lacks authority. The old order is changing, yielding place to new. The pride is changing its pack leader who has recently lost his power. The present and the future belong to his brother Michele and himself. That is where the real power struggle is taking place. The only question in his mind is which brother will be brave enough to grasp the crown.

Meanwhile Arrigo is droning on in that thin, rasping voice which conceals impatience, intelligence and genuine concern. He still has all the facts at his fingertips. His monologue lasts some ten minutes. He is listened to by all with interest, but by Giovanni with particular attention.

His speech ends with these words: "There you have it. In a nutshell. It's as plain as that coat of arms on that mantelpiece."

He pauses to let the facts sink in and to refresh himself with a draught of Chianti drunk from a gold chalice. His rhetoric begins to take effect. Several members of the group shift uneasily. There is very little eye contact. Giovanni who can see what is coming stares at one of the dogs stretched out luxuriously in front of the fire. His father is going to recommend diversification. That will undoubtedly mean more wealth for the Arnolfinis. But the family will have to pay a heavy price. Never again will it be so united.

At any rate, that is what Giovanni, the younger son, is

35

thinking in his corner. He does not have to wait long for his father to play one of his trump cards.

"So what I say is quite simply this, we must expand. Yes, expand. It's as simple as that. To stand still here in Lucca would be commercial suicide. It would be tantamount to ossification."

Giovanni cannot help noticing that his father separates the last word into five units, enunciating with equal emphasis all five syllables. He contrives to make it sound like the warning hiss of a snake about to strike.

Arrigo looks at his wife, seated on a carved wooden bench on his immediate right. Dear, sweet Antonia, she of the gentle laugh, the bewitching smile, the unexpected kindness, the companion of his marital bed, the mother of his six children. How is she going to react? Will she agree to sacrifice one of the family?

He stares intently at Antonia who steadfastly refuses to return his gaze, preferring instead to concentrate on the embroidery on her lap. But Arrigo can tell from the curve of her neck, that wisp of hair hanging down her shoulder, that slight furrowing of her eyebrows, that he can count on her vote, whatever anyone else may say.

To her right stands Michele, their eldest son. He will surely agree. He has always been a good boy, conscious of his family duties, aware that one day he will inherit this place and be head of the clan. Yes, Arrigo can count on Michele.

"May I say something, sir?"

An almost imperceptible nod of the head.

"I fully concur with what you have just said, father. To do nothing is, as you so rightly say, to ossify. This may very well be the decisive moment in our affairs. Family honour is at stake. The hour of our destiny is surely at hand."

Giovanni thinks that the speech is pompous and empty. Typical Michele, always the sycophant. Michele is Antonia's darling, Arrigo's favourite son, his grandfather's bambino, the one destined to acquire all the best crumbs falling from his father's richly laden table. "It isn't fair," thinks Giovanni, "I've always played second fiddle to Signior Have-It-All. I do all the work while he gets all the credit. I am far cleverer than he is,

36

possess much more financial acumen, have achieved greater things. Now he is going to garner all the credit and all the rewards whilst I, Giovanni, will probably have to do all the work."

He turns an outwardly placid, benign countenance towards his father. Not a trace of inner turbulence shows.

"I second Michele's sentiments, father. But what exactly had you in mind?"

There is a moment's silence while Arrigo takes another sip of wine.

"Nothing precisely at the moment. I am merely sounding out your opinions."

It is a lie which fools nobody.

Antonia smiles to herself and puts another stitch in her embroidery which shows a unicorn walking through an enchanted forest full of flowers. She concentrates on getting the beast's white horn straight. Michele is staring steadfastly at his father. Giovanni hoods his eyes for a second and then shifts his gaze to stare at Arrigo's brother who is sitting by the fire.

Niccolao is a man of the world. He has the supreme advantage of having travelled all over Europe. At present he is an arms dealer living in Paris. Under his fur hat he looks and is powerful. His opinion counts for much.

"What do you think, brother?" demands Arrigo.

Niccolao shifts in his chair and stretches his silk-clad legs out luxuriously towards the fire before replying. When he speaks, he chooses his words with extreme care. Everyone listens intently, none more so than Giovanni.

"What I have to say to you may well be news to you all. You may think, living your quiet comfortable lives here in Lucca, that you are at the hub of the business world, the heart of world affairs and that this city is the capital of the business world so far as banking goes. Let me assure you that this is very far from being the case. Lucca is an important city, yes. Lucca has an important say in the silk trade, yes. Lucca balances east and west, yes. But can the silk trade survive without Lucca? Indubitably, yes."

The last word comes out in a prolonged hiss.

37

Niccolao pauses. Even cobras have to take breath. A log in the grate crackles and spits defiantly.

There is silence for a space of time before it is broken by the old man sitting on Arrigo's left, the dome of his high forehead glinting in the candlelight.

Giannino Arnolfini, the patriarch of the family, is now in his dotage.

Many years ago, twenty-nine to be precise, he had been the most powerful man in Lucca, its Gonfaloniere of Justice. It was said that more than two score people – political opponents, racketeers, criminals, enemies, even friends – had been sentenced to death by him and executed. If there is blood on his hands, his long, delicate, arthritic fingers which stretch out longingly towards the warmth of the fire do not show it. When Giovanni was a child and heard those stories about his grandfather, he had often looked surreptitiously for signs of red staining those elegant hands.

Arrigo seems glad of the distraction.

"Of course, father. I was about to ask you for your advice. We value your opinion more than anyone's. All of us are listening carefully to what you have to say."

The implied threat in the last remark is accompanied by a swift panoramic look around the assembled company. But it is unnecessary. Everyone is paying careful attention.

Giannino draws his hands back from the fire. Too much heat hurts them. His quiet voice with precise articulation can clearly be heard by all.

"What I have to say, my son, is that since September of last year the situation is completely different. Everything has changed."

Arrigo nods gravely in deference to his father without having the faintest idea what he is talking about. He decides that he cannot bluff it out.

"How so, father?"

"Have you forgotten what happened at Montereau?"

"Not entirely, father. Just remind us of the facts, if you will be so kind. Where exactly is Montereau?"

"Aha! I thought you did not know," laughs Giannino

triumphantly for he is no fool. "Where is Montereau? Where is it indeed?"

Giannino permits himself the luxury of another long cackle of laughter before subsiding back into the gravity of an elder statesman and answering the question. He collects his thoughts.

"Montereau is a tiny town in France. It lies just a few miles east of Orleans, midway between Paris and Dijon, the respective capitals of France and Burgundy. It is in fact rather a charming town, considering it is French. Not as beautiful as most of our Tuscan towns, you understand, but not without merit. It has a particularly fine cathedral. Very small, but charming. I remember going to Mass there. Yes, charming."

Clearly 'charming' is Giannino's favourite complimentary epithet.

"And what happened there, father?"

Arrigo knows from a lifetime's experience that his father enjoys a little prompting and prodding.

Giannino shifts in his chair before replying. He has the floor and the attention of everyone. He intends to milk the situation and chooses his words with care and precision.

"It happened, if I remember rightly, on Sunday, 10th September, last year. In Montereau. A conference was to take place between the King of France, Charles VI, and the ruler of Burgundy, Jean Sans Peur. You will recall that Jean had inherited much of Flanders when his father, Philip the Bold, had married Margaret."

Heads nod around the fire. Eyes stare hard at Giannino. A history lesson is being learnt quickly.

"There are at the moment, as you know, three great powers in western Europe. England of course is one under their tyrannical and ambitious King Henry V. A dangerous man, especially after his surprising victories in France four years ago."

Giannino pauses to blow his nose loudly on a kerchief of fresh white linen before throwing it into the fire.

"Then there is Burgundy with its controlling influence in Flanders. Very important of course and very powerful. Not to be under-estimated. Finally, there is France, caught in the middle, unable fully to control either side."

"But what happened at Montereau?"

Giannino takes the implied rebuff without offence.

"Well, Jean Sans Peur of Burgundy so mistrusted the French that he spent the night before the conference in a fortress. A castle in fact on an island in the river Yonne. Now the French had built a pontoon bridge from this isolated fortress to the stone bridge spanning the Yonne where the conference was to be held right on the bridge in the Tour du Pont."

"Did Jean Sans Peur come to the bridge?"

"He did. But the Dauphin, acting doubtless on orders from his father, arranged for Jean to be murdered on the bridge of Montereau on that fatal Sunday last September. And that is what in fact did happen and that is how the situation has now changed."

There is silence as these facts are digested. Giovanni is still not sure what the relevance of the story is.

But it is Niccolao who poses the next question.

"How does that affect us, father?"

"Because, don't you see, there is now an irreparable rift between France and Burgundy. A schism if you like. The new ruler of Burgundy, and therefore of Flanders, is Philip the Good. His friend and ally is Henry V, King of England. The wool and lace and silk trades are all based in Flanders. That is where England will send her wool. That is where the power and influence of Burgundy lies. If we want to be at the centre of power, and I take it that we do, we must have someone in Bruges representing our best interests. Someone who will have the ear of the Duke. It's as simple as that."

Arrigo throws another log on the fire, Antonia puts another stitch in the unicorn, Giovanni stares at the fire. He is beginning to see which way this conference is going.

"Whom do we send?"

It is Michele who poses the question that all have been dreading, fearful that it may be he who is chosen.

"Our choice is limited," answers Arrigo. "My brother is tied up in important deals in Paris. He cannot be spared. I must stay here to run affairs in Lucca. The choice, it seems to me, lies between Michele and Giovanni."

There is a long silence while nobody catches anybody else's eye.

"Michele?"

"I will go of course, father, if it is so wished." Michele almost makes the offer sound genuine.

"But I would like to point out that my experience is limited and also that my family ties preclude my absence. Fond as I am of travel and of adventure, I am bound to say that I feel my primary responsibility is to stay at home to help my family."

It sounds gracious, as it is meant to be, but Giovanni can't help thinking that it is unnecessarily ingratiating. Not for a thousand ducats would he have made a speech like that.

"What about you, Giovanni, will you go?"

Although Giovanni knows that the die has been cast and that only the formal decision remains to be made, he is not going to waste words. Taciturnity has always been his hallmark and his strength; let Michele pontificate if he so desires.

"But of course." Arrigo looks carefully into the faces of all his family one by one. Then he stretches out his right hand so that all can touch it. He takes a deep breath and utters four words.

"So be it. Giovanni."

Nobody moves. Arrigo stands motionless, his hand outstretched. Then the old man, Giannino, places his slightly shaking right hand on top of Arrigo's. Niccolao puts his next, followed by Michele. Giovanni pauses a second, his face impassive, before allowing his long elegant fingers to rest lightly upon those of his brother.

All wait patiently for Antonia. Methodically she places a final stitch in the unicorn's horn, then sighs deeply and places her small, graceful hand on top of the bundle.

Chapter 5

February, 1420

Giovanni di Arrigo Arnolfini, who was born in 1402, second son of Arrigo and Antonia Arnolfini, has lived in Lucca all his brief life of eighteen years. Now it has been determined that he must represent his family and seek his fortune in Flanders, distant, dangerous and no doubt dirty Flanders, more than five hundred miles away, a place where they do not even speak Italian.

Just off the via del Fosso in the southern part of Lucca stands the handsome Duomo in the piazza San Martino. The front of the Cathedral is embellished with an amazing array of carved columns. Dedicated to St. Martin of Tours (he who divided his cloak with a beggar), the Cathedral was enlarged in the 11th century and given its present form in the 13th century with a Pisan Romanesque façade, a lofty three-arched portico with three rows of arches above and a separate campanile.

Towards here on a bitterly cold day in February, 1420, a few weeks after that historic family conference, hurries Giovanni. Snugly wrapped in a black velvet cloak, he is in no mood to divide it with any beggar. A broad-brimmed hat protects him from the elements and completes the air of mystery about him.

As he walks down the via San Paolino towards the Duomo, he looks neither to right nor left. Greetings from fellow citizens he ignores; the omnipresent beggars he passes without even noticing their pitiful pleas for alms. He is a man of purpose who knows where he is going – to Bruges. But first he has a vital assignation in the Cathedral.

Before he starts his long journey, he must pray for a safe and successful passage to Flanders. He knows that with the aid of his Blessed Saviour who died for him on the Cross and who waits for him, literally, in the Cathedral, he will arrive safely in Bruges.

But before he enters the Cathedral, he pauses outside, despite the cold, to look at something carved on a pillar on the immediate right of one of the great doors. It is a representation of a Roman circular labyrinth, about a foot square, beautifully incised into the stone of the pillar. You can enter the labyrinth from the south, the west and the east, but not the north. When he was a small boy, he was unable to reach the labyrinth which was five and a half feet up from the ground. Before Mass, his father used to hold him up while he traced with his finger a possible route from one of the three entrances towards the elusive centre. But he never achieved success. He usually chose, he remembered, the entrance to the east which looked as if it led straight to the centre. How deceptive appearances can be! His finger would shoot along the line until he was right next to the middle but, alas, there was no way in. It was a snare and an delusion. So he would start again with the west entrance, without success, until his father got bored and tired of holding him and they went in to Mass. He had never got to the centre.

Now on the spur of the moment, he decides to try again. He seems to remember that east and west were futile. Best try south. He places his gloved finger on the line entering the labyrinth due south. He goes up three circles until he reaches an impasse, he turns left, no choice to do anything else, starts going right round in a huge circle, turns right when his finger is due west, goes through two more circles, turns left and goes up until due north, heads south for two circles, turns left and goes round until due east, turns right and after crossing three more circles, a miracle!, he is at the centre. What a blessed and favourable omen! He crosses himself and hurries into the relative warmth of the great Cathedral.

The darkness greets him, broken only by the flickering light from the scores of candles lit by the faithful. He feels comfortable in such an atmosphere; he has always preferred the penumbra to the sunlight. He dips his fingers in the holy water and strides up the nave to the crossing where he turns left into the northern transept. There it is.

43

Hanging on the wall is a large wooden crucifix. It is an object of enormous and especial veneration to all Lucchese. Legend has it that it was carved from a cedar of Lebanon by Nicodemus himself with the help of an angel. For a long time the cross was hidden in Palestine until it was discovered by a Bishop on a pilgrimage to the Holy Land who entrusted it to the sea. It floated westwards along the Mediterranean before touching land at Luni in Italy, a Roman colony on the coast between Spezia and Genoa. There this Byzantine crucifix was found in the 8th century and brought in triumph by the Lucchese back to their native city where they deposited it in the Cathedral.

Giovanni crosses himself and kneels before the Volto Santo, as it is affectionately and universally known, the Holy Face. On a plain wooden cross, a man is hanging. He is about six feet tall, dressed in a plain, dark blue tunic which hangs in broad swathes down to his ankles. His arms are stretched painfully straight. His long, elegant fingers and hands protrude from the tunic. Nails have been driven through the palms of His hands and through His two ankles which, unusually for a crucifix, are not crossed. Around His waist is a simple gold-coloured belt with two long tassels hanging down.

If the beautifully carved body excites compassion, it is Christ's face which is infinitely more moving. With His head on one side, Christ is portrayed as a young, virile man, with a handsome crop of hair flowing over his shoulders, a moustache, beard and sunburnt features. Everything about His composure elicits pity for His suffering. But once seen, never forgotten, His wild, staring eyes are the focal point of attention. He seems to be staring down at the three Marys and St. John at the foot of the Cross.

On Good Friday, the Lucchese carry the Volto Santo in procession around their city. But before they do so, they dress their Christ in all the glory of a crowned monarch. On His head they place a glorious golden triple crown surmounted by a cross, the tiara embellished with many precious stones. On His outstretched arms they drape golden armlets embellished with scenes from the Manger at Bethlehem in gold thread. Around His neck they hang a huge golden necklace. They place a large gold decoration on His chest, a magnificent gold belt depicting the twelve apostles which supports a black skirt, richly embroidered with golden saints and angels. There is also a golden sceptre and two giant golden keys. No newly crowned king has ever been more richly decorated at his coronation.

As Giovanni kneels in front of Christ hanging there on the cross, there is no sound in the Cathedral, save the murmuring of confessions being heard in numerous side chapels. He is alone with his thoughts and His Saviour. He is waiting for a miracle to happen, as it has so often in the past and as he is confident it will again today.

His back aches as he kneels but he is oblivious to the pain. All his attention is focused on those staring, compassionate eyes. He empties his mind gradually of all secular thoughts. His father, his mother, his family and friends, ambitions, hopes, fears, all slowly vanish. Avidly he stares at the Cross, willing its occupant to grant him a sign. For what seems like an eternity nothing happens. The long minutes pass agonisingly by. His faith is being tested. The Volto Santo has performed many miracles for the Lucchese. All that is required is complete faith.

And then suddenly it happens. To Giovanni's great astonishment and joy, Jesus Christ on the Cross raises His head and for one long moment stares straight at Giovanni. Then the head drops once more, the eyes are lowered and He resumes His painful stare down to the foot of the Cross. But the sign has been given. Jesus is dying to save Giovanni's soul. He will redeem him by His supreme sacrifice.

With great difficulty but tremendous joy Giovanni lowers his eyes. He starts to say his prayers. First he salutes the risen Christ. He acknowledges the Trinity. He worships God the Father, God the Son, God the Holy Ghost. He prays with fervour for his parents, his grandfather, his uncle, his sisters and even his brother. He prays for the citizens of Lucca, the people of Flanders, the nations of the world. He prays for Pope Martin V and the Holy Catholic Church, for the poor, the sick, the dying, the dead and the bereaved. Finally, he prays for his own safety in the difficult and arduous journey that lies ahead. He finishes with three paternosters.

He crosses himself and takes one last lingering look at the Volto Santo. As he hurries from the Cathedral his faith is burning like a living flame within him. Though he has a long journey ahead of him, he is not afraid. The Lord will protect and provide.

Outside he drops a coin in a beggar's grimy, outstretched hand.

***

11th June, 1420

Giovanni starts on 1st March. His journey will last three months.

First he rides down to the nearby port of Viareggio from where he takes boat to Genoa and thence eventually to Marseille. The voyage is uneventful if unpleasant. Giovanni keeps himself to himself. In Genoa he catches a small fishing smack which carries him with no small discomfort to the mouth of the Rhône and up to Châlon-sur-Saône, across to the river Seine whence it is comparatively easy to sail down river past Auxerre and Sens to Paris where he hires horses to ride to Arras, Ypres, Turnhout and at last the spires and towers of his destination.

He has survived with stoicism several storms, one minor shipwreck, a flight from pirates, near drowning, two highway robberies, a sprained ankle, four falls from his horse, a blizzard, severe lightning, a blinding rainstorm and many other mishaps which he describes in a letter home as 'minor inconveniences and irritations'. In addition he has had to endure bug-ridden beds in filthy inns, disgusting food, atrocious wines, appalling or non-existent roads, bouts of dysentery, fever, seasickness, sunstroke, thirst, hunger, loneliness and homesickness.

But he is tough. He has travelled more than five hundred miles to make the family fortunes. On 11th June, 1420, the Feast Day of St. Barnabas the Apostle, Giovanni Arnolfini limps into Bruges.

He has arrived.

46

Chapter 6

All Saints Day, 1420

Just back from Mass in the Cathedral, Philip III, by Divine Grace His Serene and Most Eminent Duke of Burgundy, is toying with a bunch of grapes which has been presented to him on a gold plate. He feels uplifted, both from the spiritual and secular points of view.

Spiritually he has invoked the names of all the saints, confessed his sins and received absolution. Secularly he has prayed for the fair citizens of Bruges and the good people of Flanders.

From his Palace he can look out of a big bay window over the pink and brown roofs of the city. In the grey November light the city crouches like a hare, alert and wary, ready to take on the world. Smoke rises vertically from its many chimneys.

Philip likes Bruges. For him it is an exciting place in which to live, so different from his native Burgundy with its enchanting landscape. But here in Bruges he is very much aware that he is lucky to be at the apex of an international, cosmopolitan, thriving city.

His Chamberlain stands before him, holding the dish of grapes. He is wearing the Duke's livery, a scarlet tunic, edged with fur, liberally sprinkled with gold fleur-de-lis. He is a serious man with a serious face. Discretion is his middle name. He it is who keeps the Duke *au fait* with local news, who's in, who's out, who's on the way up, who is finished; he mentions that there is a new entrepreneur from Italy, a young businessman from Lucca who is causing quite a stir; he it is who has informed His Grace with a certain degree of trepidation that His Grace is now known affectionately by the people as Philip the Good, a fact which is greeted with laughter and evident satisfaction. Finally it is

47

Charles, the Chamberlain, who is in charge of all the arrangements for the Banquet which the Duke is giving this very evening.

"Remind me, Charles, who exactly is coming tonight."

The Chamberlain places the dish on a small table beside the Duke and produces from a wallet three small leather volumes. The first he hands to the Duke who studies it assiduously. Several minutes of silence elapse before he speaks.

"This is excellent, Charles. I must thank you for your impeccable arrangements."

Both men incline their heads in a brief exchange of courtesies. The Duke returns to read through the list for a second time.

"I see, I see. Very interesting. Good – all the bankers are coming, well, almost all. H'm, most of the city dignitaries, yes, including that scoundrel of a Treasurer. The Cathedral Chapter too. Remind me to have a word with the new Dean, will you? Ah yes, the Ambassadors, yes, yes, him, good, oh, he is coming, is he? Never mind. Any apologies?"

"The second page, your Grace."

The Duke is well satisfied. The list of refusals is commendably short. Few of those invited scorn the chance to sample the Duke's famed hospitality whilst meeting all the most important people in Bruges under one roof.

His Grace studies the second and third volumes to acquaint himself with the arrangements for the evening, the food and wines to be served and the entertainments to be offered, including a masque especially written for this evening. No expense is being spared. The rich and influential Burghers of Bruges will be here tonight and all will be suitably impressed by and indebted to His Grace.

"The arrangements are without blemish, Charles. You merit my felicitations. I thank you and will not speedily forget what you have done."

Graciously he inclines his head. The audience is over, The Chamberlain bows three times and leaves the room backwards. Philip pops another grape into his mouth and saunters over to his capacious library. He selects a slim leather-bound volume from the fourth shelf up. He begins to read in Latin one of Horace's Odes from Liber III, number one as he walks up and down a long Gallery, hung with fine tapestries.

> *Odi profanum vulgus et arceo;*
> *favete linguis: carmina non prius*
> *audita Musarum sacerdos*
> *virginisbus puerisque canto.*

It amuses him to translate the elegant Sapphic measures of Q.Horatius Flaccus into the vernacular.

> 'I eschew any interest in vulgar publicity.
> As High Priest of the Muses,
> I sing to youths and maidens.'

The lines strike him as curiously apposite. He permits himself the luxury of a discreet smile and retires to his private withdrawing room to rest and prepare himself for the rigours of the evening.

He settles himself on a chaise longue for another good read of Horace. All is serene upstairs in the ducal Palace.

***

Not so downstairs.

The cooks have made an early start. An astonishing amount of food has to be prepared for the Lucullan banquet that is to be served in the Great Hall this very evening.

By four in the morning all is hustle and bustle in the great kitchen and adjacent pantries, larders, sculleries and work halls. Twenty-four master chefs are creating their masterpieces on the huge scrubbed tables that run down the centre of the kitchen, as big as a cathedral nave. Dozens of sou-chefs are hard at work alongside them, scraping, sieving, paring, disembowelling, peeling, pulverising, tenderising, plucking, mixing, stewing, scalding, blanching, grilling, boiling, and generally exhibiting multifarious culinary skills. Small boys patiently turn the wheels of the spits.

Porters scurry hither and thither, bringing in mountains of fresh food.

On one table a French master chef, especially imported for

the occasion from Liège, has stuffed a sucking pig with forcemeat and closed the opening with a trussing needle and thread, employing all the delicacy and precision of a surgeon sewing up some great general's wound on the battlefield.

In another room, an army of women are plucking pheasants, herons, partridges, woodcocks, egrets, teal, quail and snipe. All the birds have been recently slaughtered, thereby making their feathers more easy to be withdrawn before their flesh has stiffened. The women hold the birds in their left hands and pluck with the right, singing as they do so a curiously unmusical rhythmic chant.

When they have been plucked, the birds are taken to another table where another host of women truss them, first cutting off their heads (except for the snipe and heron), scalding and peeling the feet, The birds are then drawn (except for the snipe), and passed to a sou-chef who brushes them over with hot fat, covers each breast with bacon and ties a vine-leaf over the bacon. Each bird is then skewered, ready for basting on a spit.

Snipe merit especial attention. From his position in the centre of the main kitchen, the Chamberlain oversees the work. His eye misses very little. He observes the select band of women dressing (but not drawing) the mountain of snipe that lie on one table. They are skinning the little heads whilst leaving them on, passing the long, delicate beak of each bird through its legs and body as though it were a skewer. It is work which requires nimble, deft fingers.

A master chef selects the best hares in one larder from the hundreds which have been hanging there for the past eight days. Carefully he feels each animal before making his choice. He is looking for smooth and sharp claws and a narrow cleft in the lip. Once he is satisfied – and he selects only about one in four – he taps with his forefinger the chosen victim which is immediately put into a huge wicker basket by an apprentice cook.

When the basket is full, the hares are taken to a table where chefs skin, draw and truss the beasts before stuffing them with forcemeat and sewing up the bodies with needle and strong cotton. The hares will be roasted in ovens for two hours whilst the chefs prepare the hares' liver, minus their gall bladders, by boiling for five minutes and then chopping finely and stewing with melted butter, onion, parsley and thyme. The liver will be pounded in a mortar until smooth, rubbed through a fine wire sieve, and reheated with the butter and some flour until a nut-brown roux is obtained. Then when the hare is served, it will be accompanied by the liver seasoned with wine.

To recount how many barons of beef are roasted, what quantity of small-boned, plump mutton is boiled, how much pork and venison and lamb and poultry and veal will be consumed is nothing more than a tedious rehearsal of impressive statistics and an invitation to indigestion on the part of the reader.

And that of course has not taken account of all those small creatures who have died to satisfy the splendour and the appetites of those upstairs – a huge husk of hares, a siege of herons, an ostentation of pheasants, a bevy of quail, a charm of goldfinches, a plump of woodcock, a spring of teals and an exultation of larks.

In another room swan chaudwyn is being prepared, always popular with the guests. The liver of the swan is chopped up and its entrails boiled with blood, bread, wine, vinegar, pepper, cloves and ginger, all to be stuffed into the swan itself which is to be roasted. Delicious!

There is plenty of fish on the menu too – bream, perch in jelly, freshwater crayfish, pies of eel and carp; but of course nothing as common as trout or salmon.

Finally, in another room, the pastry chefs are working their puff pastry magic, concocting miracles of confectionery. A soltelte represents the Archangel Gabriel greeting Mary; another shows an angel appearing to three shepherds on a hill (of cream-filled puff pastry); a third has the Kings of Cologne, the traditional Wise Men or Magi, presenting to the infant Christ their gifts of gold and frankincense and myrrh (all edible).

There are mountains of almond cream, baked quince, sage fritters, white apples, amber jelly, wafers and an Ypocras to wash it all down, not to mention fifteen vintage wines to accompany the feast.

Fifteen hours of non-stop work in hot, underground rooms

by an army of cooks sees a banquet fit and ready for the Duke and his four hundred guests, one of whom is an Italian, newly arrived from Lucca. His name is Giovanni Arnolfini.

Chapter 7

All Saints Day, 1420

In the five months he has so far lived in Bruges, Arnolfini has made extraordinary progress in his business affairs. He has brought with him wealth, contacts, business acumen, youthful audacity, a working understanding of Flemish, a considerable knowledge of the wool, silk and lace trades of Bruges, plus a burning desire to succeed. Though a mere eighteen years old, he has the financial wisdom of one twice his age.

On his arrival at the ducal Palace on that evening of All Saints Day, he is briefly but graciously received in the ante-chamber by the Duke himself.

They exchange platitudes.

"Your Grace does me an inestimable honour in receiving me." He kisses the proffered ring.

"Signior, it is I and the City of Bruges who are honoured. We feel that your presence here will be of mutual benefit. Thanks to you, our trade will flourish and you will doubtless not go unrewarded."

"Your Grace is most kind."

There is a considerable pause whilst Arnolfini studies the Duke's blue slippers with the golden studs. What a waste of money, thinks Arnolfini.

Meanwhile the Duke is staring hard at Arnolfini's inclined head. What curious ears, thinks the Duke.

"How long do you plan to stay with us?"

There is a tiny delay while Arnolfini translates the French-inflected Flemish of the Duke back into Italian before replying in his own brand of Italian-inflected French.

"Your Grace, provided that you are willing, I would like to settle here permanently. I am pleased to say that I shall look upon this fair city of Bruges as my home. I was not born here but I hope to live here until I am called by my maker."

Giovanni perceives that the Duke is gratified by his answer. He knows that the Duke has no objection to foreigners living in Bruges. Indeed his Grace actively encourages the practice. After all, he is one himself. Giovanni has heard that the Duke delights in the cosmopolitan nature of the city and its internationalism; that he wants passionately for its foreign contingent to devote their lives and business affairs to the greater glory of Bruges, not merely to aggrandise themselves by making money.

Giovanni Arnolfini is well aware that he is committing his life to the service of the Duke. From now on he will be a Man of Bruges, the Duke's man, no longer Italian. That the operation will be hazardous he has no doubt but he welcomes the challenge. The battle lines have been drawn. Unequivocally he wears the Duke's colours on his sleeve; gladly will he fight and lay down his life for the Duke.

The Duke gives Arnolfini one of his penetrating looks.

"Perhaps you will marry one of our young burgesses."

"Perhaps so, Sire, or I may search among the hills of my native Tuscany for my bride. But in any case, I shall live here. Thanks to your inspirational leadership, Bruges is where the business of the world is done. Bruges will be my capital and my home."

The Duke is gratified by the compliment. The interview is at an end. It has lasted precisely ten minutes. It has done Arnolfini no perceptible harm. He permits himself the luxury of a secret smile as he retreats backwards out of the presence of Duke Philip.

Outside, a long line of dignitaries are waiting for an audience. A Chamberlain from the household, resplendent in gold and scarlet livery, escorts him to the Great Hall where the banquet is to take place. The Chamberlain shows him to a seat on one of the long tables stretching down the middle of the hall. The table is groaning with gold and silver plate, statuaries, gold saltcellars known locally as *salières du pavillon* and great swathes of flowers. He is introduced to his neighbour, Joos Vidt, a distinguished Burgher from the nearby city of Ghent. Their talk is desultory as they await the arrival of the Duke when the banquet can commence. They have a long wait. Three-quarters of an hour pass while they admire the glorious French tapestries gracing the walls of the hall, study the gold and silver plate, debate the rival merits of Flemish and Tuscan architecture and go in some detail into the intricacies of the wool trade.

Suddenly a brazen fanfare from the Minstrels' Gallery rudely interrupts their conversation, announcing the arrival of the principal guests, who process into the Hall to take their places on the high table.

The Lord Bishop of Bruges in full canonicals heads the procession. He will be well worth cultivating. He is followed by a gaggle of clerics, lesser Bishops, Deans and Chapter members. Next come the arts on which the Duke is particularly keen, represented by.the famous painters Jan van Eyck and his elder brother Hubert van Eyck. Arnolfini has heard a great deal about these painters, almost all of it favourable. He is curious to know more. There is a rumour that they are currently engaged on a major commission in the Cathedral of Ghent. But it is only a rumour. He does not know if it is true.

The faces come thick and fast. It is hard to make a judgment on every person. His neighbour, Joos Vidt, knows them all and gives a running commentary softly into Arnolfini's right ear as the grand guests of honour parade. Arnolfini files all the information away in his pigeonhole mind.

"That's Sir Baldwin de Lannoy. He's the Governor of Lille. Trust him as you would a serpent fanged. That little man with the beard and the limp is Jan van der Buerse. He's the Burgomeister of Bruges. Worth getting to know. He did me a good turn once. That's Maurice van Versenare of the Town Council. Harmless and useless but quite good fun. Oh and these must be the Ambassadors. Don't know them, except the English one. Don't have anything to do with him. Ah, here comes the Duke."

Arnolfini with the eye of a professional admires the gorgeous blue silk gown with gold leaf decoration and fur hat which the Duke has changed into since he last saw him. He thinks that the gold chain around his neck perfectly complements the Duke's gown. The Duke is preceded by his Chamberlain carrying an ivory wand. He shouts a ceremonial greeting to all in Norman French, "Approche! Approche! Tout le monde, approche!"

Everyone claps and shouts back, "Venons!"

Arnolfini notices that after the Duke come two of his sons, languid youths, exquisitely dressed in silks and satins and beaver hats. Will they be useful business colleagues? Can they by any chance be an entrée to the ear of their father? Possibly. Arnolfini stores it away in his capacious mind.

The Chamberlain raps his wand three times for silence The hubbub gradually subsides. Stillness and silence pervade the Hall, broken only by the soft crackling of logs on the fires around the room. The Bishop pronounces grace and all cross themselves as they say Amen. There is a great clambering over benches and huffing and puffing as elaborately clothed bodies strive to find their correct sitting positions. An excited babble rises up to the magnificent hammer beam roof as strangers introduce themselves to each other. The banquet has begun.

While musicians play up in the Minstrels' Gallery, an army of cup-bearers, pantlers, carvers and servers all wearing the Duke's livery march into the Great Hall and attend to the needs of the guests. The bewildering array of courses is served with the utmost splendour. Each dish is presented to each guest with great ceremony on a gold serving dish.

If the Duke's purpose is to impress his guests with the prosperity and financial security of Bruges, then he has succeeded abundantly in the case of one young Tuscan newcomer. Arnolfini has never seen such opulence, such munificence, such sheer display of heedless extravagance. Even those extrovert Medicis in Florence would be hard pushed to match this exhibition.

He toys with a delicious mouthful of venison in a sauce which ravishes the palate. His plate is whisked away by an invisible hand and immediately replaced by another tempting offering. Each new course is greeted by the consort of musicians who play up in the Minstrels' Gallery at one end of the Hall. Arnolfini studies the programme in front of him, written on vellum with gold embossing and an illuminated capital letter. He learns that the instruments are a citole, bagpipe, three recorders, a viol, harp, trumpet, hand organ, gittern, shawm, theorbo, timbrel and cymbals. He isn't much the wiser. He considers that the noise that they are making is invariably rough, frequently discordant, occasionally angelic, always rhythmical and never boring. But then Arnolfini would be the first to admit that he is not very musical.

He studies the tapestries again. They depict mythological hunting scenes. He wonders vaguely to himself why the hunters are so obsessed with killing such exotic creatures as hydra, wyvern, griffin, cockatrice and basilisks. Heraldry has been one of his hobbies from an early age.

He glances around the room. A thousand candles twinkle in a thousand silver sconces. In the six great fireplaces, three on each long wall of the Hall, large logs burn fiercely. Everywhere that Giovanni looks, there is splendour, opulence and magnificence.

By two o'clock in the morning he has eaten much too much. The Hall is hot. He takes a long draught of Rhenish wine from his goblet, wipes his mouth and his forehead with his napkin (for it is insufferably warm) and turns for a serious talk with his neighbour.

Joos Vidt and he have already had some desultory conversation during the meal about the food being presented, the quality of the tapestries, the relative differences between Tuscany and Flanders, Ghent as a place to live and work, the international situation, the difference between Chianti and Sauternes, the weather in Tuscany, the future of the Medicis and various other topics. But, if the truth be told, there has been so much food to consume that there has been little time for sustained conversation. But now, with a temporary hiatus between courses, their goblets recharged and the servants all departed, the two men find themselves discussing an exciting artistic project in which Arnolfini's neighbour is involved. At least Joos Vidt is clearly excited by the scheme. Arnolfini is not quite so sure. Cultural matters have never been his strong suit.

Arnolfini finds out that Joos Vidt is "an Alderman of the City of Ghent and a Churchwarden of the Cathedral Church of

St. John the Baptist in that fair city", as he puts it. He makes it sound all rather grand. Arnolfini wonders to himself just how much power and authority the offices carry. Probably not quite so much as Vidt thinks they do.

Joos Vidt explains to an attentive Arnolfini, who has always been a good listener, that he has commissioned on behalf of the Cathedral "two famous artists to paint for the Cathedral an enormous picture which will contain fourteen panels on one side and twelve more on the other, all on the same theme, a picture which will hang in one of the chapels of the Cathedral." The project sounds so ambitious that at first Arnolfini cannot comprehend the scale. He asks a question.

"What is the theme, sir?"

"I have spent all my adult life in the service of the church. Forgive me if I adopt the language of the pulpit."

He taps the side of his nose and gives Arnolfini the ghost of a wink. Arnolfini reciprocates by offering the flicker of a smile.

"The picture will depict the Redemption of Mankind by the supreme Sacrifice of the sacred Lamb which is of course a symbol for the Crucifixion of Our Blessed Lord Jesus on the Cross."

Arnolfini nods wisely without having comprehended what is being described. Why is this lamb being sacrificed? He decides to let Joos Vidt continue with his explanation. There will be plenty of time for questions later. Joos Vidt continues excitedly with his explanation.

"The Lamb will be surrounded by God in majesty, the Blessed Virgin Mary and St. John the Baptist." Joos Vidt's eyes twinkle with childlike delight as he outlines the story. "And there will a host of rulers and knights and hermits and apostles and pilgrims, hundreds of them, all converging on one spot to worship the Lamb, standing on an altar. The Mystic Lamb."

He is so excited by what he is describing that his speech spills out in a torrent of affectionate prose ending with an ecstatic sigh as he says the last three words.

Arnolfini listens intently, catching some of Joos Vidt's palpable enthusiasm. He lets the excitement subside for a moment or two before asking a question.

"Hundreds of Apostles, sir?"

"Well, twelve actually."

Both men laugh.

Arnolfini asks another question.

"Fourteen panels on one side, you say, and ten on the other?"

"No, no, sir, twelve. It is what is called a polyptych."

He separates the syllables fastidiously.

"It will be the greatest work of art in Northern Europe when it is finished," he pronounces with what almost amounts to smugness. "The whole project will take at least ten years, maybe more, to complete. But when it is finally installed in the Chapel of St. John the Evangelist on the south side of the nave in St. John's Cathedral in Ghent, the pilgrims will flock from all over Christendom to marvel and admire. Mark my words."

"You say that it is to be called The Mystic Lamb?"

"That is correct, sir."

"Wonderful!" breathes Arnolfini who feels instinctively that this paean of praise for a work of art which he has not seen yet merits a compliment. Tact has always been one of his secret weapons. "And who is painting this great work?" asks Arnolfini who has already guessed the answer.

Joos Vidt's eyes turn and gaze up the table towards the high table, past the Duke, past the Bishop and other dignitaries to where two men are sitting.

"There! Those two. Hubert and Jan van Eyck," he says with quiet pride. "That is Hubert on the left, in the blue gown with the fur trimmings. Jan is the one in green, with the gold chain around his neck, wearing the red turban."

Under pretence of drinking, Arnolfini stares long and hard at the two famous brothers about whom he has already heard so much from many quarters. Jan looks the more intense of the two – his long aquiline nose, sharp, inquisitive eyes and firm mouth bespeaking intelligence and perceptive observation. Hubert possesses the fuller, more mature face with heavy, drooping eyes.

A decent interval has now elapsed between the fourth and fifth courses. The diners have begun to get their third wind. The

Duke claps his hands softly twice. As if by magic, the musicians begin playing again and the army brings in the splendours of the fifth course.

"If you like," confides Joos Vidt to Arnolfini as he toys with a roast snipe, "I will tell you in more detail what is going to be in each panel of The Mystic Lamb. That is, if you are interested."

Arnolfini's attention is interrupted by a servant presenting him with a gold salver on which sits demurely a curlew, looking for all the world as if it may be about to lay an egg. Arnolfini neither knows nor cares anything about birds. Birds to him are objects which people shoot for fun or food. But he gets aesthetic pleasure from the pretty picture on his plate. With his hands he breaks open the soft breast of the curlew and dips the meat in a dish of almond cream.

"Yes," replies Arnolfini in his formal Flemish, "I should very much like to hear all about The – what do you call it – Mystic Lamb."

If the truth be told, he is not particularly interested in the picture and its subject, but what does interest him are the artists. He wants to learn more about the van Eycks. They could be very useful to him. He gnaws at his bird as Joos Vidt begins his story.

"It all starts," says Joos Vidt, his mouth stuffed full of snipe, "with the Cumaean Sibyl."

As Arnolfini listens and chews on the leg of his curlew, he gazes at the younger of the two famous painters. One day, he thinks, perhaps Jan van Eyck will paint my portrait. Now that really would be something.

Chapter 8

All Saints Day, 1420

"Forgive me if I plead ignorance. Who exactly is or was the Cumaean Sibyl?"

The Banquet is over, the debris cleared, the long trestle tables dismantled, the musicians and masquers departed. Amid gracious farewells, the Duke has retired.

Guests are strewn around the Hall, digesting their gargantuan meal. Many are asleep, snoring loudly. In front of one of the many fires, Joos Vidt and Giovanni Arnolfini are sitting on a wooden settle with a high back, topped by lattice work. Dogs are rooting around on the floor, finding a plentiful supply of discarded food. Joos and Giovanni stretch out their feet on the rush-strewn floor. Their stomachs groan. But excited by the wine, the food and the heat, their minds are hyper-active.

"The Cumaean Sibyl? I am not in the least surprised, my dear sir, if you know nothing of her. I have met few people who have heard of her. Even learned theologians and academics profess ignorance."

"Oh, I am glad that I am not the only one in the dark. Where does she come from?"

"By a curious coincidence, she comes from your home country."

"Italy?"

"Precisely, Italy."

"Strange. I have never heard of her."

"I am not surprised. She was somewhat of a recluse."

"Where did she live in Italy?"

"In a cave, near the sacred grove of Artemis and Apollo at Cumae."

"And where exactly is that?"

"Near Naples."

"I see. And what could this sibyl do?"

"Ah, like all sibyls, she possessed the gift of foretelling the future. Furthermore, she was like us two."

"Really? Like us?"

Arnolfini looks puzzled.

"She was literate!"

Both men laugh.

"She wrote her prophecies on leaves which she bound into nine books. Once upon a time she had nine books of prophecies. These she offered to Tarquin Superbus, King of Rome."

"When was this?"

"Oh, about five hundred years before Christ."

"And?"

"And Tarquin, being a proud man as his epithet suggests, disdained her offer and refused them."

"What a fool! What did she do?"

"She burnt three of her books and offered the remaining six to Tarquin at the same price as the original offer."

"What did he do? Don't tell me. He accepted under duress."

"Oh, no. He refused again."

"He refused! What a stubborn man! What did she do?"

"She burnt three more books and repeated her original offer. By that time Tarquin the Proud had learnt a very hard lesson for him, true humility."

Arnolfini laughs, a rare event. It takes a good deal to make him amused.

"So what did this humble king do then?"

Joos Vidt beams at Arnolfini and wipes his sweating forehead with a linen napkin before replying.

"He bought the last three books, known as the Sibylline Books, which were consulted by the Roman Senate. It was the Cumaean Sibyl, incidentally, who accompanied Aeneas to the Underworld on his visit to his father, Anchises. But that is another story for another time."

Giovanni Arnolfini leans forward and stares with hooded eyes at Joos Vidt. He likes knowledge. Knowledge is power. He determines to find out all he can about this masterpiece in the making.

"So what is this Sibyl prophesying?"

"She is using the words of St. Augustine – *Rex altissimus adveniet per secula futurus scilicet in carne.*"

Joos Vidt does not insult Arnolfini's intelligence by translating the Latin. For his part Giovanni understands that the Sibyl is prophesying that a king most high will come in human form on earth for eternity.

"I see. Are there any more prophets in the picture?"

"Of course, you've guessed it. There are three," replies Joos Vidt. "The Erythrean Sibyl will use the words of Vergil from the Aeneid. *Nil mortale sonans afflata es numine celso.* You could translate that as meaning, 'He speaks with no mortal tongue but is inspired by power from on high'."

"Quite," says Arnolfini who has understood perfectly what Vergil has said but is too polite to say anything. "And the other two?"

"The other two are great Christian Prophets, Zacariah and Micah. They foretell the coming of Christ. These four prophets will be depicted in four lunettes at the top of the Retable."

"What is a Retable?"

"That's the polyptych when it is closed, in other words, when the two outer panels are shut."

"I see."

Giovanni has kicked off his red slippers. He stretches out his stockinged feet voluptuously towards the fire.

"So we have these four prophets on what you call the Retable. I think you mentioned that there were twelve pictures. What else will there be?" he asks as he luxuriates in the warmth.

Joos Vidt smiles benevolently as he considers his answer. He likes giving mini-lectures. It makes a pleasant change from sermons.

"Below the four prophets there will be a room, painted on four panels, a beautiful, mysterious chamber. At the rear there will be a colonnaded arch through which you will be able to see an elevated view of an imaginary city. A city very like Ghent, say, with its Cathedral. From this room, you will be able to look down on an elegant and busy street scene with the citizens of

63

Ghent going about their daily business."

"So we have a room with a view. Is there any furniture in the room?"

"Not as such, but there will be a niche with an ewer, a basin and a towel for ablutions."

"Ah, that pre-supposes the room is used by someone," observes Arnolfini who is intrigued by the puzzle.

"You are right. There are two people in the room."

There is a tiny pause as Arnolfini ponders the possibilities.

"Don't tell me, let me guess. Not two more sibyls surely?"

Joos Vidt shakes his head.

"Two more prophets of the minor sort?"

A giggle.

"Well, two saints perhaps? No? How about two honest burghers of Ghent? I know. It is the Duke and the Duchess? No? I see I'm hopelessly at sea. Go on, tell me, please, who is it?"

Joos Vidt looks round the room before replying to make sure no one is overhearing their conversation. Clearly what he is about to say is, for the present, confidential. He leans forward and grips Arnolfini's arm firmly. Giovanni can't help noticing that there is more perspiration on his brow. His voice quivers with suppressed excitement.

"What Hubert van Eyck has conceived is a contemporary representation of the Annunciation."

"I see."

"He is going to place the Archangel Gabriel and the Blessed Virgin Mary in an ordinary Flemish room."

"Yes."

"A room which is not very grand but which we shall all recognise as belonging to someone who is living today in a city like Bruges or Ghent."

"How will he paint the Archangel and the Virgin?"

"What do you mean?"

"I mean will they be realistic, contemporary figures, will they be stylised or what?"

"Oh, I see. They will be painted in an ivory monochrome, as though they were carved out of stone. I have seen the preliminary sketches and cartoons – they are enormously exciting, infinitely daring."

Joos Vidt's face glistens in the candlelight. He takes a long draught of wine from a silver goblet before wiping his mouth on the back of his sleeve. Arnolfini notes the social solecism with surprise. He has seen Tuscans behave like this but thought that top Flamands, especially members of the church, knew better. Ah well, life is a learning process and every day brings surprises, especially in Bruges.

Once more the eyes of Joos Vidt transfix Arnolfini's as he settles back in his seat to continue his description.

"You must understand, sir, that such a picture has never been painted before. The Archangel Gabriel with huge wings will carry Madonna lilies to symbolise his purity. From his aristocratic attitude and his lively features Gabriel will be one of the most striking figures of the whole retable. His ivory-coloured garment harmonises perfectly with the oak beams of the ceiling and the soft hues of this cosy room. And Mary will have the Holy Ghost in the shape of a dove hovering above her head as she crosses her hands reverently over her breast."

"You spoke of texts written above the prophets and sibyls. Are there any words in this room?"

"I'm glad you asked. Yes, above the Archangel is written in gold *Ave Gratia plena Dominus tecum* or, as you well know, *Hail, thou that are highly favoured, the Lord is with thee.*"

"And over Mary presumably there will be her response which is, if I remember correctly, *Ecce Ancilla Domini, Behold the handmaid of the Lord.*"

"Precisely. Yes, those three words will appear over her head. But – and this is a big but – there is a surprise in store for you. The words will not appear conventionally."

Joos Vidt starts to giggle. It is a minute or so before he can control himself and get the next words out.

Arnolfini waits patiently. He is in no hurry. He is enjoying Vidt's exposition too much to be in a hurry. But the explanation when it comes totally surprises Giovanni.

"The words, don't you see, will be upside down."

"Upside down?"

"Upside down, I do assure you."

65

"But why on earth?"

"Why on earth – that is the subtle point. Can you not hazard a suggestion?"

Arnolfini thinks for some moments.

"So that they are incomprehensible."

"No, but you are warm. Try again."

Arnolfini ponders anew.

"So that ordinary mortals, like you and I cannot read them unless...unless...unless they live in a topsy-turvy world and stand on their heads."

"I like it, I like it, I love it. But you are hopelessly wrong, my dear sir."

This is said with the utmost benevolence. Both men roar with laughter.

When they have recovered their composure, Arnolfini confesses himself baffled.

"Very well. Let me put you out of your agony. The words are painted upside down so that only the Holy Ghost and no one else will be able to read them."

Joos Vidt sits back in triumph and mops his brow.

Giovanni considers the implications for a minute before replying.

"Amazing," he murmurs, "what a daring concept!"

"Indeed, indeed, it will be a remarkable picture. You must also realise that the whole room will be completely realistic but that the figures therein, the Archangel and Mary, will be sculptural."

There is silence for several minutes as both men think about the picture. The crackling of the wood in the fire, the cracking of bones in the jaws of hungry hounds and the symphony of snoring from exhausted guests are the only sounds in the great Hall.

Arnolfini has thought of another question and starts another discussion.

"Is what you have described so far – the four prophets and the room with Mary and the Archangel – the whole of the retable?"

"Oh, no," exclaims Joos Vidt excitedly, "Below the

prophets and the Annunciation scene there will be four figures, all of them almost life-size."

"Four?"

"Yes, they will be set in stone niches. The two central figures will be painted in monochrome to look like stone."

"Who are they?"

"On the left will stand John the Baptist holding a Lamb; on the right John the Evangelist with a chalice. So there you have them, the two Johns, representing on the left the Coming of the Saviour and on the right the Fulfilment and Atonement of Our Lord. Utterly appropriate to our great Cathedral, don't you think, sir?"

Giovanni is quick to see the point of St. John the Baptist without fully grasping the significance of St. John the Divine. He asks for an explanation.

"Don't you see, my dear sir, the two Johns – how perfectly appropriate they are? Our Cathedral in Ghent, formerly St. Bavon's, is now dedicated to John the Baptist. Now within that great edifice, in one of the chapels on the south side of the nave, will hang The Mystic Lamb, as the whole polyptych will be called. And that chapel is dedicated to St. John the Divine, author of the fourth Gospel."

"And of course the last book in the New Testament," adds Giovanni who knows his Bible.

"Yes, sir, St. John's Revelation with his apocalyptic vision of the world as seen from the island of Patmos."

"Precisely. So I take it that the two great saints will stand there in their stone niches, sanctifying and lending dignity and authority to the story of The Mystic Lamb as well as being singularly appropriate to the Cathedral."

"Exactly. You have explained it most pertinently. I congratulate you."

Joos Vidt pauses and looks around him astonished. He has suddenly noticed something.

"My goodness, it is full daylight already. I must go home. I have a thousand things that need my attention. The rest of The Mystic Lamb must wait for another day. But I hope I have whetted your appetite."

"You have indeed, sir. But you never told me who is going to occupy the last two niches of the bottom line. Somebody pretty important I presume. More saints?"

At that Joos Vidt laughs long and loud, as a servant helps him on with his heavy, scarlet cloak.

"John the Baptist and John the Divine may be dead, Signor Arnolfini, but I can assure you that these two people are very much alive."

He looks quizzically at Arnolfini who shrugs his shoulders to signify his inability to guess who it may be.

As he pulls on his gloves, Joos Vidt puts him out of his misery.

"The one on the right will be a woman, the one on the left a man, both of them citizens of Ghent."

His blue eyes shine and his bald head perspires as he enjoys teasing Arnolfini. A servant hands Vidt his silver-headed stick.

"Come on, sir, have a stab, who do you think it is? I'll give you a clue, you've met him."

Arnolfini thinks long and hard; he hazards the name of the Duke and his bride.

"No, no, no, my good sir, you are well wide of the mark. The person occupying the right hand niche will be my wife, Isabelle Borluut. And the man on the left will be none other than the humble and at the same time very proud servant you see standing before you."

"You?" cries Arnolfini incredulously.

"Me!" replies Joos Vidt and his little eyes twinkle. "Good day to you, sir, and God's blessing go with you. I have very much enjoyed the pleasure of your company and conversation."

With a parting giggle and a wave of his hand, he limps out of the Hall.

Arnolfini is left pondering. As he puts his red slippers back on, a thought strikes him about the great picture which Vidt has been describing.

"Funny old bird, that Vidt, but not without considerable charm. Obviously a man of influence. Well worth knowing. Fancy getting the van Eycks to paint his portrait. That is clever. H'm, I wonder. I wonder. Why not? Maybe one of them will paint my portrait. Now that really would be something to write home about."

Giovanni Arnolfini walks down the long curving marble staircase of the Duke's Palace and out into the bright sunshine of Bruges.

Chapter 9

Scheveningen, 1422

Cities excite me. I am by nature a townsman. Built beside a river or straddling it, clustered around an ancient cathedral with imposing civic buildings, a city has a sense of purpose, of order, of progress. It is a civilised place where one meets civilised citizens going about their civil duties. Men of culture live in cities. It is only the hermit, the barbarian or the peasant who forsakes the city.

Speaking personally, I do not find Scheveningen, this tiny hamlet beside the sea, very exciting. To tell the truth, I am not particularly enamoured of the sea itself. For me the ocean is merely an uncomfortable and unpredictable barrier across which one sometimes has to voyage to reach one's destination. I do know what I am talking about. I have had to make several voyages and doubtless will go on more. Very uncomfortable.

The sea gives me no pleasure; I do not find it aesthetically pleasing. I am quite sure I shall never paint it. There is nothing to paint, just a low horizon and endless repetitive waves. It is featureless. True, it can change its mood, prove extremely fickle. So can a wild animal but that is no recommendation to an artist.

The most fascinating landscape for me is the human face. I can explore for ever its hills and valleys, its outstanding features and hidden charms, its mysteries and meanings. Human beings are infinitely variable, endlessly intriguing.

Over there, across that bleak sea, beyond that low horizon, lies England. Inhabited as it is by a race of barbaric people led by their warmongering King Henry V, I certainly have no desire to go there. No thank you, I would far rather go south or east or even north. Anything but west.

Here I am, walking on the beach at Scheveningen, waiting

for my brother who has suggested this absurd rendezvous.

What exists on a beach? Pebbles and sand. Look at this pebble. It is like a million others here. Totally devoid of character and significance. And this beach is like a million others. If I throw this stone into the sea – as I do now – it vanishes. It makes no mark. It creates a minute splash that is over in the twinkling of an eye. My action has made no difference to humanity, to the beach, to the sea, to the future of the world.

If I were to repeat my action a million times, it would still make no difference or have any significant effect. What can you do with sand? Very little. I grant that it can be useful in the building trade. But every adult in Flanders could come here with a horse and cart, help himself to a load of sand and there would still be millions of wagonloads left for the French, the Scandinavians, the Spanish, the Portuguese and the rest of the world. So much for the strand and the sea.

Now where is my brother Hubert? He should be here by now and there's no sign of him. He told me to meet him on this beach at Scheveningen between the hours of ten and eleven o'clock. Here I am. I've walked out from 'sGravenhage whose skyline I can see behind me. I wonder why he has chosen such a God-forsaken spot. I think of my clever, elder brother as essentially one who loves domesticity, a town-dweller, an indoors man.

But then I have never really understood him. Brother Hubert has constantly surprised me by his genius, his unpredictability, his capacity to have thoughts beyond the limits of man's imagination, his astonishing virtuosity with paint, his mastery of oils, his profound knowledge and understanding of human beings, his intense interest in religion, his compassion for all human beings and, above all things, his undying love of Christ.

Yes, he's a strange man. I do not really understand him but I do know that I love and admire him as much as I do any of my other brothers and sisters. I certainly think that he is the cleverest man I have ever met and the one who has taught me most about my craft as a painter. In fact I can say in all honesty that I owe everything to brother Hubert.

What's that dot to the north? Someone coming from Wasenaar. Ah, I recognise that loping stride long before I can distinguish the features. That unmistakably is my brother.

"Greetings, brother Hubert. I salute you in the name of our respected and hallowed mother and father whose memories we shall always treasure and revere. You are well met in this strange, nebulous place, neither sea nor land. As always, I take great pleasure, comfort and inspiration in your company."

We embrace each other warmly.

Before he replies, Hubert gives me a long, quizzical look, as though he is assessing my mental and physical health.

"I thank you, brother Jan, for your gracious greeting. Well met indeed. Let us walk towards 'sGravenhage. I have had business in Wasenaar and am heading for Delft which is why, knowing as I did that you were working here, I suggested a meeting at this spot. Not, I grant you, a very propitious or prepossessing place but it serves its purpose. It will serve," he adds cryptically, as we trudge inland over the dunes. For a time we walk in silence, partly savouring the pure pleasure of being reunited in each other's company once again, partly short of breath negotiating the steep sand dunes that lie ahead of us. When we have achieved a measure of level ground, Hubert addresses me.

"I must say, as always, brother Jan, I take immeasurable pleasure in being reunited with you. I may be head of the family now that our parents are dead, the one with his major achievements behind him. But you are the white hope for the future, the one whose enormous talents are as yet to be realised."

When I make as if to protest, Hubert silences me with a gesture.

"It is true. You may not realise it now but for us who live by paint and the brush there is no doubt about your talent. For me The Mystic Lamb is the culmination of all my artistic endeavours. But you assuredly have greater triumphs ahead of you, unsuspected even by you. I may not live to see them, but I rejoice in the certainty of their coming. They will come, Jan, they will come."

This is said with a gentle shaking of his head and a light gripping of my elbow. I smile at the graciousness of the compliment and the warmth of brotherly love displayed. Modesty and a curious lump in my throat prevent my replying. I would like to embrace brother Hubert again but northern sensibilities, the unrelenting pace that he is setting on the walk and the keen north wind which forces both of us to keep our heads down preclude such a display of affection.

Further conversation does indeed prove impossible until we have negotiated the muddy outer streets of s'Gravenhage (not a gracious town) and penetrated to the centre of the city where, in the market square, we enter a tavern, more from need for sanctuary from the biting wind than the desire for refreshment.

When we have settled down in front of a blazing fire in the hearth, Hubert asks me, "How goes your work in Den Haag?"

I give him a brief account. Then it is my turn to ask a question, in this case a leading one.

"What about The Mystic Lamb, brother?"

"I am glad you ask me, Jan. That is what I want to talk about to you. You know that I have been working on the project for two long years."

I nod. I am only too aware of the enormous task that my brother Hubert has set himself. What I am not sure is how my brother has been getting on for I have not seen him for, how long? Oh it must be nearly nine months. So I listen to his account with the keenest of interests.

"On the outer panels, the Retable, I have completed the four prophets at the top who announce the Redemption of us all through the Sacrifice of the Lamb. I am reasonably satisfied with that work."

"That is good, brother, I look forward to seeing them shortly."

"Now down at the bottom I have painted in monochrome, as though they were carved in stone, the two Johns. I hope you will like them."

"I am sure I shall, brother."

"But what exercises my mind and my hand at the moment is the large scene in the middle of the Retable."

"What is that?"

"It is the Annunciation. A contemporary room in which we find the Archangel Gabriel on the left, the Blessed Virgin Mary on the right with several windows looking out on a modern city scene."

"All that sounds very impressive. But have you started on anything in the main picture?"

"Only God in Majesty. That is going to take me some considerable time."

"Why?"

"On account of the amount of jewellery involved."

"Of course. I see."

"But now I want to discuss with you what portion of the Lamb you are going to undertake. As you know, I have made significant progress in the past two years. But the size of the task daunts me. As I envisage it, I have over three hundred portraits to paint, to say nothing of an extensive landscape with a profusion of different species of flowers and trees, numerous architectural features in the townscape, a large number of gowns, quantities of jewellery and, oh yes, quite a few horses."

"That sounds an enormous task."

"It is. I am worried that I may not have enough time left in my life to complete the whole venture. After all, I am seventeen years older than you. I feel in excellent health at the moment. My strength is unimpaired. But you never know, God may call me whenever He chooses."

For a moment his voice seems to falter. I keep silent for a space to allow him to recover. Then I put a simple question to him, a question which I know he is hoping I will ask.

"What would you like me to do? I am ready and willing to help in any way I can. That is, if you require my services."

I stare into those warm, compassionate eyes. He takes a sip of wine before replying.

"Well, brother, I am excessively grateful for your offer which I gladly embrace. Your forte is undoubtedly portraiture. That is something with which I imagine you would agree."

I nod.

"I require two more portraits on the Retable. Without them,

the exterior of the Lamb is incomplete. Already we have the four prophets at the top with Gabriel and the Virgin in the centre. But I now need two more people, one on each side of the two Johns at the foot of the Retable."

"The donors?"

"Precisely," replies Hubert, smiling at my perceptive guess.

"And they are?"

"Joos Vidt and his wife, Isabelle Elisabeth Boorluut."

"Ah, it so happens that I know this Joos Vidt. I met him briefly, brother, at that banquet we both went to which the Duke gave in Bruges two years ago. For foreigners. You remember?"

"Of course."

"Yes, well I spoke to Vidt for a few minutes. He was closeted with some Italian man of business. I rather liked what I saw of Joos Vidt. Of the Italian gentleman I am not so sure. He was a strange-looking person. But I will gladly undertake to paint the donors."

"Good."

"Kneeling of course?"

"Of course."

"In monochrome or colour?"

"Well, the two Johns are in monochrome. Vidt and Boorluut would contrast admirably with them if they were painted in colour. I see them in red predominantly."

"I agree."

"I think you will find Joos Vidt an interesting man to paint. He has been very influential in the affairs of the Cathedral where of course The Mystic Lamb is going to hang. He has been most enthusiastic about the venture, to say nothing of his financial support. His wife, incidentally, keeps a watchful eye on all his doings. You will like painting her."

"Why?"

"Oh, because she is a most compelling individual with a strong personality and a mind of her own. I suspect she exercises a considerable influence on her husband and may even control the purse strings."

"Really? Well, that sounds very interesting and I look forward to meeting them both and painting them. So that

75

accounts for two panels. Now is there anything else I can do? What about inside?"

"Here we have problems, many of them, which must be resolved. There are the varying scales, the sheer size of the composition, the iconography, matching the colours, choosing the appropriate holy texts, balancing the Old and New Testaments. I can assure you that the difficulties are multitudinous. I pray daily for divine guidance."

"Are you receiving it, brother?"

"Undoubtedly."

He smiles at me and I smile back. The warmth in that room is generated by more than the fire. We feel very close to each other.

I ponder the position and realise that he must make the suggestion. I have made an offer; it is for him to lay down the ground plan. His knowledge and experience are far superior to mine. Furthermore, he even knows my capabilities better than I know myself. He is aware only too well what I can and cannot achieve.

"What would you like me to do?"

His long, slender fingers toy with the stem of his glass as he thinks for a moment. When he speaks, he weighs his words carefully.

The enormity of what he now says to me in a few words sinks fully into my consciousness only days later. At the time the words seemed so simple, so easy to say. I remember that the landlord walked through the room as he said them, that a cart rumbled by outside and that I even smiled as he said them. I now realise that these words were probably the most significant in the first half of my artistic career.

What brother Hubert said to me is, "I think you should paint Adam and Eve."

Chapter 10

Aviz in the Kingdom of Portugal, 1429

To the right worshipful Giovanni di Arrigo Arnolfini, at Bruges.

Right worshipful sir, I recommend me unto you in the most goodly wise that I can; and forasmuch as you desired of me to send you word of divers matters here, I write to you of them such as I can.

It has not been an easy journey. It has been arduous. Not to put too fine a point upon it, it has been hell.

I hate the sea and voyages upon it, however short. This one has been long and tedious. At first I was sick, very violently. I did not master the movement of the ship for at least four days during which I went through purgatory.

Then everything on board a ship is unstable and creaks – the rigging, the sails, the deck, the mast, even sometimes the crew. It is impossible to find a level place. My brain and body are in continual turmoil.

I was under the impression that the Venetians were the finest sailors in the world. In the light of my experience, I must now revise my opinion. Venetian sailors are foul-mouthed, blasphemous, incompetent, licentious, cowardly braggadocios. But I quite like them, when they are sober. They have interesting faces and tell good stories, even though most of their yarns are lies.

I can assure you that the two galleys they sent us from the Adriatic were far from seaworthy. Most of us were sick, almost before we set sail from Sluis. Certainly, Master John Hilbert, the Secretary, and Peter de Vauldres, the Cupbearer, were vomiting all over the deck. Of Sir John de Lannoy, Lord of Rouhaix and Harzeele (who calls himself a diplomat), Councillor and first Chamberlain of the Duke, I saw little. Wisely he kept himself to his cabin, incidentally the only one on the ship, apart from the Captain's. I hazard a guess that even all those grand titles did little to save him from the terrors of the deep.

This is my third mission for the Duke. I went on a secret pilgrimage two years ago (about which I may say nothing – my lips are sealed); again I set sail last year and now here I am in this year of Our Lord, 1429, on this accursed voyage. To make matters worse, I shall not see for at least one year my wife, Margaret, whom I married on 2nd August, 1426, – the Feast Day of the blessed St. Basil the Great, bishop and doctor.

On the 18th September, two years ago, occurred the saddest moment of my life so far. My beloved brother, Hubert, so much more talented than I, a truly great man and a divine painter, died. My grief is still so immured within my soul and body that I can write no more on this subject.

You ask me to paint your portrait. I am flattered and interested by your request but must decline. I am saddled with finishing The Mystic Lamb, an immense task which will take me years of labour. I will tell you about the Lamb, but not now. I will paint your portrait but not now. Find a good wife and I will paint you both, but not now.

What I will now recount to you is what a dreadful voyage we had and some of the incidents on the way. It may amuse you to suffer with us from the sanctuary and stability of dry land some of the hazards which we had to endure.

As I said before, we embarked at Sluis in Flanders on 19th October, 1428. Our mission was to sail to Lisbon, to meet King John the First of Portugal, for me to paint the portrait of his daughter, Isabella, and to bring her back for Duke Philip to marry in Bruges.

It all sounded simple enough on dry land when the proposals were discussed with the Duke. But what a performance we had once we put to sea! Sir John de Lannoy was the head of the mission, accompanied by his brother, Sir Baudouin de Lannoy, whom I had met when he was Governor of Lille where I was working two years ago. He was a man I both liked and admired. I felt I could trust him.

Then there was Master Giles d'Escornaix, Doctor of Law,

Provost of Harlebeke and Court Referendary, a pompous man if ever I saw one, but clever as a ferret and as sharp-nosed; Andrew de Thoulongeon, Lord of Mornay, Councillor and Chamberlain (no fool he, but dangerous and untrustworthy); and a number of minor dignitaries whose names are unimportant but whom I list here for the sake of veracity – Hector Sacquespee, Baldwin d'Ognies (known as the Bastard of Bavaria, presumably a title of distinction, but having met the man I have my doubts), John de Baissi Esquire, Oudot Brain Esquire, and two Poursuivants, Renty and Portejoie. All in all we were a motley crew, far more impressive on land than at sea.

As for the real crew, those of them who were sober, and their villainous Captain, Master Caballero, we soon enough discovered their deficiencies in seamanship. A violent storm sprang up almost immediately after we had set sail. No sooner had we left the shelter of the estuary of the Zwijn than we felt the full force of the wind. A very strong south-east gale blew us straight across the English Channel. It was precisely the opposite direction to where we wanted to go. We landed the next day at some god-forsaken spot on the coast of England. I believe the Captain found out by looking at his charts that it was called Sandwich (I think that was the spelling, Heaven knows how it is pronounced). Nothing to see there – a few hovels, one small stone church, endless sand dunes. The whole landscape was flat and uninspiring. How can people live in such an uninteresting country? Such natives as we met seemed unintelligent, evil-looking and evil-smelling, barbaric and unintelligible. It is difficult to imagine how these dreadful people only a dozen years ago under their late King Henry V achieved such an astonishing and overwhelming victory over the full might of the French at a village called, I believe, Agincourt.

We were forced to wait in this foul place for over three weeks. I took the opportunity of the enforced delay to ride up to London. I was not impressed by this small, dirty, smelly city, straddling a broad river whose name I never mastered. Two buildings and only two gave me some pleasure. One was the parish church at the south end of the only bridge over the city's river. The church of St. Mary Ovarie was in a disreputable village called Southwark. I liked its slender white tower which I sketched.

The other edifice which could not help but catch my eye was the Cathedral of London, dedicated to St. Paul. It stands on a low hill and its spire is immensely tall. I cannot estimate its height but am confident that it is taller than any other spire in the whole of Europe. I made a detailed drawing of the Cathedral with its buttresses topped by its immense spire and the north transept. A very fine building.

Otherwise I am forced to say that London is a singularly undistinguished city which I am confident will never match the splendours of those in Flanders or Italy.

I rode back to the south coast of England over several pretty hills but sadly little else to attract my admiration unless you count innumerable sheep. Back at the little port we waited for what seemed an interminable time. Eventually two more galleys arrived from Venice to accommodate our extensive party more comfortably. I myself was accorded the luxury of a cabin to myself.

We set sail on 13th November, the Feast day of St. Brice, Bishop of Touraine. More vile weather. The persistent south easterlies kept blowing us westwards along the coast of England.

We sheltered at a place called La Chambre (I believe the English call it Shoreham or something like that), then we crept on to a port at the mouth of the river Plym. Here we found an excellent harbour with safe anchorage. Finally, we arrived at the mouth of the river Fal on 25th November where we stayed a week. We encountered more barbaric natives whose language was even less intelligible than those of Plymouth.

On 2nd December the winds abated and shifted to the north, God be praised! Despite our lack of faith in him, our Venetian Captain sailed on the tide and we had a good crossing, for which God be thanked. Nine days later we reached Bayona in Galicia, a small town on the Atlantic coast between Vigo and the mouth of the Minho. Paradise! We spent three days in this delicious place with its charming and courteous inhabitants before we sailed on to Cascais, a small seaport fifteen miles to the west of the immense Tagus estuary, the gateway to Lisboa. With what joy and thankful hearts did we sail up the majestic broad estuary of the Tagus to land safe and sound at Lisboa, capital of the powerful kingdom of Portugal.

How gratefully I knelt on Portuguese soil at the dockside and kissed the blue and white tiles of its pavement, giving thanks for having survived such a terrible and terrifying voyage, sixty-one days of pure torture.

We learnt almost immediately that His Majesty was at Estremoz, a small town in the province of Alentejo, some three or four days' travel.

The Herald Flanders informed the King of our arrival and the object of our mission. His Majesty sent a gracious and favourable answer which immediately caused us to advance to Arriollos and thence to Aviz where on 13th January, the Feast Day of St. Hilary of Poitiers, the King of Portugal and his royal family graciously received our Ambassadors who presented their letters of credence from Duke Philip.

On the next day at a formal convocation the Duke's proposals were made known to the Portuguese court in a Latin oration delivered by Giles d'Escornaix. A Doctor of the King's Council replied, also in Latin, albeit with a pronounced Portuguese accent. For the next few days the Ambassadors spent much time discussing the Duke's proposals with the Council.

Meanwhile I was closeted with the Infanta whose portrait I had come to paint. Let me say at once that I found her charming. She spoke no Flemish, I no Portuguese. The language we used was gestures with our hands, expressions on our faces, laughter in our throats. But I must hasten to add that she was far from flirtatious or immature. When I asked her to pose for me, she sat astonishingly still for long hours at a stretch.

Although I had never painted a portrait in oils before, the moment I started I felt at home and extraordinarily confident, almost dangerously so. Hitherto I had painted some miniatures, done some polychroming on figures outside the Town Hall and painted the full length nude Eve in The Mystic Lamb (for whom of course I had used a model).

You may well wonder, therefore, how I came to obtain the commission. There were three factors. The reputation of Hubert was so great that merely being his brother and an artist carried enormous weight. Secondly, my work on The Mystic Lamb had so impressed the authorities that I received the commission. Finally, my portfolio of portraits in crayon which I showed to the Duke convinced him that I was the right man for the task.

I determined to make the portrait as truthful as possible. In my make-shift studio I posed Isabella on my left. From a northern window poured that hard southern light which we never enjoy in Flanders. I painted her from the waist upwards, her torso at an oblique angle to me but with her face turning back towards me. Thus I created a slight tension between the head and the body as well as between the subject and the spectator. She wore a beautiful green gown, edged with fur. (Green, incidentally, is one of my favourite colours). Her hair was braided and bound in a single gold bandeau.

Isabella possessed a very high forehead which I accentuated. She had no eyebrows to speak of, a long, sensual nose, thin determined lips and a small, pert chin. Below her long, slender neck, when I painted her body, I deliberately changed the scale so that the head was fractionally bigger than the body. Finally, at the bottom, I placed her folded hands in the centre of the picture, exaggerating slightly the length and slimness of each finger.

I gave her a serious expression, but not too solemn. For her age of fourteen she looks much more mature than one might expect. But behind the hauteur I like to fancy that one can detect a sense of what the French call *joie de vivre*.

For four weeks I worked frenetically, doing preliminary sketches before I painted the finished portrait on a panel of wood which I had brought with me from Bruges, prepared with thirty-two layers of gesso grosso. Finally, I made an exact copy.

By the end of January, I had finished. Isabella liked it with certain reservations. His Majesty professed himself very satisfied. I had certain professional doubts. Ambassadors were despatched to the Duke, two by sea and two by land, each bearing a portrait of the Infanta.

So my task is complete. I take this opportunity to send my epistle by the Ambassadors going overland. You will read what I have done up to now. You may anticipate that I shall avail myself of the opportunity of making a pilgrimage to the important and famous shrine of St. James of Compestella at Santiago in Galicia. Presumably, once their mission is accomplished, the Ambassadors will return, contracts will be signed, and our vast fleet will sail for Flanders with the Infanta on board.

Much as I dread the thought of that voyage, my terrors are mollified by the thought of returning to Bruges, to my beloved wife, to all my friends amongst whom I number you, and to my work.

Meanwhile I am delighted that your business affairs prosper. You are truly one of us now, a citizen of Bruges. I look forward to renewing and strengthening our acquaintance some time next year. Who knows, some day I may well paint your portrait.

Written of mine hand, St. Valentine's Day, 1429, at Aviz

God be with you

Your friend, Johannes de Eyck.

Chapter 11

Ghent. 6th May, 1432

The morning of Tuesday, 6th May, 1432, dawns bright and clear. It is going to be a glorious day. Over the steep gabled houses of Ghent the sun rises with hardly a cloud in the sky.

As soon as it is daylight, the narrow streets are thronged with the good citizens of Ghent. All move in one direction, all seem to be wearing their best clothes, all have a sense of purpose, all are extraordinarily excited. By 8 o'clock, the nave of the Cathedral Church of St. John's is packed. Hundreds upon hundreds of eager citizens are jammed into the nave where they await patiently the nobility and the Cathedral Chapter, the famous and the unknown. Shoulder to shoulder they stand. Save for a very few lucky ones who 'go to the wall' – the old, the infirm, the expectant mothers – there are no seats. Soon the temperature in the Cathedral, hitherto chilly, begins to rise uncomfortably. The first of many faintings occur. A rumour even spreads, completely unconfirmed and without authority, that a woman has given birth in a side chapel.

The 6th of May is the Patronal Festival of the Cathedral, the Feast Day of St. John the Baptist. He will be celebrated with a High Mass. The real excitement will begin when Mass is over. Today, the new treasure of the Cathedral, known to all as The Mystic Lamb, or The Adoration of the Lamb, will be unveiled. It has been placed in the south side of the Cathedral in the Chapel dedicated to the other John, St. John the Divine, St. John the Evangelist, author of the fourth Gospel and the man who had such an apocalyptic and eschatological vision on the island of Patmos which produced his final masterpiece, the Revelation.

It is rumoured among the crowd that all the most important

people in Flanders and even further afield will be coming. What the congregation chiefly wants to see of course is the Duke and his new Portuguese wife. She has not been seen in public since her arrival from Lisboa. She is rumoured to be incredibly beautiful. As well as her and the Duke, Chancellors, Cardinals, Bishops, Ambassadors, Diplomats, soldiers, goldsmiths, painters, and other eminent citizens are all expected to attend. Standing patiently, Dirc says to his neighbour, "This is going to be a sight for sore eyes, Hans, we're not going to see anything like this again in our lifetime. Let's make the best of it and enjoy it while we can." Hans merely grunts in reply but then he does have an elbow resting across most of his face. It is doubtful if he is going to see much today.

By 9 o'clock expectation has reached fever pitch. No fewer than twelve of the congregation have fainted and been carried away. A loud altercation in one corner reveals that a pickpocket has been successfully at work. The air is heavy with the scent of rosemary which has been liberally spread along the centre aisle as a carpet for the great and good.

Suddenly, a piercing fanfare from long trumpets rings out from the transepts. The enormous west doors of the Cathedral are flung open and a procession of great dignity makes its slow and solemn way up to the Sanctuary. It is time for the congregation to gape and gawk.

First comes a Virger in black silk cassock, holding his staff of office, a long silver rod. He points it out in front of him, looking for all the world like an ecclesiastical water diviner. Where he indicates with his silver virge, his four junior Virgers accompanying him push the crowd back.

The great processional cross is carried aloft into the Sanctuary surrounded by four Censers. Next come the Choir in surplices, led by their Cantor. They are singing a processional Introit, *Rex omnipotentiae*. Behind them comes the Chapter of the Cathedral, the minor Canons, all of them coped and vested, including Canon Van der Paele, severely crippled by arthritis, limping along on a stick. Several Bishops follow, with bejewelled mitres and croziers. Then in all his glory His Eminence Nicolas Albergati, Archbishop of Bologna and Vicar of Santa Croce in Gerusalemme, attended by two acolytes holding his scarlet robe. As he processes, he blesses the people on either side of the narrow gangway with a kindly smile and benevolent twinkling of his friendly eyes. Those fortunate enough to be within touching distance, kiss his ring. Almost all, as he passes, genuflect or bow their heads.

In striking contrast to the all-pervading sartorial splendour around him, Nicolaes van Maelbaeke, the 29th Provost of the Abbey of St. Martin at Ypres, stands out in his simple, plain black Dominican habit.

Jean Rolin, Bishop of Autin, makes a curiously diffident entrance, overshadowed by his eminent forerunner. The Cardinal Bishop of Ghent, who is to celebrate Mass, concludes the spiritual procession which winds its way up to the Chancel.

If the splendour of the clerics' copes excited admiration and awe, it is eclipsed by the magnificence of the secular entourage which follows. Another Virger heads this part of the procession.

First come eminent representatives of the Painters Guild. They are led by Meester Jan van Eyck, esteemed Burgher of Bruges, co-author of The Mystic Lamb and brother of the legendary Meester Hubert. Jan van Eyck wears a brown velvet gown with long sleeves, trimmed with fur around the collar. The gown falls in natural folds to the knees where it is again edged with fur. He has a surcoat, red chaperon and red stockings over his pointed leather shoes. He carries a long ebony stick and walks with a slight limp as his piercing eyes seem to examine every member of the congregation.

Behind him there follow some distinguished painters, not all of them in the public eye. From the fair city of Bruges come some of Van Eyck's fellow artists – Petrus Christus and the much esteemed Hans Memlinc; from Tournai emanates Robert Campin, and all the way from Brussels, the great Rogelet de la Pasture, later to be called Rogier van der Weyden. From Louvain comes Dieric Bouts walking alongside van der Weyden who has such an influence on his style. Finally, bringing up the rear, citizen and artist pre-eminent of this great city of Ghent, the painter who will so impress the Italians, Hugo van der Goes. These men constitute at this moment the cream of Flemish painters. Of this number Jan van Eyck is the undoubted doyen.

The Guild of Craftsmen from Ghent, Bruges and Antwerp follows – Master weavers, lacemakers, wood carvers, carpenters, jewellers, ironsmiths, shoemakers, hosiers, silversmiths and two goldsmiths, both very distinguished in their very different ways, Jean Peutin and Jan de Leeuw.

There is in this group also a young man in a red gown wearing a green turban. His name is Gilles Binchois, poet and musician extraordinary at the court of Philip the Good. Some of the music to be played later in this service has been composed by him.

A frisson of excitement runs through the crowd as the next great personage is spotted. Preceded by another Virger, Nicolas Rolin of Autun (father of the Bishop), the Chancellor of Burgundy and Brabant, makes his impressive entrance. Now aged fifty-six, he not only looks powerful, he is also immensely influential. There is something cruel and sinister about that bullet-headed, closely cropped head. And yet appearances can be deceptive. Nicolas Rolin is in fact a very devout and humble man, albeit a ruthless one.

Later in his career he will found the Hospital of Beaune. He is a well-known benefactor and friend of the poor. Yet how severe he looks. (Hans and his friend cower under his glance). His beige, fur-trimmed gown, magnificently inlaid with intricate gold motifs, speaks eloquently of his wealth and prestige. He glances neither to left nor right as he makes his relentless way up to the Chancel.

Another Virger, another famous man. Baudouin de Lannoy, Lord of Molembaix, but known behind his back to one and all as The Stammerer, treads imperiously up the aisle. He it was who accompanied Jan van Eyck all those years ago on that perilous voyage to Portugal. Van Eyck did not much like him then and his predilection has not changed since. The Stammerer wears a perpetual scowl on his heavy jowelled face with that long chin and pimple on the left cheek. Like Chancellor Rolin, he is dressed in a beige gown with gold motifs. He carries a thin stick, his wand of office. Around his neck he wears the Order of the Golden Fleece. Duke Philip founded the Order on 10th January,

1430. Baudouin is inordinately proud of the fact that he was the first recipient of the collar on the very day on which it was inaugurated. The Golden Fleece glitters menacingly on The Stammerer's chest. It would take more than Jason and a score of Argonauts to wrest it away from Baudouin's proud grasp. As this powerful man strides arrogantly up the aisle, the people avert their eyes; instinctively they know who their friends and enemies are.

The gap between the rich and the poor is so immense that it is inconceivable that anyone can cross it. The divide between Lazarus and Dives is as great as when Jesus preached about it. Nothing can bridge the chasm. Better not even to look at the Promised Land from afar off across the river Jordan. "We shall never cross it," says Dirc to Hans, as he looks at the back view of The Stammerer. "That's for sure." Hans agrees.

The Burgomeister of Bruges, Jan van der Buerse, and the Burgomeister of Ghent in their chains of office step solemnly up the nave behind their mace-bearers and Town Councils which include Joos Vidt.

Lastly, the climax of the procession, its *raison d'être*, the man and woman whom everyone has come to see. First walk two Virgers. Then processes Colard Le Voleur, Valet de Chambre and, despite his name, trusted confidant of the Duke. Four Heralds with their heavily embroidered tabards walk stiffly before their lord and master.

To the delight and acclamation of the congregation who burst into spontaneous applause at the sight of their beloved ruler, Philip the Good, the third Duke of Burgundy and of Brabant, escorts his new bride, Isabella, daughter of the King John the First of Portugal, up the aisle to the two thrones placed for them in the Sanctuary.

It is the first time that she has been seen in public since the wedding more than two years ago (7th January, 1430). The question on every woman's lips is "Is she? Isn't she?" The consensus of female opinion in the Cathedral on this sunny May morn in the year of Our Lord, 1432, based on keen critical appraisal, is that she is not pregnant. Not yet.

The Duke is wearing a black velvet hat, tied under the chin.

His black velvet tunic with puffed sleeves comes down to mid-calf. His coat is open from throat to waist, revealing a scarlet silk shirt on which glitters the Order of the Golden Fleece. In his right hand he carries a baton which his wife lightly touches; on his left side his hand rests on a short, silver poniard. Black tights and narrow, pointed shoes complete an ensemble that conveys at one and the same time authority, fashion and humanity.

His wife's scarlet gown trimmed with ermine is neatly set off by a coiffe of six layers of finest Bruges lace worn over the traditional huvé hairstyle, swept back on the high forehead. The fact that Isabella is already fairly fluent in Flemish has endeared her to those of her new compatriots fortunate enough to have met her. She is much liked. If she were to give the Duke a son and heir, she would be even more popular.

This immense procession which has taken half an hour to proceed up the Nave finally reaches the Chancel. When all are seated, the choir sings a Gloria.

Gloria in excelsis Deo.
Et in terra pax hominibus bonae voluntatis
Laudamus te. Benedicimus te. Adoramus te.
Glorificamus te.
Gratias agimus tibi propter magnam gloriam tuam.
Domine Deus, Rex Caelestis, Deus Pater omnipotens.
Domini Fili unigente Jesu Christe.
Domine Deus, Agnus Dei, Filius Patris.
Qui tollis peccata mundi, miserere nobis.
Qui tollis peccata mundi, suscipe deprecationem nostram.
Qui sedes ad dexteram Patris, misere nobis.
Quoniam tu solus Sanctus. Tu solus Dominus.
Tu solus Altissimus, Jesu Christe.
Cum Sancto Spiritu in gloria Dei Patris.

Amen

The sound of that final, triumphant Amen soars around the triforium of the great Cathedral.

There is silence for the space of half a minute.

Then the voice of the Archbishop comes, distant but firm, as he prepares to celebrate Mass.

"Dominus vobiscum."

A rustle goes round the Cathedral as all cross themselves. A sound like the soft surging of the sea on a bed of pebbles comes back to the Archbishop and with it the congregation's response.

"Et cum spiritu tuo."

***

High Mass has been celebrated. The vast Cathedral of St. John's, so recently thronged, is now almost empty. Gone are all the Ghent citizens from the Nave. But in one chapel, half way up the Cathedral on the right hand side as you face the altar, there is a distinguished gathering. Let Jan van Eyck do the talking and explain what is happening.

"Your Grace, my Lady, my Lord Archbishop, Your Eminence, Honoured Guests, my Lords and Ladies, it is first my gracious and pleasant duty to welcome all of you to this Chapel, dedicated to St. John the Baptist on his Feast Day, the first Tuesday after the second Sunday after Easter.

So far you have graciously listened to my explanation of the Retable. You have heard the oracular pronouncements of the Sibyls and Prophets at the top. You have seen in the middle of the picture the Annunciation. You have witnessed at the foot the stone statues of the two St. Johns and you cannot fail to have noticed the two human beings flanking the saints in their own niches at the bottom.

May I present two people who are standing next to their portraits. On the right is the gracious Isabelle Borluut and on the left her husband, our much loved Churchwarden of this great Cathedral, Joos Vidt, without whose generous benefaction this whole project would not have been accomplished." There is a spontaneous burst of applause as the assembly acknowledges Vidt's generosity.

For Joos Vidt, perspiring slightly in his heavy wool gown, this is the happiest moment of his life, happier even than when he became a Churchwarden or when his wonderful wife bore him seven children. True, the work by the brothers van Eyck has cost him a fortune, a Duke's ransom if the truth were known. It has left him relatively impoverished. But he does not care. He has never intended to lay up for himself or his family treasures upon earth where moth and rust doth corrupt. He is happy, with an inner peace that passes all understanding, his soul purged of all impurities, ready to face his Maker.

Forty years earlier, as a young and inexperienced Burgher of Ghent, he had been involved in a financial peccadillo of petty embezzlement. Though he was acquitted at his trial, the stigma has remained, if not in his townsmen's memories, at least in his own heart. Now he feels that he has at last been vindicated and that his sin has been expiated by this very generous benefaction to the Cathedral. Enraptured, he listens to van Eyck's words.

The slightly nasal voice of Jan van Eyck continues with his peroration. "So far you have seen the twelve pictures on the outside, the so-called Retable. We are now about to open the two panels to reveal fourteen more pictures. Before Joos Vidt and I do that, I would like to pay tribute to my brother, Hubert van Eyck. He is the true author of this work. This huge picture or collection of images was his idea, his alone. Everything you have seen, everything you will see, was conceived and planned by him. Six years ago he died. Since then I have laboured to complete his great work. When you view the whole polyptych, do not ask what is his and what is mine. That would not only be an impertinent question, it would be irrelevant."

There is a brief but dramatic pause while the audience assimilate this information before Jan continues.

"This is a work of art, painted by my brother and me, which is dedicated to the greater glory of God. Its theme is the Redemption of Mankind by the supreme Sacrifice of the sacred Lamb."

Van Eyck nods to his good friend Joos Vidt. Together they open the two panels of the Retable to reveal for the first time to public eye the glories of The Mystic Lamb.

The reaction of that distinguished gathering is interesting and unpredictable. At first there is silence. It is not the silence of indifference; rather is it the silence of astonishment. Then as different people notice different things in the plethora of images presented to their amazed eyes, audible gasps and exclamations escape from their lips. With more than three hundred figures to look at, a heavenly landscape, rich costumes, precious jewellery, musical instruments, horses, God in majesty, different scales to be measured and reconciled, not to mention the two first realistic nudes ever painted, no wonder that it is several minutes before His Grace the Duke breaks into spontaneous applause which all emulate.

When the clapping subsides, Jan van Eyck briefly acknowledges the tribute before explaining simply the significance of the different panels. He takes a long wooden pole from a corner and uses it as a pointer to show the various elements which he is describing in the picture.

"Let me start at the top. You can see before you Adam and Eve, our grandparents, who committed the original sin, admitted into the blessed company of singing and musical Angels. They surround the Blessed Virgin Mary and John the Baptist seated on either side of Christ in Majesty.

The five lower panels contain one extended landscape in which knights and judges, pilgrims and hermits, disciples, holy men and women flock together around the Altar on which the Lamb is making the supreme sacrifice under the wings of the Holy Dove."

Van Eyck rests his pointer whilst his audience assimilate and digest this information. How can the assembled company express adequately their wonder and admiration of so palpably great a work?

It is the Duke who solves this problem. Words would have been totally inadequate. He merely does something very simple. Whilst everyone applauds, he walks forward and embraces Jan van Eyck.

In one corner of the Chapel, Isabelle Borluut is watching her husband. Never has she seen him so happy. Beneath the sparse and fluffy hair, his upper eyelids are tightened over his eyeballs; his lower lids droop so as to reveal the whites of his eyes. His brow is wrinkled with age, three or four prominent pimples stand out on cheeks and forehead, arteries break through at the temples, cheeks are flabby; in short, he's not much of a catch. And yet, and yet, she loves this man, warts and all, faithfully recorded for posterity by Jan van Eyck. Her own portrait she does not like. In her opinion the artist has made her far too severe. She thinks she looks like an Abbess whose regime has been so severe that there are no nuns left in her Abbey! But she loves the painting of her husband just as she loves this good and wise man, this honest, sincere, deeply faithful Alderman, her husband, the father of her children, patron of this Chapel, whose flabby cheeks are at this moment running with tears, tears of joy at a life's ambition fulfilled.

And still the Duke goes on embracing Jan van Eyck, and still the company applauds, and still Isabelle watches her husband as the tears continue to course down his happy cheeks.

Chapter 12

6th February, 1433

To my right worshipful lady, Giovanna Cenami, be this delivered in haste.

My most precious and best-beloved mistress and fellow Lucchese,

I recommend me unto you as lowly as I may, evermore hoping to hear of your good welfare; the which I beseech Almighty Jesu to preserve you, and to keep you in His pleasure and to your gracious heart's desire.

From the city of Bruges I send you greetings and abundant affection appurtenant unto me. To your parents my respectful salutations wing their way on the south wind. To your sister Joan, soon to be my new sister, I say all hail.

As you are undoubtedly aware, your esteemed father has happily given his gracious consent that I may formally make my addresses to you. That you will listen patiently and reverently to my impassioned pleas I know from your previous letters I may be assured. I flatter myself that my entreaties shall go neither unheeded nor unremarked.

But of course your response to my entreaties must be a matter for your conscience and your judgment after you have besought God to guide you in your choice. That you will choose wisely I have not one scintilla of doubt.

Soon I shall be walking beside the Seine with you on my arm. I intend to arrive in June, God willing. My business affairs (which flourish) keep me very active at this time of the year; June will be less hectic.

Bruges is very dank this month. It rains and rains. The streets are filthy, the Flemish citizens noisy, ill-tempered and rude. I have not been well treated by them. My Master, Duke

Philip the Good, could not have been more courteous. But because I am a banker and make a great deal of money out of wool trade, the citizens of Bruges resent it. They think that usurer, a mountebank, a Jew! Me!! A Jew?

am not ashamed to own that I am an Italian. So are you. I citizen of Lucca. So are you. I am proud of that fact. So I an. are are you.

We come from the fairest city in the fairest country in all the world. And you, my beloved, are the fairest of the fair, my Madonna, my Venus, my Aphrodite. How I miss you, as I last saw you, standing in our fair land under that hot sun and blue skies.

What of Paris? In the course of my business travels I visited it once and much admired it. Throw an Angel into the Seine and make a wish that you and I may be happily married before the Zodiac has run its full course.

In the meantime, I yearn to fold you in my arms. You are the most beautiful and precious jewel in all Europe.

To your esteemed father, Gugliemo, I send my respectful and profound greetings.

The Trinity have you in His mercy and keeping. May Our Saviour, the blessed Lord Jesus, send you God speed in all your affairs.

Written in haste on the Feast Day of St. Amand the blessed, Missionary Bishop of Maastricht.

Very heartily, with infinite affection,
your servant,
Giovanni di Arrigo Arnolfini

6th February, 1433
St. Walburgastraat
Bruges

To Giovanna Cenami
Rue Royale, Paris,
Seine, France

Chapter 13

Wednesday, January 22nd 1947

Painfully, with raw chilblains and frozen fingers, John is writing up his diary, as he has done every day of his public school life. What he writes is frequently trivial, usually bland and often boring. But in fifty years' time it may have some interest for an acquisitive school historian or archivist.

"Typical Easter term weather. An Arctic wind whistling over the downs has descended on this defenceless school. It is freezing cold and starting to snow. My dormitory is like an ice-box. The prefects, not noted for either their superior intelligence or humanity, have decreed that in order to maintain the school's reputation for toughness all windows in the dormitory must be kept open. Result: conditions which Scott at the South Pole would have found intolerable.

Let me tell future generations what I have on my bed. I start with two sheets and three blankets. Then I place over that a rug, two overcoats and a curtain. I top up the whole absurd concoction with all my games clothes and underwear. In fact I have used the entire contents of my chest of drawers except my handkerchiefs, socks and razor! I reckon that a Gillette blade gives little warmth. With all that weight the only problem is getting into bed!

To make matters worse, there is no heating because there is no fuel. Honestly, that wretched so-called Minister of Fuel, Emmanuel Shinwell, should be shot. People are already sick and tired of this awful Labour government under that little squit, Attlee.

No fuel, no food, no money, what a catastrophe! A hundred Colonel Blimps, all of them Tories of course, are saying in every town throughout the country that England has gone to the dogs.

Disgusted from Tunbridge Wells has a diatribe on the Letters Page almost every week in *The Daily Telegraph* or *The News Chronicle*. I'm inclined to agree with him. What did we gain from the War which we are supposed to have won? Why did everyone vote Labour two years ago? I shall have the vote at the next Election and I'm pretty sure it will go to the Conservative Party, whether it is led by Churchill, Eden or someone else.

After lights out in dorm last night, Michie said that the Conservatives under Churchill if they were in power would be doing just as badly as Labour. It was what he called post-war depression. Worlidge argued strongly for the Liberals. I stuck up for the Tories. The political debate ended with a pillow fight. Labour won."

This term John is sharing a study with Bill with whom he has a lot in common. Both have a love of literature, especially poetry and 18th century novels, an interest in art and the history of western painting (without much knowledge), a love of the cinema and Hollywood's latest offerings, anything to do with the United States, an unstinted loyalty to the Chaplains and the spiritual life of the school Chapel where both are servers at the Eucharist, and last but certainly not least a passion for all sport, especially cricket.

The rest of life they take as it comes with open minds, ready to accept or reject as the whim takes them. Actually John and Bill are a couple of invalids this term, feeling more than a bit sorry for themselves. The dormitory word for them is 'cripples'. Not very polite!

Bill has developed asthma and the school doctor has put him leave-off games. (There is a school legend about this doctor who took part in the London Olympics of 1904 as a long distance runner but whose stamina is not matched by his medical knowledge. One boy had broken his wrist which old Niffy, as he was known, set in plaster. "Come back and see me on Monday," he said to the patient. Back returned the boy on Monday only to be greeted by Niffy in his surgery with the memorable words, "Well, can you walk on it?")

John is also barred from rugby football. Last term he was badly tackled in a game of rugger and tore his cartilage. He had an operation in the holidays on his knee and of course is unable to play any rugger this term. Both boys are very frustrated by this turn of events. They love their sport – Bill is a distinctly useful full back and John had been hoping to make the second XV as fly half. Now both are condemned to cheering on the first XV from the touchline and playing a little desultory fives.

They are sharing study number twenty-two in New Court. They have spent the afternoon decorating it by sticking up pictures on the wall. The new Art Master has lent them *The Triumph of Death* by Pieter Bruegel the Elder, a picture which John finds gruesome but exciting. Bill has brought back a good reproduction which he bought in the V. & A. of *The Cornfield* by John Constable, which John thinks is a wonderfully placid painting, so evocative of East Anglia and summertime. Every summer before the war he and his parents used to spend their summer holidays at Southwold. When they got bored with Southwold's stony beaches, they would take a bus ride inland. It was these trips which reminded John so forcibly of Constable's landscape.

On the third wall there hangs a Nativity scene by Botticelli which both boys love very much without exactly knowing why. The picture contains so much mystery and adoration. Last holidays they went to see it in the National Gallery, now re-opened, thank God.

There have been changes on the staff. The old art master, 'Podge', as he was universally known, has at last retired. He had been at the school for donkey's years, practically since the school was founded, or so legend has it.

"Universally beloved," as the Headmaster put it in his valedictory encomium, "he will be a hard act to follow". John and Bill reckon that is Headmasterly shorthand for 'good riddance'. A young classics beak who can be relied upon to drop bricks and commit gaffes spoke of cleansing the Augean stables, wherever they are. To everyone's faint surprise, 'Podge' is missed not one jot or tittle.

The fact is that he had become stultified if not downright lazy in his teaching, the art school was a boring, uninspiring place and few boys, apart from the exceptionally talented, ever bothered to visit it.

But this term, it is different. In the world of art a new broom has arrived, Tony Simpson, young, personable and avant-garde. He has brought with him a whiff of glamour – the thrill of the Slade, news of interesting exhibitions at the Tate, the Royal Academy, even the Jeu de Paume, the Mauritshuis and the Kunsthistorisches. Furthermore, he has started taking boys up to London to see the latest shows. Bill and John have been privileged to see the magnificent Constable exhibition at the V. & A.

The school has taken Tony Simpson to its heart and paid him the highest compliment it can bestow. No pejorative nickname for him. He is known universally merely by his initials. TS has introduced art appreciation lessons at every level of the school. The sixth-formers are now enjoying a double period with TS every Wednesday afternoon. The Art School has become an exciting place to visit.

The effect on the school has been electrifying. Suddenly rugger is out (or at least not quite so important); culture is in.

TS is not the only cultured beak on the staff. John enjoys his lessons with 'Janks', who has a passion for the dramatic monologues of Robert Browning, especially *The Bishop orders his tomb at St. Praxed's Church* and *Soliloquy of the Spanish Cloister*. He teaches what is known as 'General Studies'. In his lessons he welcomes the Red Herring, provided that a) it is on an interesting subject and b) it lasts no more than ten minutes.

For example, in the third period today, Lloyd asked him what special qualities were needed to make a good schoolmaster. 'Janks' accepted the diversion and expatiated on the subject. As I recall, he said that you must have three gifts. "First of all the ability to interest others in what you yourself find intensely interesting; secondly, an iron stomach that can digest anything; and finally the faculty of being able to go to sleep immediately your head touches the pillow at the end of the day."

Various suggestions were then made from the form.

"What about enthusiasm, sir?"

"What about it, Thomas?"

"Do good teachers have to have it or can they get by merely on knowing their stuff?:

"Enthusiasm goes automatically with good teaching."

"Knowledge, sir?"

"Quite unimportant, Peacey. If you don't know something when asked by a boy in the form, you merely say, 'That is a very good question, Peacey, go and look it up in the half and tell me the answer in the next period.' It never fails to work. Boys are very gullible, you know.

General laughter.

A bright spark at the back of the class chirps up with

"What about girls, sir?"

"That you must find out for yourself, Wilkins," says 'Janks' with a twinkle in his eye. "And doubtless you will. Shortly."

Gales of laughter.

"Is the pay good, sir?"

"My dear old fruit, a lavatory cleaner at Clapham Junction gets more than I do."

"And it's a more skilled job," mutters Lambert, sitting next to John, under his breath. Luckily 'Janks' does not hear this *bon mot*.

***

'Janks' played a dirty trick on John's form today. They were having a double period with him on Law. One period was before the half, the other immediately afterwards. Because there were two law questions written up on the blackboard, everyone anticipated that there would be a written test after the break. Of course during the half they all mugged up the answers to those two questions and returned after the half, fortified by their bun and cocoa, confident that they could answer both questions impeccably. Imagine their horror and indignation when 'Janks' turned the board around to reveal two brand new questions on the other side.

"At least you know the answers to those two questions" was his wry comment.

He told them about a boy he had once taught who had been set some poetry to learn by heart. The boy had tried and tried but simply could not memorise the poem. In desperation he had come into the classroom well ahead of 'Janks' and the rest of the class. He wrote the poem out on the board. 'Janks' strode in and sat down on his dais, facing the class with his back to the board, noticing nothing amiss. He was suitably impressed when he heard the boy recite the poem perfectly.

Dear old 'Janks', thinks John, he always tells a good story against himself.

In the evening Bill and John have Tony Simpson in for a cup of coffee in their study. They talk for an hour and a half, managing to avoid school gossip entirely. Their subjects cover Arsenal's prospects in the 5th round of the Cup, the Nuremburg Trials, President Truman's track record, and the Nationalisation of the coal industry. But then inevitably they get on to art. Very enjoyable it is too.

TS seems to know intimately all the art galleries of Europe and every major painter in them. The conversation ranges from Post Impressionists through Dutch landscapes (Ruisdael, Cuyp and Hobbema) to Leonardo, Vincent van Gogh's last pictures painted at Auvers in the summer of 1890 before he shot himself, and Hogarth's Progresses.

Finally they come to the Flemish school. TS starts talking about Bruges. He waxes lyrical about its mediaeval beauty so miraculously preserved, the Hospital of St. John with its Memlincs, about Gerard David's paintings, about an unknown Leonardo in the Cathedral and a wonderful van Eyck in the city art gallery.

"Have you got any slides of the Flemish?" asks John.

"Dozens."

"May we see them? You give us art talks once a week on Wednesday afternoons. It would be awfully sporting of you if we could see them then. I mean we are genuinely interested, aren't we, Bill?"

"Yes. You bet."

TS agrees readily and they break up at half past ten. John struggles into mittens with gloves on top of them before putting on his duffel coat with two scarves. Finally he hooks over his arm the obligatory umbrella (carried in all weathers, even heat waves), symbol of his sixth form status. Thus encumbered, like a mediaeval knight in full armour, he staggers over to House and his icy bed.

***

TS is as good as his word. They have a gorgeous double period on Wednesday (after CCF activities), looking at Flemish slides. He starts by telling them that Michelangelo did not approve of Flemish artists.

"Why, sir?"

"I'll tell you. The great man wrote, 'In Flanders they paint with a view to external exactness'. By which sentence Michelangelo is saying, if I have understood him correctly, that Flemish artists lack harmony, symmetry and proportion, which of course is what the great Renaissance painters of Italy at that time were striving to achieve. And of course were being astonishingly successful."

"Like who, sir?"

"Oh, heaps of people. Leonardo, Masaccio, Giotto, Mantegna, Ghirlandaio, Raphael. The list is endless. I could go on for hours."

"Don't, sir, please, we want our supper."

Laughter.

"And we want to see the Flemish slides." This from Bill.

"Very well. Let's forget Michelangelo if we can and concentrate on the Flemish, those strange, wonderful painters north of the Alps who had, I might say, a considerable influence on the great Italian painters."

"In what way, sir?"

"In their brilliant and original use of oil painting. Van Eyck particularly was a pioneer in oil painting. But let me tell you four great qualities the Flemish painters have which compensate to some extent for their lack of symmetry, harmony and proportion. First of all, they have a meticulous attention to detail. Look at this slide, for example, by Pieter Bruegel the Elder. It shows the building of the Tower of Babel. You can see the King in the foreground planning his ridiculous skyscraper with his architects and behind him the absurd Tower reaching up into the clouds

102

with hundreds of tiny figures labouring on the futile project. The attention to detail is meticulous, as I have said."

"Where does this picture hang, sir?"

"In the Kunsthistorisches. In Vienna."

"Will you take us there, Sir?"

"Certainly. After the Cold War."

Laughter.

"Now the second quality which the Flemish have is an absence of sensationalism. They look at Man in his environment and record with a dispassionate eye and a delicate hand what they see and find. Here's a *Madonna and Child* with saints and donors which is in the National Gallery – utterly peaceful, almost mundane, nobody's getting excited or writing to the papers or shouting from the rooftops. It's all very domestic. Do you agree, Harvey?"

"In a way, sir, but I can't get worked up about it. Quite frankly, it's not my cup of tea."

"Fair enough. Now the third property is that dreaded word symbolism. Flemish paintings have hidden meanings. You've got to scratch around a bit to see what the artist is getting at. Here's a lovely scene – a farmer is ploughing, a shepherd is neglecting his flock as he gazes up into the sky, a man is fishing lower left, and a stately galleon sails serenely across the ocean towards a little port. But if you look carefully, you can see a pair of legs sticking out of the water. Just there. Now what is Bruegel saying in this painting which he entitles *The Fall of Icarus*? You are all so well educated that you can tell me about Icarus. Thomas?"

"Well, sir, Icarus and his dad whose name I can't remember."

"Daedalus, stupid!"

"Thank you, Worth, see me afterwards."

Laughter.

"As I was saying, when I was so rudely interrupted, Icarus and his dad, Daedalus, a clever inventor, flew away from Crete where they were imprisoned by Minos, I think. He was a well known tyrant as most kings were in that age."

Laughter.

"But Icarus flew too near the sun and the wax melted on his

feathers, causing him to plunge into the sea where he was drowned. End of Icarus. Moral: Don't use wax on your feathers if you want to fly. Stick to Gripfix in more senses than one."

Laughter.

"Very good, Thomas. Thank you. Now what Bruegel is saying in this picture is that although an astonishing and unprecedented event is taking place in the air, the peasants in the picture are completely indifferent to that event. What matters to them is that the earth must be ploughed, the fish caught and the sheep guarded. The symbolism is carefully hidden but it is there all the same. Do you see?"

Silence.

"May I take your silence to indicate agreement?"

"You may, sir."

"Thank you, Jones. Now the fourth Flemish quality is the ability of their painters to place people correctly in space with realistic perspective and a miraculous control of light. If we look at this triptych of *The Seven Sacraments* by Rogier van der Weyden, you can see, I hope, the painter's marvellous control of perspective and light. Look at the way the interior of the church recedes. Your eye can go right down the nave and into the chancel. Remember that van der Weyden is painting this on a flat piece of wood; he gets a wonderfully realistic sense of recession. And if you look in all the side chapels, where the seven sacraments are taking place, you can see his control of light. Do you agree, Wickham?"

"Yes, sir. But who is right? Michelangelo or the Flemish painters?"

"Both."

Laughter.

"They are both right. That's the beauty of art. There is more than one way of painting a picture. – you can paint a portrait or a landscape or an abstract or a still life or a religious allegory or a mythological subject, call it what you will. Generally speaking, people's tastes are a hundred years out of date. That is to say, Constable's landscapes or Vincent van Gogh's pictures were derided and not understood when they were painted. Now they are respected and revered. You see, it takes several generations to get them in perspective."

"What about Picasso, sir?"

"What about him?"

"Well, sir, to me and I suspect a lot of other people he seems to be all about women with two faces, distortion, exploding light bulbs, rude colours, you know what I mean."

"No, I don't, Jones. Are you still taking the pills?"

Laughter.

"No, quiet please everybody. Jones has got a point of view which deserves to be considered seriously. He does not appreciate Picasso. That is exactly what I am saying – Picasso is too close to us to be fully understood. He will come into focus only fifty years after he has died, when we will all think that his pictures are simple. We won't understand what all the fuss was about. Honestly!

But go and look at *Guernica* in the Museum of Modern Art in New York or *Les Demoiselles d'Avignon*. These are the great pictures of the twentieth century, a century of incalculable cruelty and violence, a century which has got the painters it deserves who reflect accurately its violent moods. Picasso and Braque and maybe Matisse are the greatest painters of this century. But they will not, Jones, be properly understood for another fifty years. Fair enough, Jones?"

"Fair enough, sir. Let's just say that we agree to differ. And by the way, sir, can you lend me the fare for the Queen Mary so that I can pop over the Atlantic to see the Picassos in New York?"

"I might just do that. See me afterwards. O.K., now let's have some slides. Yes, Wickham? It's time for your trombone lesson, is it? Well, it's your loss, not mine. If you think that the trombone is more important than van Eyck, there's nothing I can do to cure you of your philistinism. Please go and as you leave, kindly turn out the lights. Thank you."

And so they settle down to a feast of painters, most of whom John had never heard of before. Jan Gossaert (also known as Mabuse), Robert Campin, Rogier van der Weyden, Dieric Bouts, Hans Memlinc, Gerard David, Hugo van der Goes, (TS waxes lyrical about him), Geertgen tot Sint Jans, Pieter Bruegel the Elder and above all the great Jan van Eyck.

John loves Bruegel's *The Birdtrap*; Gerard David's *St. Nicholas of Myra* giving thanks for his birth, inventing Christmas presents and restoring three boys to life who have been slaughtered and salted down by an inn-keeper in time of famine; a very theatrical *Adoration* by Hugo van der Goes in the Uffizi; and a wonderfully gentle *Nativity* by Geertgen.

But for John personally the pictures by van Eyck take the biscuit. TS shows them *Madonna and Child with the Chancellor Rolin* with its miraculous and ravishing little city and the bridge crowded with people in the distance through the arches, a portrait of *Timotheos* in the National Gallery. – "very cool, very dispassionate," he calls it – *A Man in a Turban*, which TS suggests may be a self-portrait of van Eyck, several more Madonnas and finally, the *pièce de résistance*, the Arnolfini wedding portrait.

TS doesn't say much about the painting, there isn't time. He is just about to launch into an elucidation on the painting when the bell goes for the end of the lesson and supper.

"Sorry, chaps, as usual I've run out of time. Go and look for yourselves in the National Gallery. You'll find all the answers there. Enjoy your supper. Next week the Impressionists."

Everyone files out except Bill and John. TS is busy dismantling the projector when he notices them.

"Bill, John, how can I help you gentlemen? Incidentally, thank you very much for that delightful evening the other night. I thoroughly enjoyed myself and kept you up far too late."

"Not at all, sir. We enjoyed having you. You must come again."

"I'd love to. Now, what's the problem?"

Diffidently John poses his question.

"The fact is, sir, I'm having trouble with the Arnolfini picture which I must admit is my favourite. I think it is absolutely riveting. I am fascinated by it."

"Good. So am I. But what's the problem?"

"Well, the picture is usually called the Arnolfini wedding portrait, isn't it?"

"That's right."

106

"Why is it called a wedding portrait? What's the evidence? It doesn't look like a wedding to me."

TS keeps his cards close to his chest. He lets John do the talking.

"Tell me why it's not a wedding."

"Well, have you ever heard of a wedding taking place in a bedroom? With a dog present? I mean, all the usual trappings of a wedding are missing."

"Such as?"

"Oh, I don't know." John gropes for corroboration. "A bride in white, a church, organ music, a congregation for Pete's sake, the mother of the bride in tears, confetti, er, a parson wearing the right clobber and, you know, lots of other things."

He turns for help to Bill who is laughing.

Bill offers "a photographer".

"Exactly. Thank you, Bill, oh, and yes, a Best Man. Where's the Best Man?"

"Perhaps it was van Eyck," suggests TS gently.

"Where's van Eyck in the picture?" asks John aggressively.

"In the mirror," replies TS.

"Yes, I see," says John slowly who hasn't understood the complexities of the painting but is now beginning to realise that there is more in the picture than he had initially realised.

TS is coiling a length of flex as he asks the next question.

"Tell me, John, if it's not a wedding, what on earth is going on in the picture?"

John summons up all his courage.

"Well, you may think this is potty but I think, sir, that Arnolfini is not marrying the woman."

"What is he doing then?"

John takes a deep breath.

"What he is doing is divorcing his wife."

There is silence in the classroom for a few seconds as this statement is digested and a lens is detached from the projector. The enormity and outrageousness of John's suggestion takes the breath away. It is TS who breaks the spell.

"That's very interesting, John. Extraordinarily interesting. I think I require notice and a little time to think out the implications of what you have said."

He glances at his watch.

"Look, you are missing your supper. Go and have your meal and we'll talk further on the subject. Goodnight and thank you both for your interest and kindness."

Out in the court, it is intensely cold. Frost glitters on the double row of lime trees lit by a pale moon.

Somehow, John doesn't feel the cold. He hurries towards the Dining Hall with Bill, warmed by the memory of all those glorious reds and blues and greens in van Eyck's paintings; by the quiet dignity and serenity of his people, above all, by the sight of that man in the strange hat raising his right hand in that ritualistic gesture, a man who reminds him so strongly of his lost father. Yes, of course it could be a divorce. He isn't going to be shaken so easily.

As they toy with their reconstituted scrambled egg, John makes some banal comment about Arnolfini and his 'bride'. He almost feels like airing again his theory about their getting divorced, not married. But his innate shyness gets the better of him and he falls back on platitudes and safe questions.

"There's no doubt in my mind, Bill, that van Eyck is a good egg which is more than you can say for this disgusting mixture that we are eating. Tell me, what did you think of the little dog?"

Bill looks at John quizzically.

"What about the little dog?"

"I've got a theory about the dog which you might like to consider. Jam, please. Thanks. If you think about it, you could never get a real dog to stand still like that in front of the couple. In my opinion, it's not a real dog."

John is busy spreading what passes for raspberry jam on a thick hunk of bread.

"How do you mean?"

"That's not a real dog. It's a cardboard cut-out."

"Oh, come off it, get away! You cannot be serious."

"Honestly, Bill, and I'll tell you something else too."

"What?"

"Mr and Mrs Arnolfini aren't real either. They're cardboard cutouts too."

108

They both relax into laughter and a deep, unspoken friendship as they finish their supper and walk across the court to their study.

Before they settle down to prep, Bill makes one final observation about the picture.

"I've been thinking, John, about what you said. I've got a new theory about the picture."

"Oh, yes, and what that might be?"

"I think you're a cardboard cut-out too!"

Liddell and Scott's dictionary flies through the air, making sufficient noise to bring a prefect.

"What are you chaps up to?"

"Nothing," says Bill, wrestling with an iambic hexameter.

"Nothing," says John, reading the opening lines of *l'Allegro*.

"Well, keep quiet," says the prefect fiercely, closing the door.

From Study twenty-two there is no sound save the noise of suppressed laughter.

John recites under his breath Milton's opening anathema to the departed prefect beyond the closed door:-

Hence, loathèd Melancholy,
Of Cerberus and blackest Midnight born,
In Stygian cave forlorn,
'Mongst horrid shapes, and shrieks, and sights unholy!
Find out some uncouth cell,
Where brooding Darkness spreads his jealous wings,
And the night-raven sings;
There, under ebon shades and low-browed rocks,
As ragged as thy locks,
In dark Cimmerian desert ever dwell.

John's entry in his diary that night reads, "Studied van Eyck's Arnolfini so-called Wedding Portrait. Smashing picture. Arnolfini looks uncannily like Daddy. I advanced the theory that it is in fact a divorce that is taking place. Derided by all and sundry. I'm fascinated by the picture, completely hooked. I shall damn well get to the bottom of it, even if it takes me fifty years. Cardboard cut-out indeed!"

Chapter 14

1433

To the right worshipful and esteemed Johannes van Eyck, Master Painter of the Guild of Painters, Bruges.

I commend myself unto you and am ever desirous of wishing you good health and happiness.

Knowing that you craved from me an account of my recent journey to Paris, I hasten to furnish you with such details as I judge you may not find over-tedious. Our friendship over the past four years has meant much to me, not overburdened as I am with citizens of Bruges whom I can in all honesty call companions, let alone true friends.

I remember with admiration and astonishment your extraordinary account some five years ago of your voyage to Portugal with all its vicissitudes and dangers. Your adventures were arduous in the extreme, all born with Christian fortitude and forbearance for which you are justly celebrated. I shall try to emulate your skill in story-telling even if I cannot hope to match your stoicism.

You told me in your epistle from Portugal how much you disliked London on your brief visit there. Let me reciprocate by saying on the contrary how much I like the city of Paris. It is a fine and noble city, second in Europe, I would have thought, to the incomparable Constantinople. Not that Paris does not have its darker side. Many of its streets are narrow, both ill-favoured and foul-smelling. But I am not talking about that aspect.

Nor am I talking about the southern part of the city, that which they call the rive gauche or Quartier Latin, leading up to the so-called Montagne St Geneviève (in truth, the 'Mountain' turns out to be no more that a small hill. But then the French have always had a propensity towards hyperbole). True, there is a new University there, known as the Sorbonne, which may one day produce some fine scholarship. But on the whole the left bank is undistinguished. I am not talking about that aspect.

On the north bank, the rive droite, stands the Castle of the Louvre, the Citadel of the city. It has crenellated walls and stone towers which I found not unimpressive. But closer inspection of this apparently impregnable fortress revealed to me that the whole edifice was somewhat decrepit. I predict that the Louvre will not last more than another century or two, when we shall have heard the last of it. No, the rive droite holds few treasures or pleasures. I am not talking about that aspect of Paris.

Through Paris runs the river Seine, winding sensuously and surprisingly hither and thither. The Seine constitutes the heart of Paris. On its bosom are cradled two islands which contain its finest buildings. These two are called the Island of the City and one dedicated to one of France's favourite kings, Louis IX or St Louis as he is affectionately remembered. At the risk of boring you or telling you something which you already know, let me relate the life of Louis IX for it is a fascinating story. I have been reading his Life, written by John of Joinville, his friend and companion on the Crusade.

When Louis IX became king of France two hundred years ago in 1226, he was a mere twelve years old. Seven years later he married Margaret of Provence, elder sister of Queen Eleanor, wife of Henry III of England. It was a happy marriage, blessed as it was with eleven children. In 1242 he defeated Henry's army at the battle of Taillebourg and made a generous treaty with the same Henry in 1259. But that is unimportant. What merits our attention and admiration was his conduct from the time when he took over the government of the country after the regency of his jealous mother, Blanche of Castile. Louis was an ideal monarch – deeply and sincerely religious, lacking in bigotry, impartial and merciful in the administration of justice, insistent on every citizen's rights, an acute and trustworthy statesman, a man of peace and an efficient soldier.

One of his admirable characteristics was his horror of profane or blasphemous language; he would neither ever use it himself nor tolerate it in any of his subjects.

111

In 1248 he led a crusade to the Holy Land. He captured Demote in Egypt with ease but in 1250 his army suffered a heavy defeat at Mansard where he himself was taken prisoner. After his release he withdrew the remnants of his army to Akka in Palestine. Little could be done there and he returned to France after an absence of six years. The dynamism of the crusades was spent.

Nevertheless, in 1270 Louis again sailed with an army which he had mobilised with much difficulty. Eight weeks later he died of dysentery at Tunis. Twenty-seven years later he was canonised, a public veneration richly deserved in his case because of his superlative integrity, the quality on which he set such great store. And St Louis brought back with him, from the Holy Land, a sacred relic which I will tell you about shortly. Let me now return to the purpose of my visit to Paris, namely to meet my affianced.

It was on these two islands in the middle of the Seine that my lady Giovanna Cenami and I delighted to wander on fine summer days, exploring its many exciting and exotic treasures.

You reach the islands by boat of course. Although there are scores of professional watermen on the Seine, plying their trade, eager for customers, they are untrustworthy and even at times dangerous.

On one occasion my lady and I made the mistake of sailing upstream. When we disembarked, I found to my consternation that my purse had been cut. There was nothing that I could do. The villain of a boatman was already out in mid-stream, paddling strenuously.

No, I do not recommend travelling by boat in Paris. It is a city made for walking. To reach the Island of the City you cross the Seine by its only bridge, the so-called Pont Notre Dame. It is a very fine bridge where Giovanna and I took pleasure in lingering. There is something about the atmosphere of Paris which is different from any other city that I know. In Bruges during the summer the air can be heavy and oppressive. Not so in Paris. The air is sparkling and clean, one feels a spring in one's step, what the French define as a joy of living. It is hard to describe but it visibly animates its citizens who have what I

112

would call buoyancy in their steps and vivacity in their faces. You would certainly like to paint them!

Standing on the Pont Notre Dame, one is immediately impressed by the astonishing number of gabled houses huddled together on the bridge. There are so many, so contiguous to each other, so leaning over drunkenly to touch the neighbouring houses opposite, that when one is on the bridge, one is unaware that it is a bridge at all.

But I believe that, proud as Parisians may be of their fine bridge, its six arches beneath the superstructure seriously impede the flow of the river which makes navigation hazardous. There is talk of knocking the bridge down and building a new one, a Pont Neuf so to speak. We shall see.

The island dedicated to St. Louis is a fascinating place. Actually there are two islands which have been artificially joined together to form one island. There we find fields with herds of cattle, flocks of sheep and other farmyard animals grazing, something which one does not expect to find in a city. The houses are undistinguished and by the standards of Bruges very modest. Along the spine of the island there is one street with an open sewer running down its middle. This is the rue St. Louis with the parish church standing in the centre, a modest edifice barely worthy of mention.

I am bound to say that Giovanna and I avoided the dubious pleasure of walking along that filthy, stinking street. No, what gave us delight was wandering around the farmland surrounding the central village. We enjoyed our bucolic perambulations around this rural scene set in the heart of a great city.

The other island, the Island of the City (Ile de la Cité), is the true heart of Paris. Here stands proudly its new Cathedral, dedicated to the Blessed Virgin. Less than two hundred years old, this magnificent Gothic structure with its flying buttresses ricocheting off in all directions impressed us both enormously, both inside and outside. It was in this Cathedral, incidentally, that the new boy King of England, Henry VI, was crowned less than three years ago. A curious business that. In the same year, as I am sure you recall, the King of France, Charles VII, was crowned not in Notre Dame here in Paris but at Reims, the

113

traditional place for the coronations of the French monarchy.

Outside the west façade of Notre Dame, in a square which they call the Place Notre Dame, Giovanna and I spent a pleasant hour watching children playing games. Then we strolled on past the main prison of Paris called the Conciergerie, a dark, forbidding place. Hurriedly to escape its menacing presence we rounded a corner and there it was! The most beautiful building that I have ever seen. It is called La Sainte Chapelle, the Holy Chapel. Four-square and unbelievably elegant it stands, seeming to float effortlessly upwards towards heaven. Fifteen stained-glass windows rise fifty feet high to a star-studded ceiling. The windows depict in reds, golds, blues and greens more than a thousand episodes in Christianity. All this magnificence has been built to house the Crown of Thorns which King Louis, venerated saint, brought back from the Holy Land after his crusade.

Uplifted by our visit to this enchanting building, Giovanni and I walked to a little garden which stands at the very tip of the Island of the City. There, gazing across the busy river at the bustling city, we sat and talked of many matters – of our beloved Tuscany, of Giovanna's sister, of my family back in Lucca, of her life here in Paris, of my business aspirations in Bruges, of the children playing with such happiness and invention in front of Notre Dame and of the future. We were very happy, very close in spirit to one another, mutually affectionate and respectful the one of the other.

Such a propitious moment might not occur again. I had previously obtained her father's permission to present my suit. I went down on one knee, ignoring the vulgar comments of a passing waterman and humbly begged the hand of Giovanna in marriage. I am not a man given to many words. I will use one or two where others make speeches. My world is business, finance and trade. But beneath what some have perceived as a cold exterior, I can assure you there beats a passionate heart. I am Italian, after all!

When I had proposed, for a long moment Giovanna said nothing. I thought that I had perhaps offended her in some way. With those elegant, hazel eyes of hers seeming to strip my soul bare of any artifice she looked steadfastly at me. In her presence I felt naked. Just as St. Louis had adored the Crown of Thorns, so I was ready at that moment to worship her. I gazed and gazed; she gazed back. Then she lifted her eyes and looked across the roofs of Paris, as if seeking for inspiration, for some answer. I remember noticing three tiny details – that a pair of storks flew lazily downstream making strange creaking noises with their wings; that the bell of St Sulpice started tolling; and that there was a tiny dimple in her chin which I had never spotted before. That such minutiæ are etched in my memory puzzles me. Presumably, as a painter and professional observer of human faces, you must remember many such instances. That is your trade. You are such an accurate observer of other people that all men accord you veneration. I can only marvel at your skill.

But to return to the matter in hand, Giovanna took one long sweeping look at the city before she placed her elegant left hand in mine and raised me off my knee.

"If you will have me, sire, I will gladly consent to be your wife."

Thus were we affianced. How we walked back through the streets of Paris to her father's house, what we said and felt I do not feel incumbent upon me to relate. Suffice it to say that we were very happy, very happy indeed, as were her parents when we broke the news to them. Signior Cenami opened three prized bottles of vintage Chablis from his cellars in our honour.

Subsequently we spent many joyful hours discussing the wedding arrangements. We were to be married in the Cathedral of Notre Dame in Paris within three months. Her dowry was to be most handsome – an elegant cassone or wedding chest filled with her trousseau as well as a marriage bed (a four-poster with curtains) and a sum of money sufficient to furnish her with all the appurtenances necessary and proper for her rightful station in society.

I send you this letter in haste that you may be the better acquainted with all my news and movements. I intend to return to Bruges in a month or two. I shall accord myself the great honour and privilege of calling upon you at some time and date to be agreed. We have already discussed the possibility of my portrait being painted by you. I am of course keenly aware of your artistic commitments and the pressure of your commissions. Yours will be the prerogative to name a time.

In the meantime, I would count myself the most fortunate of men if I were to receive a letter from you in which you were to recount some of your more recent artistic and diplomatic ventures.

I have the honour, sir, to sign myself your esteemed and devoted servant and your friend, Giovanni di Arrigo Arnolfini

Written of my hand, upon the Feast of St. Jarlath of Tuma, being the 6th of June in the year of Our Lord, 1433, in the fair city of Paris.

May God be with you.
Your friend,
Gionvanni Arnolfini.

Extract from a letter written by Jan van Eyck to Giovanni Arnolfini

2nd September, 1433
…as you are doubtless aware. But I can say no more on this matter. It behoves me to be discreet. When the Duke entrusts me with diplomatic missions of such delicate importance, part of my mandate is that I cannot and must not divulge the nature of my employment. My lips are sealed.

You will recall that five years ago I gave you an account of my voyage to Portugal with all its vicissitudes yet happy outcome. Since then the Duke has employed me on more than one occasion. For example three years ago in 1430 I was sent to Hesdin in northern France on behalf of the Duke. I do not resent these expeditions though I do begrudge the time I must perforce spend away from my studio.

I discovered that Hesdin is a small town, west of Arras and north of Abbeville. It possesses little architecture of distinction to merit comment. I cannot in all conscience tell you any more about this mission. All I will say is that northern France is very flat and tedious. The inhabitants of Hesdin I found to be imbued with the same qualities as their landscape. They were to a man exceptionally unsophisticated inhabitants of a totally uninteresting part of France. To say that they were all peasants would be to sully the name and reputation of the work force of most nations whose way of life and dedication to the task in hand I invariably respect and admire. But let that pass.

Whilst I was in Hesdin with some time on my hands, I sketched several interesting faces. In my work I can always make use of new faces.

When I returned to Bruges, Cardinal Albergati sat for his portrait in my studio. His Eminence had been sent from Rome by the Holy Father to promote peace between France, England and Burgundy.

I found him a very warm man with whom to converse. He possessed an interesting face to draw and was a spiritual leader of profound conviction

As is my custom, I did a preliminary drawing in silverpoint with detailed notes on the subsequent colours to be used. It might interest you to learn what I wrote. For example I noted in my native language

Dat onderste vanden vorhoefde
tusschen den augen sanguinachtig
boven ten hairwair bleicachtig
Die wratte purperachtig

Which, since I know your Flemish is still somewhat limited, I will translate for you as:-

The lower part of the forehead
Between the eyes sanguineous
Close to the hair polish
The wart purplish

I also made the following observations which I reproduce here in both languages:-

Den appel vanden auge
alrenaest den swarten um
bruyngeelachtig Ind'omtrent

alrenaest den witten blauachtig
Dat witte auch geelachtig
which may be loosely translated as:-
The apple of the eye
around the pupil
dark yellowish
and in its circumference
close to the white bluish
The white of the eye yellowish
And again I wrote:-
Die nas bruynsanguinachtig
gelyc den kinbac af den wangen
die lippen zere witachtig purper
die stoppelen vanden barde
wal grysachtig
Die kinne roodachtig
Which translates as:-
The nose dark sanguinish
Like the cheekbone
down the cheeks
the lips very whitish purple
The stubbly beard
rather greyish
The chin reddish
Finally I noted:-
Dat hair… voren…
Okerachtig (grau) grys
or
The hair in front
Ochreous (ash) grey

I apologise if you find these notes tedious but you did once express to me an interest in my technique and methods of painting a portrait.

Whilst I painted the Cardinal, he told me he hailed from the City of Bologna which boasted the oldest university in Europe. He had entered a Carthusian Order there from which he was elected Bishop of Bologna in 1417. He must have been quite outstanding as a Bishop because Pope Martin V elevated him to the College of Cardinals in 1426 when he took as his titular church Santa Croce in Gerusalemme, the Church of the Holy Cross in Jerusalem, which is of course, despite its name, in Rome.

I realised at once that I was painting an exceptional man, as I tried to show in my portrait. His outstanding virtues were a burning sense of the importance of his mission, call it zeal if you will; and a piety and humility extraordinary in one so powerful. Be that as it may, the evidence of his strength, intellect and importance is manifested by the fact that the Holy Father sent Cardinal Albergati on no fewer than nine embassies on behalf of the Vatican. It was in early December, 1431, that he spent three days in my studio.

I am quite pleased – I am never wholly satisfied – with the final portrait which I like to think has dignity, sincerity and a certain latent ruthlessness. But if the truth be told, I prefer the greater immediacy and candour of the preliminary line drawing in silverpoint. Any humdrum journeyman painter can depict a decent likeness; but it is the soul that we painters strive to catch. I think I get nearer to the Cardinal's soul in the drawing than in the finished painting. But you must tell me what you think when you visit my studio and see the two works in juxtaposition.

Incidentally, I chose to paint Nicolas Albergati, as befits a Cardinal, wearing a scarlet gown trimmed with fur. The Cardinal wanted to pose for me in his customary habit of a Carthusian monk. But when I pointed out the technical problems of painting him in an all-white habit, he reluctantly agreed to the change.

When I come to paint your portrait, I shall endeavour to close the gap between the original sketch in silverpoint which I shall make of you and the finished portrait in oil. I look forward to that venture. If I may say so without any intended impertinence, you have an interesting face.

Last year I have been preoccupied with painting the portrait of a young man. As you well know, *The Adoration of the Mystic Lamb*, my brother Hubert's masterpiece, was finished by me and dedicated in 1432. It had kept me a prisoner in its service for over six years since my brother died in 1426.

I celebrated my freedom by painting for my own pleasure this young man who is leaning on a stone parapet, holding a roll of manuscript. He wears a green bonnet and a red gown trimmed with fur. He is seen three-quarter face, looking off to his right. Incidentally, that is my favourite pose.

On the stone parapet I have painted as though it were carved into the stone the following inscription "-

TYM. W EOC.

LEAL SOVVENIR

Actu ano dni. 1432. 10. Die octobris. A. ioh. De Eyck

Perhaps this inscription needs a short commentary. Let me explain. The top line alludes to Tymotheos of Miletus who was a musician of distinction in ancient Greece.

Beneath that name I have written LEAL SOVVENIR, in other words Loyal Remembrance. Then, as is my custom, I have signed the portrait and dated it with the final day when I completed the last varnishing, 10th October, 1432.

The sitter is Gilles Binchois, a soldier turned eminent musician. He is at present working at the Court of the Duke who commanded me to paint this portrait of Binchois which I imagine will hang in one of the Duke's Palaces. I found Binchois's face intriguing, full of character and intelligence.

Binchois himself has written several chansons, some motets and a quantity of sacred music. I believe he is a young man who will go far.

I am present working on another portrait you will be able to see when you visit my studio which I hope will be shortly.

I thank you for your perceptive and penetrating descriptions of Paris, a city that I intend to visit soon.

Written of my hand upon the Feast Day of St. Stephen of Hungary, 1433, whose blessing for your safe return I pray.

Your friend
Johannes de Eyck
Bruges

Extract of a letter from Giovanni Arnolfini to his affianced Giovanna Cenami

...and now to news of your wedding gown which you will remember we discussed at such length. I think it was a happy choice that in the end we agreed that it should be my duty to supply the gown. I only regret that we wasted so much time and effort in fruitless discussions with so many couturiers in Paris. It was disappointing to say the least that, after divulging all the precise measurements and details which they demanded, none of them was capable of producing the garment which we required. You recall that I was confident that Bruges could do better. I was right! I am glad to say that when I returned to Bruges I found exactly the cloth for which we had been looking and of course there are many skilled craftsmen capable of making it up into a beautiful and elegant gown which will be admired and extolled by all who are privileged to see it. Let me attempt in my inadequate language to describe what you will be wearing.

The finest woollen cloth, green on both sides, has been woven for you. Immediately I can hear you asking me precisely what sort of green it is. What a difficult question! If I say it is the colour of the meadows surrounding Paris on the south side where we took that memorable walk to look back at the Conciergerie, I am deceiving you. For it is a darker shade of green. If I describe it as liturgical green with which you will be familiar, I am still not being accurate enough. No, I have on rare occasions seen the sea this shade of green. There is a tree in your garden which has leaves of this colour but I am unable to recall its name. Ah! I have it! You remember that I showed you *The Mystic Lamb* when we were in Ghent. In the bottom register there is a continuous and extended landscape. Several of the plants depicted there have precisely the same colour as your gown. Let me see. One is *Vitis vinifera*, the common vine. Another is the greater plantain, *Plantago major*, whose leaves are almost exactly the colour which your gown will be. Or of course *Ficus caric* with its large pear-shaped leaves precisely replicates the colour. Have a look at the fig tree in your garden when you next walk there. Remember those delicious figs we ate?

I believe that the gown which is immensely heavy and very full in the skirt will give you that full-bellied look which is so fashionable at the moment. When you pick up the front and hold it up, you will even look as though you are great with child! Who cares? I shall take that as a happy omen of an event that will surely occur all too soon with your willing and blessed co-operation.

The sleeves of your gown are edged with the finest fur. Below at the bottom of the sleeves there is an immense area of intricate dagging that is sure to elicit attention and commendation. It is very fine workmanship which has taken hundreds of hours' work. I am confident that you will both like it inordinately and approve wholeheartedly of my choice and its workmanship.

Beneath the gown, edged with fur all round, I have chosen for you a blue silk dress. Again this is magnificent workmanship. I think the two colours, the dark green of the gown and the royal blue of the underdress will complement each other very well. Fertility and Virginity as bedfellows! What a curious paradox!

At your wrists will be gold bracelets; around your waist will be another gold bandeau.

You will be wearing two gold wedding rings on your left hand, one on your elegant little finger, another with a ruby on your second finger. I have commanded these rings from a Master Goldsmith who has already manufactured them for you. They are exquisite. (He has of course had to guess your size; I am sure they will fit you).

From the same smith I have bought a double rope of gold for you to wear around your slender neck.

Your hair will be braided of course and bound in a huvé. On your head, you shall wear five linen coiffes, all made in Bruges, partly as a tribute to the City of Bruges; partly to commemorate the five years of our courtship and my residence in this city; partly to remind us of the Stigmata – Christ's five wounds on the Cross.

There you have it. I depart in three weeks' time for Paris and our marriage in Notre Dame. I hold you in my arms.

Your passionate servant and impatient suitor,
Giovanni

Written this Feast Day of St.Gertrude of Helfta, 16th November, 1433

Chapter 15

28th December, 1433

Giovanni di Arrigo Arnolfini has just been talking to Giovanna Cenami, his bride-to-be. The air has been thick with compliments. "So beautiful, so pure, so Italian". She arrived here in Bruges after an arduous journey from Paris which took more days than one would have thought possible. But she is not only handsome, she is also young and resilient. A couple of days' rest and she will be fully recovered. Arnolfini's mind, usually stuffed with financial impedimenta and minutiae, is now full of romantic and erotic thoughts. Wedding arrangements must be made.

All the carefully made plans of Giovanna and Giovanni to be married in Notre Dame a couple of months back have gone out of the window. How could they have possibly foreseen that Paris would have been afflicted with an outbreak of the Black Death, that thousands upon thousands of its citizens would have died in the past three months? It had been obvious that it would have been the height of folly and extremely hazardous to remain in Paris whilst the Plague was decimating the city's inhabitants. The Cenami family had fled to the village of St. Cloud outside Paris for their own safety. Arnolfini had reluctantly agreed to postpone the wedding until next year and return to Bruges.

Now, three days after Christmas, 1433, the figure of a man, bundled against the cold, could be seen striding along the Oude Burg towards the Cathedral of St. Donatian. No, Arnolfini is not going to the Cathedral but to the handsome house next door, the Deanery, where he is hopeful of making arrangements for his imminent wedding.

Now immensely wealthy, Arnolfini is used to getting his own way. He owns a fine stone house in Bredelstraat, just off the central square, the Burg. He employs a large number of liveried servants. French cooks, imported from Burgundy, use their skills to tempt jaded Bruges palates with exotic dishes.

His house is full of beautiful furniture, illuminated manuscripts, pictures, tapestries and gold, silver and ivory objets d'art. His financial opinion and advice is sought by all the wool merchants and weavers of Bruges and Ghent. After twelve years' residence in Flanders, he speaks Flemish fluently, albeit heavily accented.

Arnolfini has power, position, wealth and influence. But to tell the truth he has few friends, one or two men of the arts, a couple of his fellow countrymen and, oh yes, especially Jan van Eyck. But for the rest, his business associates regard him as a cold fish, a mere outsider with some financial acumen who happens to have struck it lucky and who is merely exploiting his position. The whisper round the Bruges dining tables is that 'this damned Italian is on the make to see how much he can con us Flemings out of our precious gold to send back to his Lucca.'

As he strides down Magistraat, Arnolfini mulls over these unpalatable home truths of which he is only too aware. Maybe when he is married, the charm of his bride will stem some of the ugly rumours.

He decided last year after one particularly wounding insult from a fellow banker that he must find a wife. He wrote to his father back in Lucca for advice and suggestions.

Three months later, back came the answer.

"My son,

I thank you for your letter which the whole family and I have discussed at length in formal conference. You know the format and the scene. I would add that we were unanimous.

Of course you must marry.

Of course you must marry soon.

Of course that someone must come from Lucca.

On that we are adamant. We cannot possibly weaken our family name by your marrying anyone from Flanders.

There is only one possible choice, Giovanna Cenami, a charming girl from an eminently respectable and desirable family.

Let me remind you of her impeccable pedigree and

antecedents. As you know, Cenami is a famous Lucchese family, celebrated throughout Tuscany, with respectable credentials. You will recall that Grandfather Gioffredo Cenami had been Gonfaloniere in Lucca in the 1380s and 1390s like Giannino Arnolfini, your paternal grandfather. It was Gioffredo Cenami who set up businesses in Venice, Bruges and Paris, selling buttons and ribbons, one of our chief exports.

Giovanna is a sweet child. Just sixteen years old, she is eminently suitable to be your wife, blessed with serene beauty both in countenance and temperament. Her maternal grandmother came from another powerful and famous Lucchese family, the Rapondi. Philippa Rapondi was the niece of a wealthy international banker called Dino.

Giovanna's father, Gugliemo Cenami, is the eldest of five sons born to Philippa and Gioffredo Cenami. More than thirty years ago, in the 1390s, he lived and worked in Bruges. By 1403 he was conducting his business in Paris where he sold cloth to rich clients. He has settled on the Boulevard St. Michel on the rive gauche and married Jeanne Langlois. There they still live with their six children, one of whom is Giovanna.

Go to Paris, my son, and offer your hand in marriage to Giovanna Cenami.

You have the blessings and good wishes of your mother, your family and your devoted father who signs himself,

Arrigo Arnolfini"

As we have seen, Arnolfini obeyed his father's instructions and journeyed to Paris where he has proposed to and been accepted by Giovanna Cenami. Then came the Plague.

Now in December, 1433, the Cenami family have travelled from Paris to Bruges to attend the marriage of their beloved Giovanna to Giovanni di Arrigo Arnolfini in the Cathedral. They hope and are reasonably confident that the wedding will take place in January. Surely nothing can go wrong a second time.

All the detailed planning is in hand. It has been left to the bridegroom to make the final arrangements. Thus it is that we find Arnolfini walking through Bruges on this cold, snowy, late December day.

He himself resides in the parish and diocese of St.

Donatian. All that is needed now is a priest and a church. He has consulted the Cardinal Archbishop who has advised him to see Canon van der Paele in the Deanery.

Arnolfini quickens his pace, impelled by his desire to receive ecclesiastical permission and to seek sanctuary from the cold.

The great brass knocker in the shape of a sea serpent on the heavy oak door of the Deanery stares at him impassively. Arnolfini raps it three times. The sea serpent and Arnolfini watch each other warily.

Although he looks authoritative, Giovanni would admit privately that he is nervous. Used to having his own way, issuing orders and being obeyed, he does not find it easy to have to beg for a favour.

A servant opens the door; he is ushered into a large hall. The servant divests Arnolfini of his cloak, bows like an acolyte at the altar and goes in search of his Master. Arnolfini sits down and waits.

He has decided to dress opulently for the interview the better to impress the Canon. Accordingly he is wearing his red woollen gown with the enormous pleats and heavy sleeves, trimmed with fur at the wrists, skirt's edge and collar. It looks and is very expensive. A garment of the same colour on the inside and outside always costs the earth in Bruges. He trusts the Canon will be impressed.

Around his waist, he wears a black velvet belt from which is suspended a large purse. He has every intention of buying his way into St. Donatian's.

He is examining a very fine ivory Madonna and Child, exquisitely carved, standing on a pedestal, which he guesses to be German. He is just wondering how much it cost when, to his surprise, a bookcase swings open and Canon George van der Paele hobbles into the room. The Canon proffers his hand. Arnolfini drops to one knee and tries to kiss his ring.

The Canon will have none of it.

"My Lord, welcome, welcome, welcome. I trust I find you in good health despite our barbaric Bruges weather."

Here a hearty laugh.

"I am very well, I thank you, reverend Father. And you, I trust you are well?"

Another great gust of laughter shakes the Canon's frame as they walk into a large chamber.

"We shall not talk about my health, sir. Sit down, sit down, I beg of you."

In the great room with its roaring log fire and fine pictures on the wall, softly lit by a number of candles in silver sconces, Arnolfini sits down on an oak settle. He has a chance to observe the Canon.

Even with a cursory glance, it is obvious that the Canon is far from well. The veins on his forehead indicate high blood pressure, he is going bald, is overweight, short of breath and crippled with rheumatism.

But transcending all these physical ailments, his spirit is unquenchable. Clearly he has an insatiable lust for life and a glorious and unshakeable belief in the Redemption of his sins through the Grace of Our Lord Jesus Christ.

His eyes twinkle in his podgy face. The formalities begin.

"May I, my dear sir, offer you a glass of claret?"

It is gracefully offered, graciously accepted.

There is a short silence while both men sip their wine. Protocol demands that nothing too serious should be discussed for the first ten minutes. The Canon embarks on a short encomium about claret wine. He speaks knowledgeably about St. Emilion and the Châteaux of Cheval-Blanc, Ausone, Magdelaine and Figéac. It is obvious to Arnolfini that the Canon knows a great deal about his subject, knowledge which can only have been acquired through frequent acquaintance. Perhaps that accounts for his high blood pressure.

The subject lapses. It is Arnolfini's turn to start another topic – not his impending marriage, that would be rude and clumsy so early in the proceedings. It has to be something unimportant, preferably religious.

He makes a few platitudinous remarks about the Cathedral church of Notre Dame in Paris. The Canon listens politely and gravely but it is clear that he is not very interested. Arnolfini decides to strike nearer home. He fires an arrow and hits the

128

Gold.

"Tell me, my dear Canon, who exactly was St. Donatian?"

Van der Paele gives a snort of delight.

"I am glad you ask me, sir, for St. Donatian was a very interesting person, a very interesting person. He was Bishop of Bruges almost exactly one thousand years ago. And apparently he was a very good Bishop indeed, very good indeed, very good indeed."

Arnolfini cannot help wondering if the Canon's verbal habit of repeating himself has been acquired from constantly attending Mass and hearing the repetitive nature of the liturgy.

> *Lord have mercy upon us*
> *Christ have mercy upon us*
> *Lord have mercy upon us*

The Canon intertwines his podgy fingers together and begins a homily, as though in the pulpit. His voice is just a trifle too loud.

"It happened in this wise. One day St. Donatian, or rather plain Donatian as he was then, for he had not yet been canonised, was walking by the canal here in Bruges. Doubtless he was contemplating the mysteries of the Trinity for his next sermon, or some equally weighty theological matter. At any rate, he was walking along the tow path, rapt in contemplation, when he was suddenly assailed."

"Assailed?"

"Yes, assailed, sir, assaulted, set upon, vandalised."

"By whom?"

"By a bandit, a ruffian, a footpad. Somebody who wanted to rob him."

"What happened?" asks Arnolfini who feels that it is his duty to feed the Canon easy questions to keep the narrative flowing.

"Well, the thief was too strong for poor old Donatian. Not only did he steal his purse, he also stole his life."

"What do you mean?"

"I mean he killed him."

"Killed him?"

"Yes. The villain struck Donatian such a fearful blow to the head that poor Donatian was knocked into the canal. His body disappeared beneath the murky grey waters."

"What happened then?"

"Well, the citizens of Bruges were in a terrible state of shock when they found out and mourned their beloved Donatian. So upset were they that they sent a delegation to Rome to seek the help and advice of the Holy Father. Pope Justinius considered the matter, consulted his expert advisers and delivered himself of this judgment. He told them to make a wheel of wood and fix candles on it all the way round the rim. Then they were to carry the wheel to the canal, light the candles and float it downstream. When it arrived directly over the body of Donatian, it would stop."

"And did they take the Pope's advice?"

"Indeed, indeed they did. They made an ordinary wheel, fixed candles on it, lit them and carefully floated the whole contraption downstream through the centre of Bruges with vast crowds watching from either bank."

The Canon takes another sip of wine and mops his brow for he is sweating profusely. He remembers something.

"One of those who was watching events anxiously was the man who had assaulted Donatian and thrown his body in the water. He had been caught immediately afterwards and brought to trial. He was found guilty by the court but could not be sentenced because there was no body. If they found nothing, he would go free. If Donatian was discovered, the assailant would suffer a horrible death. You can imagine his feelings."

"Indeed. And did they find anything?"

"Of course they did. O, ye of little faith! Amazingly it worked."

The Canon beams from ear to ear.

"At the very spot where his body had come to rest on the canal bed, the wheel stopped and suspended itself over the cadaver, despite a strong current. Whereupon a score of enthusiastic volunteers dived down, found the body and brought it to the surface where it was restored to life."

"You mean Donatian recovered?" asks Arnolfini incredulously.

"Oh yes, no question. Not only was he fully restored to life,

130

but he also led an active existence thereafter and became a much loved Bishop of this city."

"That is an incredible story."

"No, it is not, my good sir, with respect. You are forgetting one thing."

"What is that?"

"That Our Lord can work miracles. That was a miracle."

He taps for emphasis the finial on the side of his armchair, a genial-looking lion.

"That was a miracle."

The words are said so simply, with such conviction and burning zeal, that Arnolfini is silenced for a moment in the presence of such blazing faith. Where for him there is a modicum of doubt or even scepticism in the validity of the story, for Canon van der Paele there is total commitment and acceptance.

Giovanni stares thoughtfully at the ivory Virgin and Child for a long moment before nodding slowly.

Shyly he says at last, "I agree with you, Canon, that was a miracle. Thank you for telling me that story. Strange to say, I have never heard it before, even though I have worshipped in St. Donatian's these past fourteen years."

He takes a sip of claret. The Canon replenishes his glass. The introductory formalities are over.

"And now, sir, what is it that you wanted me to do for you? How can I be of any service?"

The fat fingers fold themselves comfortably together and are laid on the ample lap.

Arnolfini explains to the Canon that he wants to get married, that his bride-to-be comes from his native Italy, his home town of Lucca in fact, that the wedding should have taken place in Paris but an outbreak of the Black Death put a stop to that, that she and her family have arrived in Bruges and that they would like to get married next month in the Cathedral. Arnolfini concludes by reiterating that he has been a parishioner of St. Donatian's for the past fourteen years and is of course a devout and practising Catholic.

Normally a man of few words Arnolfini likes to use one

where most people employ three; say something in three or four words where others would make a speech. It is not that he practises taciturnity for its own sake; it is merely that he dislikes the wanton and reckless misuse of language. The speech he has just made is for him abnormally long. He looks at the Canon to see what impression he has made.

The Canon is nodding appreciatively.

"Good, good, good. Everything sounds in order. I understand the situation perfectly. Let me just consult my missal."

With several puffs and pants he levers himself out of his chair and goes to a desk whence he produces a prayer book. From a side drawer he extracts a pair of tortoiseshell spectacles. Holding them on his nose with one hand and peering through the thick lens at the missal, he begins to read carefully. From time to time he turns a page laboriously.

Little grunts of impatience and snorts of comprehension come from him. Suddenly he lets out a shout of acclamation.

"By St. Boniface, I have it. The Presentation of Christ in the Temple, commonly called the Purification of Saint Mary the Virgin, a Tuesday, that is when you shall be married in St. Donatian's."

The thin boyish face of Arnolfini gives the glimmer of a watery smile.

"And what date is that, Father?"

"My goodness me, sir, I thought everybody knew when Candlemas was."

"I confess that I plead ignorance."

"Why, it's February the second."

"Then I take it you can see no objections why we should not be married on Candlemas in the Cathedral."

"None at all."

"And I hope that you will pay us the gracious compliment of performing the ceremony. I shall of course endow the Cathedral with a Chantry and pay for a daily Mass to be said for the repose of all souls."

The Canon's sharp eyes glitter when he hears this. His head nods several times like a doll being shaken. When he replies,

132

there is a slight quaver in his voice.

"Of course, my dear sir, of course."

He beams effusively and then adds as an afterthought, making it sound quite different from its predecessors, "of course."

Courtesies, pleasantries and farewells are exchanged. Arnolfini leaves the Deanery. Confidently he strides through the streets of Bruges. No longer does he feel the cold; he is to be married in little over a month's time. He smiles at passers-by and even stops to give a beggar a coin. All seems set fair.

But St. Donatian's never does receive its Chantry.

Chapter 16

November, 1993

The Chairman
West Dorset Decorative & Fine Arts Society
Beaminster
Dorset

Madam,

This being the season of the year when societies fix their lectures for the next year, I am taking the liberty of writing to you to see if you would be interested in one of my lectures.

I append a list of the lectures which I am offering and look forward to hearing from you.

Yours faithfully,

John Arnold M.A.

These are my subjects, all copiously illustrated with slides:-
FLEMISH PAINTING – Flemish painters from about 1430 to 1550.

I start with Jan van Eyck and move on via Campin, Memlinc, David, Gossaert, Van der Goes and others to finish with the great Pieter Bruegel the Elder.

THE MYSTIC LAMB – Painted by Hubert and Jan van Eyck and unveiled in 1432, the great polyptych of 26 pictures hangs in Ghent Cathedral, one of the most important works in the history of art, a complex and fascinating masterpiece.

LANDSCAPE IN ART – An attempt to show the many facets of landscape painting – landscape in general, the extended view, the beachscape, the icescape, the riverscape, landscape in the service of religion, the mythological landscape, the imaginary landscape and many other aspects. It's a fun talk!

DUTCH GENRE PAINTINGS OF THE 17th CENTURY – 'Genre' = scenes of everyday life. So no portraits, religious pictures, still lifes or landscapes – merely ordinary Dutch folk doing ordinary things in their homes. But there is more to it than meets the casual eye. It's a big subject which includes a number of Love & Music pictures containing a good deal of hidden sexual innuendo.

EVERY PICTURE TELLS A STORY – an examination in detail of some famous pictures (Holbein's *Ambassadors*, Seurat's *La Baignade, Asnières*, and the *Wilton Diptych* among others) which are enormously enhanced for the viewer if he or she knows more about the pictures in question – the background to them and the techniques of the great masters.

JAN VAN EYCK – The masterpieces of Jan van Eyck, including especially the *Arnolfini Wedding* double portrait in the National Gallery, the *Chancellor Rolin with the Virgin and Child* in the Louvre, the *Madonna with Canon van der Paele* in the Musée Communal des Beaux-Arts, Bruges, and several important portraits.

ARNOLFINI – The entire lecture could be devoted just to the *Arnolfini Wedding* double portrait which I have studied intensively and extensively and about which I have some interesting new ideas.

THE BAYEUX TAPESTRY – The events leading up to and including the invasion of England in 1066, as seen through the Norman eyes of Bishop Odo, William's half brother. There are more than one hundred and twenty slides illustrating the seventy-nine scenes in the Tapestry.

***

January, 1994

"More coffee, Jim?"

"Thank you, no, Heather, that was delicious."

"Anyone else? Sylvia? Charles? Harry? Myrtle?"

There is a general murmur of polite refusal. Heather

135

proceeds briskly with the agenda. As the newly appointed Chairman of the Society, she has fought her corner for the retention of her traditional title. Chairperson, Chair, Convenor and other ghastly epithets, even the odious Mrs Speaker have been hotly debated at the last meeting. But Heather has stuck to her guns. Chairman she remains and Madam Chairman she insists on being called.

"Item four on the agenda. What did we think of the last speaker and his talk? Charles?"

"Speaking as a former schoolmaster, Madam Chairman, I would give it Beta Gamma plus. I couldn't hear all of it and what I could hear I couldn't understand. I thought the slides were poor and his lecture technique, to say the least, flabby. Them's my views so who's afeered?" For some reason best known to himself, Charles concludes his little speech by lapsing into broad Dorset.

"Oh dear, I can see you didn't like it. Thank you, Charles. What about you, Myrtle?"

"I agree with Charles, though I must say I wouldn't go quite as far as he does. Not very good, shall we say? Oh, and I could hear perfectly but that might have been because I was sitting in the front row."

Myrtle ended with a simper.

"Thank you, Myrtle. Harry, can you do any better?"

"Well, I'm just the Treasurer, Heather, and I must confess that I wasn't there. So I can't really say anything. Sorry."

"That's quite all right, Harry. I quite understand. How is your poor wife, by the way?"

"Much better, thank you."

"Oh good, I'm so glad," said Heather in the tone of one who has just performed a two hour operation in the hospital theatre. "Jim, the floor is yours."

"Thank you, Madam Chairman."

Here a fierce look around the table from under bushy eyebrows.

"Am I alone, I wonder, in finding last week's lecture a thoroughly entertaining, well presented and I may say informative talk on a subject about which I knew very little? I realise that Japanese flower-arranging is a somewhat esoteric subject but I for one enthuse. In fact, I will go further. I have astonished my wife and visitors by arranging all the flowers in our bungalow in the Japanese fashion. I can tell you that after initial objections my wife now thinks a single chrysanthemum in a vase complemented with a twist of ivy is thoroughly decorative. I am of the opinion that the vast majority of our members found the talk stimulating and interesting. He gets my vote, Chairman."

"Madam chairman, please. Thank you, Jim. Point taken. There seems to be a slight dichotomy around the table. Sylvia, your views, please, dear."

Sylvia fixes her reading glasses on her nose and produces from the bowels of her capacious shopping bag a writing pad, liberally sprinkled with notes. She glances at it to refresh her memory before launching into a diatribe against the lecturer for his subject, technique and presentation, and her predecessor, the Membership Secretary, fortunately now retired, for ever booking such an unhappy choice in the first place. She has been speaking for three minutes when she pauses, mainly to draw breath. Heather seizes the initiative.

"Thank you, thank you very much, Sylvia, for that cogent and witty speech. I think we have all got the drift of your remarks by now. Can we all vote now, please? May I remind you that we mark out of five. Five is excellent, four good, three average, two indifferent and one downright bad. On the piece of paper in front of you, write your score on the ikebana talk. And don't of course put your name. Fold them once, that's right, and pass them up to me. Thank you."

The papers are marked and handed up to Heather who announces the result after perusal.

"He scores two. Not very good, I'm afraid. I do not think we need to invite him again. Sylvia, would you please make a note? Thank you. Item five on the agenda, next year's speakers. Sylvia, please."

"Madam Chairman, we have fixed seven talks. Let me remind you that we already have Holbein and the Court of Henry VIII, Spanish religious paintings, Piet Mondrian and the

137

Abstract, the History of the Sofa, the Palace of Versailles and three Royal Beds – that should be fun – our usual pre-Christmas talk, Nativity Paintings, which is always very popular, you know, supplemented with mincepies and a glass of mulled wine, – and finally Stanley Spencer at Burghclere (I'm not sure how you pronounce that place)."

"Burr Clear."

"Thank you, Jim."

"Right, Sylvia, so, correct me if I am wrong, we are left with one slot to fill. What about this Arnold fellow? You've all got his programme in front of you. He sounds quite good. I must admit I have done some snooping around. He spoke to the East Berkshire Society last year so I rang up their Chairman in Sunningdale who said he was excellent. I think we should go for him. Agreed?"

Five fingers are raised around the table.

"What subject would you like, Jim?"

"Personally, I would like to hear him talk on the Bayeux Tapestry. I am sure that would be very interesting. Them's me view, Madam Chairman"

"Oh, come on, Jim, that's old hat. We've all seen it and most of us know all about it."

"You speak for yourself, Charles, we're not all as well educated as you are. Anyway, that's what I think."

"Thank you. So what would you like, Charles, if you don't want the Bayeux Tapestry?"

"Well, he has a number of attractive subjects. But I think I go for Dutch Genre paintings. Everybody likes Dutch paintings and it would be fun to find out about the underlying meaning."

"I agree with you, Charles."

This surprising intervention stems from a somnolent Harry.

"No, I really feel that I must exercise my chairman's veto on that one. He does say that many of the paintings have a sexual connotation and I cannot allow pictures with a salacious undertone to be exhibited in my lecture hall. Not while I'm chairman. Let me remind you that many of my members are elderly ladies who would undoubtedly take umbrage. So let's choose one of the others. Myrtle?"

"Well, I rather like the look of the Flemish painters."

"Good idea. Sylvia, do you agree?"

"I agree in a sort of way. But, correct me if I am wrong, we did have a lecture a few years ago, I seem to remember, on Flemish religious triptychs which included some Memlincs and Davids, I think. Why don't we just have van Eyck and Arnolfini? That sounds very fascinating."

"Arnolfini? All agreed?"

There is a general murmur of assent.

"Right, that's it then, I'll write to John Arnold and book him. Thank you all for your time and trouble. So we meet next month for our first talk, on *The History of the Flea*. I'm just itching to hear it."

Heather's braying laugh accompanies the committee out into the street where they disperse to their separate homes. As for Heather she retreats to her 'Den' and her PC to lure John Arnold into her spider's web.

Chapter 17

January, 1434

Superficially the city of Bruges resembles the human heart with its network of narrow, cobbled streets, interlocking canals and four 'chambers' or districts. In this year of Our Lord, 1434, Bruges is vigorously pumping its commercial lifeblood to all corners of its prosperous and populous town. No city in western Europe at this time has better living conditions for its inhabitants, finer streets or more churches.

Indeed from the top of St. Gillis's tall Gothic spire, a panting and perspiring climber can see like a bird all of Bruges spread out beneath him. Over to the north he can spot the spire of Santa Clara, a perpetual reminder in stone to St. Clare of Assisi with her 'privilege of poverty' granted to her by Pope Innocent III; to the west the Cathedral of St. Salvator and the church of St. Amand of Maastricht, the 6th century Flemish missionary Bishop; to the south, the church named after that mysterious nun from Wimborne in southern England, Santa Walburga, pushes its elegant spire heavenwards; to the east is visible Santa Anna and the church of Jeruzalem (sic). Here, in the centre of the city, near St. Gillis itself, stands St. Maartens and St. Jans. From the tower of Onze-Lieve-Vrouwkerk, the church of Our Blessed Virgin Mary on Katelijnestraat, the bell announces to a busy city that it is 10 o'clock.

The fishwife selling her cheap salmon and cod in the Vismarkt hears it and starts calculating how much she has made this morning since 5 o'clock; white from head to foot, the miller hears it in the far east of the city in his creaking windmill called Sint Janhuysmolen as he humps for the umpteenth time another sack of freshly ground flour; in the Customs House on St. Salvatorskerkhof – the Oud Tolhuis – Thierry, the Customs 'fficer, gratefully stamps the documents of the captain of the last barge to register that day and prepares to shut up shop and repair to a local hostelry for his breakfast; in the Great Hall of the Stadhuis with its famous wooden, polychromed, hammer-beam ceiling, the Lord Mayor, heavily encumbered with fur and chain of office, takes his cue from its sound and bangs his gavel for order in court; in his studio in St. Gillis Niuew Straat Jan van Eyck certainly notices it as he painstakingly works in silverpoint; Hans Memlinc in the St. Janshospitaal is so grossly immersed in the painting of his triptych of *The Mystic Marriage of St. Catherine* that he is oblivious of it; Canon van der Paele on his knees in his private chapel sighs deeply, puts away his spectacles and the Gospel which he has been reading and climbs painfully to his feet. It is time for the office of Tierce. He lumbers joyfully off to St. Donatian's, full of stoical acceptance of the arthritic pain which the good Lord has sent for him to endure.

The clothmakers hear it, as do the lacemakers and the silversmiths, the goldsmiths and the blacksmiths, the coppersmiths and the diamond cutters, the barge hands and the candlemakers, the fruit importers, the brickmakers, the cobblers, the fur importers, the carpenters, the notaries and the lawyers, the manciples and the poor prisoners shivering in their unheated cells.

For it is cold, bitterly cold. Out of a cloudless sky, the sun shines mockingly onto a freezing Bruges as the east wind whistles mercilessly Mind you, for January in that part of Flanders the temperature is about average.

At the end of Sint Gillis Nieuw Straat, opposite Schottine Poorte, a watchman notes the time. Desperately he is trying to keep warm by feeding a blazing brazier with wood, his thick woollen hose and leather jerkin scant protection against the biting cold. A small group who are walking down the street stop to enjoy the warmth from the fire. The party comprises two women, two men and a dog. The two women are wrapped in voluminous fur coats and hats. The two men are well protected. Even the little long-haired Belgian griffon wears a coat.

Obsequiously, without even being asked, the watchman

stands back to allow the posh toffs, as he thinks them, their proper station and due share of the heat. The two women are jabbering away in a language which he does not understand.

A few minutes later the party reluctantly abandons the warmth and continues its walk down Wapenmakerstraat towards the centre of the city. They do not accord the watchman even a cursory thank you or grateful glance for his gift of temporary warmth. After they have gone, he returns to his fire and rubs his bemittened hands over the blaze. He looks with contempt at the departing party. "Bloody foreigners," he thinks and spits after them. It is a futile gesture but he feels the better for it. If no warmer.

Meanwhile Margaretha van Eyck and Giovanna Cenami, accompanied by Lambert van Eyck walk away from the brazier towards the centre of Bruges, the Burg. Behind them, straining at his leash, follows Hendrik the dog, held by Pieter. Margaretha is six months pregnant with her first child. Jan and she are hoping for a boy. She is keeping well but her thin, pinched face betrays the strain. And she feels the cold.

Her companion, newly arrived from Paris, does not speak a word of Flemish. French is their *lingua franca* in which they jabber away with much invention, gesticulation and giggling. Giovanna Cenami is rapturously happy and very excited. Her Latin temperament scarcely allows her to contain herself. She has come to marry her Lucchese lover, her clever, handsome, rich and adorable Giovanni Arnolfini. What about the cold? Pooh! What cold? She has not even noticed that it is freezing.

Lambert van Eyck, the younger brother of Jan, is a banker by profession which is why he knows Arnolfini. He is following orders. Brother Jan has suggested tactfully but firmly that they should all walk into town and dine at a tavern, thus allowing him a little peace and quiet in his studio where he is painting an important commission, a portrait. Besides, Giovanni will be in the tavern where he can have a *tête-à-tête* with his beloved. Furthermore, 'Hendy' needs a walk and can have the privilege and pleasure of meeting his new master. Giovanna has brought the dog from Paris as a wedding present (amongst others). He is

142

a nice doggy, as Giovanna is explaining in broken French to Margaretha. "He is sleeping in my chambre during night. On the bed. How do you say? At the feet. After we get marriage, maybe my husband not want dog on bed." Here there is much giggling on the part of the two women.

Lambert who is not listening to this tittle-tattle inclines his head in a grave bow to a passing citizen who merits his attention. The greeting is reciprocated. Hendrik finds a fascinating smell in the street and tugs at his leash. Pieter reprimands him with a sharp tug but refrains from hitting him because the strange lady from France who is meant to be his mistress is looking. Giovanna is so pleased with her new dog. He behaves so well and is so intelligent. Not once, not a single time, she tells Margaretha proudly, did he 'misbehave' during the long coach ride from Paris to Brussels.

And so they pass merrily along, past steeply-gabled stone houses, past a group of horsemen cantering slowly westwards, past a man on a ladder mending a casement, past long and short-gowned citizens, past a group of men playing Kolf on a frozen section of a canal, past old women hurrying to Mass, past houses shuttered against the cold, past a flock of hooded crows feeding off horse-droppings, past a peasant leading a long string of heavily laden pack mules, past a school teacher at the head of a crocodile of excited schoolchildren, their bird-like voices chirruping in the frosty air, past tantalising smells emanating from a bakery, past disgusting odours reeking from a slaughter house, past sounds and sights and smells which excite, disgust, stimulate or depress the imaginations of the two women, the two men and the dog.

Lambert who has seen it all before notices nothing. Giovanna, on her first day in Bruges, subconsciously is aware of many things that are different from Paris. Margaretha concentrates on Giovanna's reactions. Pieter watches Hendrik like a hawk.

And Hendrik? He loves every aspect of Bruges. It looks good, it sounds good and by St. Donatian it smells good too. He is in his seventh heaven, the one where dogs are given the freedom of the city, especially the butchers. Provided he receives another good meal of meat this evening and does not have to endure another horrible bath from Pieter, there is a distinct possibility that he is going to enjoy himself.

It is half past ten, dinner time for the adults. Lambert and party arrive at their rendezvous in the Burg where Giovanni awaits them. At the tavern where they dine it is warm and comfortable, the food is plentiful, rich and appetising, the wine imported from France excellent and the company delightful.

Not so on Nieuwe Gillis straat where the watchman's brazier has run out of wood to fuel it. His job done for the day, he makes his frozen way home to a cold house, a nagging wife and a miserable repast of lentil soup. "Ah well," he thinks as he trudges along full of self pity, "them rich folks do no work at all and still have all the best things in life. They can afford useless things like dogs. Me? I can't even keep a cat. Unless you count me wife. Slap me hand! It's a miserable existence, but that's me lot."

As he ruminates on the mystery and unfairness of the universe, he trudges past St. Gillis church. The bells chime eleven o'clock. It has been a long day already. He spits sadly but accurately into the central gutter which runs down Spaeniaerd straat. His gob of spittle starts its slow inevitable journey towards the canal, the Rhine and the North Sea.

Chapter 18

January, 1994

John Arnold, M.A. Esq.,
Weybridge
Surrey

From the Chairman of West Dorset Decorative & Fine Arts Society

Dear Mr Arnold,

Thank you so much for your letter of November last. I must apologise for the tardiness of my reply. Blame it not on me but on the procrastination of my committee!

I am so pleased to tell you that we would love to have a lecture from you – in May of next year, if that is convenient. Perhaps I could speak to you on the phone and fix a precise date.

My committee debated long and hard over your choice of lectures. We were very tempted by the Dutch Genre and the Bayeux Tapestry. In the end we plumped for the van Eyck Arnolfini Wedding portrait. It sounds a fascinating subject and I know that you have done a great deal of research on the picture. We all know the picture superficially and long to hear your views and interpretation of it.

So let's leave it like that. Details such as the precise date and your fee can be fixed when I ring you.

Looking forward to meeting you.

Yours sincerely,

Heather Hepton
Chairman
West Dorset D.F.A.S.

***

January, 1995

West Dorset Decorative & Fine Arts Society
Beaminster
Dorset

My dear Mr Arnold,

How nice to hear from you and have such a long conversation on the phone last week. I can tell you, my husband was getting quite jealous!

Now, all is in order. You are coming on Tuesday, May 30th, arriving at my house (see enclosed map) by 12.30 pm, please. Then we can have a nice, quiet lunch with one other couple, whom you will like!

We leave for the Arts Centre at 2 pm which will give my projectionist plenty of time to load your slides into the carousel. We provide the screen of course, an electric pointer and a throat mike.

One word of friendly warning. Recently we had a lecturer who gave her talk pointing constantly at the screen with the red torch. Unfortunately she did not have a very steady hand. Members spent the entire lecture watching a red dot quivering like an inebriated Tinkerbell instead of listening to what the lecturer was saying. It was all most unfortunate. But I am sure that your lecture technique is impeccable.

Our WDDFAS meetings start at 2.30 pm promptly. I am sorry but I shall have some dreary old notices to give out before introducing you. But then of course the floor is yours and I am confident that you will be a succès enormously fou with our members.

At the end there will be time for questions (if you don't mind), followed by tea in the parlour. The whole event should be over by 5 pm when you should be wending your way home. There will be a fat cheque for £150 from our Treasurer in your pocket.

I hope that has made everything clear to you. If you do have any further questions for me, do not hesitate to get in touch. I am generally at home in the mornings. The glories of West Dorset await you and we are impatient to meet you and to hear your talk.

Yours most sincerely,
Heather Hepton

***

25.5.95

Heather,

Just a quick postcard to confirm that I shall be arriving chez toi at about 12.25. So looking forward to meeting you, and your husband. Hope you like this Pieter de Hooch. Actually it's not quite as innocent as it looks!

Love,
John

Chapter 19

February, 1434

It is early February in the year of Our Lord, 1434, in Bruges. A man wearing wooden pattens picks his way warily through the detritus produced by the busy Woensdag market. He pauses for a moment beside a fish stall where a thin-faced woman in a dark blue woollen dress is cheerfully and expertly gutting four large cod. Behind her the top half of a salmon sits on a marble slab staring benevolently at all and sundry. Cod and salmon, especially the latter, are cheap. They are the staple diet of many of the poorer citizens of Bruges. Meat they cannot afford, certainly not fresh meat. But this man is rich. He cannot remember precisely when he last ate cod or salmon. Certainly a long time ago. Vaguely he wonders what they taste like. Probably rather fishy.

He works his way through the market and finds Schottine Port on his right. Here the great barges are tied up which make their way all over Europe, carrying the riches of Flanders to its customers. Cloth and lace for the wealthy senoritas of Spain and Portugal; fine woollen gowns for fine French dames; satins and silks for the signoras of Italy. And the barges return to their home port laden with grain from the Baltic, timber for the ships and houses of Bruges, holds full of fish for salting, furs from the Black Sea, carpets from Kurdistan, spices from the Orient, almonds, oranges and ginger from Seville, hemp to make ropes, tar for caulking timber, honey to sweeten bitter foods; even wooden pattens, such as Arnolfini is wearing, from the Levant. If the Mediterranean provides the citizens of Bruges with their luxuries, it is the North which supplies them with the necessities to see them through the harsh winters.

The wooden pattens leave the river and clack their way left

148

up Sint Gillis Nieuw Straat. Immediately their owner is struck with how handsome and rich this street is. He would very much like to live here. But how would its inhabitants take to him? He doesn't even bother to answer the question to himself.

On either side of a broad and clean thoroughfare stand elegant stone-gabled houses, three or four stories high. A few well-dressed citizens are conversing in the street. They see this foreigner, observe his presence as he passes by and ostentatiously ignore him. For his part, as an expatriate Italian, he is used to being ostracised. It is the price that he pays for his wealth.

He stops at number eight on the left, a particularly fine stone house, and knocks imperiously. While he waits, he pulls his broad-brimmed beaver hat firmly down over his curiously shaped ears. But he knows in his heart that the gesture is futile. The painter is sure to notice them. Nothing escapes his eagle eye. Ah well, he thinks, let him paint me, warts and all. The important factor is the truth.

He shifts uncomfortably on his pattens, by now muddy from the filth of the market floor. Truth to say, this new pair he finds uncomfortable. The left one does not fit him properly and gives him a slight limp. He will be glad to be disencumbered of them as soon as he gains admittance to this house.

The door opens. In his heavily accented Flemish, Giovanni Arnolfini announces himself and enquires of the servant if the Master is at home. Pieter replies that the gentleman is expected and please to follow him. Arnolfini steps inside the house and gratefully kicks off his pattens. In his thick woollen stockings enclosed in a thin pair of silk slippers he pads up three flights of stairs behind Pieter.

By the time he reaches the top he is somewhat short of breath. Pieter indicates which door it is and goes down stairs by himself. Giovanni pauses a moment to get his breath back. He can hear Pieter whistling as he goes downstairs. Then a knock on the heavy oak door and he finds himself in the holy of holies, Jan van Eyck's studio.

Arnolfini is surprised. The room is curiously bare of furniture. Somehow he was expecting something grander. At one

149

end there is a shallow raised dais where the painter's subject obviously poses. The studio is lit by a huge window facing north and another smaller one.

In the middle of the studio, there is an easel. At the far end, in front of a window overlooking the street, stands a trestle table on which are the tools of the Master's profession. It is on a subsequent visit when Arnolfini expresses his curiosity that van Eyck gives him a guided tour of its contents.

There are jars and jars and jars of brushes, varying in width from several inches down to some with a single hair. A slab of marble and a muller or stone used for grinding pigments stand next to the brushes. There is some vellum; an earthenware vessel containing gum arabic; jars labelled ultramarine, cobalt, Saxony blue; ten jars of yellow paint, all different shades and ten of black, eleven of white, ten of blue, ten of green, nine of violet and eight of red. A quantity of chalk, some size and a jar of turpentine complete the picture. It is an impressive, orderly clutter.

Against one wall lean some oak panels, primed with layers of chalk and glue (what van Eyck calls "gesso grosso"), ready to be painted.

Courtesies are exchanged. Neither man has time for small talk. Van Eyck wants to start sketching; Arnolfini wants to be painted. He finds himself being posed on the dais.

Artist and subject have had several preliminary discussions over the picture. At first, the idea, suggested by Arnolfini, is that van Eyck should paint two separate portraits, one of himself, another of his bride-to-be. The idea was mulled over without much enthusiasm by van Eyck. Then on the third visit, van Eyck had a brainwave. Instead of painting two separate portraits, why did he not do something which had never been done before, paint them together in one single picture, making it a double portrait? The idea was so revolutionary yet so breathtakingly simple that it was some time before Arnolfini concurred. But once he grasped the concept, he was enthusiasm personified.

So it has been agreed that the double portrait is to be full length of them both, he Arnolfini looking to his left whilst holding with his left hand his bride-to-be, Giovanna Cenami, as

150

she gazes at him. The picture will commemorate by a clever ambivalence both their engagement and their wedding. In the room where the 'ceremony' is to take place, van Eyck proposes to place certain artefacts which will unmistakably hint at the wedding. He has not told Arnolfini what these are to be. To keep spontaneity and freshness in his sitters, he prefers that they should not know too much about the finished picture. All of this has been explained to Arnolfini at some length in that courteous manner for which van Eyck is justifiably renowned.

There is another factor which has played an important part in the creation of this painting. Alas, there has been another crisis in the Cenami family which has necessitated a further postponement of the wedding. Tragically, Giovanna's mother, even though the whole family moved out of Paris to St. Cloud, as has already been said, caught the plague and died within three days. That happened in August of last year. The Cenami family have been devastated, not least Giovanna. The wedding of course has had to be postponed a second time.

Etiquette demands a minimum period of six months' mourning. The marriage will not now take place until July. Meanwhile, to escape further ravages of the plague and to help herself acclimatise, Giovanna has arrived in Bruges.

Giovanni has now been tragically denied marriage in two cathedrals. But married he will be, in Bruges this very year, Pope or no Pope. The family back in Lucca would like some permanent reminder and token of this union.

All of these ideas have been communicated to van Eyck who has pondered the situation with that amazingly clear mind of his. He has had some interesting and innovative ideas about the double portrait which he has not divulged to his sitters. All that Arnolfini knows is that, although both he and Giovanna will be in the picture holding hands, van Eyck would like them to pose separately for their joint portrait.

Giovanna has made an extraordinary suggestion which has really put the cat amongst the pigeons. She has asked if her pet dog, Hendrik, can be included in the picture. Van Eyck has not committed himself. He is thinking about it. He is not overfond of dogs because they present technical difficulties and their behaviour can be unpredictable. At the moment he is inclined to refuse but may change his mind, simply because the dog presents a challenge and could well be a useful symbol. He may not like dogs (he was bitten by one a few years ago) but he does like symbols.

Meanwhile van Eyck has taken great care and considerable time and trouble to pose Arnolfini on the dais. There is a debate about whether Arnolfini should wear his hat or not. It is agreed, that as the double portrait will portray both the engagement and betrothal of the couple, he should wear his hat as is customary at this time.

Jan van Eyck is fascinated by the texture of the hat and the subtleties of the way in which the light will hit its different surfaces. It will give him also a chance to show his virtuosity in the use of black. Arnolfini readily agrees because he hopes it will hide his ears.

The painter stands in front of his subject and looks long and hard at the banker's face. Several times he advances and moves Giovanni's head a fraction. He does this by placing three of his fingers and a thumb on Arnolfini's cleft chin and swivelling the head minutely. Every time he does it, he steps back to look critically at the source of light and Arnolfini's right cheek. Three, four, five times he makes his infinitesimal adjustments until at last he appears satisfied. He goes back to his easel and writes himself a note.

Having placed Giovanni's head exactly as he wants it, van Eyck now concentrates on Giovanni's right hand. It is to be raised, as if he is in the act of making a vow. Several postures are tried. The arm is moved left and right, the fingers separated slightly, the thumb given its own special position. Nothing is left to chance. It is agreed that he will wear a ring on the middle finger of his left hand, as a token of his betrothal.

"What about my finger-nails?" enquires Arnolfini somewhat shamefacedly. "I have been examining massive bales of cloth and there is a great deal of dirt under my nails. I am positively ashamed of them. Shall I wash and attempt to clean them?"

"Certainly not, my dear sir. That is the sort of authentic

detail which I am hoping to incorporate in your portrait. That sort of detail represents authenticity and the truth if you will of your living presence. I like them; please leave them exactly as they are. After you are married, you may clean them as much as you like."

Both men smile at this frank exchange. Instinctively they feel that they are getting on well with each other. Arnolfini asks about the position of his left hand but is told by the artist not to worry about this at the moment.

Satisfied with the pose at last, van Eyck returns to his easel to start making a preliminary drawing in silverpoint. Conversation is desultory. After what seems like twenty minutes of tension, van Eyck breaks the silence.

"How goes the silk trade?"

Arnolfini is surprised at the question. He cannot believe that a great artist is interested in something as mundane as business matters. His answer, when it comes after a moment's consideration, is perfunctory and uninformative.

"Well, I thank you, sir."

There is another long silence, broken only by the scratching of the crayon. At last the artist speaks.

"You may ask me questions."

Look. Scratch.

"If you so desire."

Look. Scratch.

"But not about this work."

Look. Scratch. Scratch.

"About my other paintings. If you so desire."

Look. Scratch. Van Eyck writes a note.

"If you know them. Or about my brother."

Look. Another look. Scratch.

"The one who died. Hubert."

Arnolfini is relieved that the ice seems to have been broken. Gratefully he accepts the invitation.

"When did your brother die?" he asks and then wonders if he has been impertinent.

Van Eyck stares at Arnolfini for a long minute, goes back to his paper on the easel in front of him, makes a minute mark with his crayon, again looks long and hard at his subject, then at the paper before writing a note on the edge of the paper. Only then does he reply.

"Hubert died on the 18th September, 1426."

Another short silence.

"In Ghent."

"Were you with him at the time?"

"Unfortunately, no. I was out of the country on a pilgrimage for the Duke. I had been polychroming a statue of St. Antony for Robert Poortier in March."

The artist walks over to Giovanni Arnolfini and moves his chin a fraction to the left before returning to his easel.

"Yes, I left my beloved brother in Ghent hard at work on his great masterpiece, *The Mystic Lamb*. By the time I had returned in, let me see, October he was dead. No sooner had I come back from Lille than I had to set out in January of the following year on another secret mission. Finally, in 1428, I spent more than a year, as I described to you in a letter, travelling to Portugal to paint King John's daughter, Isabella, for my Duke.

"That must have been very frustrating for you."

"It was. Would you move your head a fraction to the right. No, too much. Back a little. That's perfect. Thank you. Keep it like that."

Van Eyck makes another mark, writes another note.

"Chin a little lower. Don't look at me – look across the room, slightly down, as though you are gazing at someone who is coming through the door. Yes, that's right. Try to keep that position. I must now put all this down on paper."

Van Eyck starts writing busily.

Eventually he says, "Please keep talking to me; it helps my concentration."

"Was your brother as good a painter as you are?"

The painter observes his subject before making a mark on the paper.

"Better, far better. I am a talented and innovative craftsman; he was a genius."

"In what way was he a genius?"

154

Van Eyck looks at Arnolfini in surprise.

"Have you seen *The Mystic Lamb*?"

"Yes, I was in Ghent last year on business. Their merchants needed a great deal of cloth which I was able to supply. I availed myself of the opportunity to slip into St. John's Cathedral and see *The Mystic Lamb*. I spent two hours in the Chapel."

"Well then, I don't have to answer your question. The concept of the whole polyptych was Hubert's. Hubert conceived the idea of painting the Retable with the four prophets, the Annunciation, and the effigies of the two St. Johns with donors on the outside."

This speech is spoken while the artist is wiping his hands on a cloth.

"Yes," answered Giovanni, "I had dinner many years ago with Joos Vidt who explained to me the whole thinking behind the Retable. When I arrived in the Cathedral last year, the Retable was on show and the audience – there must have been twenty people – was able to study the marvellous details. That extraordinary room with the Archangel and the Blessed Virgin and the contemporary view out of the window. I could swear it was Ghent, or maybe Bruges, and yet I couldn't recognise it. Tell me, Master, where was it?"

Van Eyck looks at Arnolfini and almost smiles. He takes a sip of wine before replying.

"It was nowhere. Hubert invented it. It is what you Italians would call a *capriccio*, pure fantasy. But it's meant to be a typical Flemish town. There are deliberate echoes of buildings in Ghent, Bruges, Brussels, Antwerp, Lokeren, Mechelen, Turnhout, Roosendaal, even distant London."

"Oh absolutely, I agree, its very typical of any Flemish town. The castle, the spire, the gable houses, people hurrying up and down the streets, the skein of geese flying over. It reeks of reality."

"Most Flemish town streets do smell."

Both men laugh.

"And all of that was Hubert's work."

"No, I'm not saying that. All of it was the product of Hubert's imagination. But unfortunately he did not live long enough to realise the completion of his project."

"Then if I had to guess, I think he painted the four prophets and the Annunciation scene. Maybe he did the two St. Johns but I would hazard an opinion that you painted Joos Vidt and Isabelle Borluut."

A serious man by nature, Jan van Eyck rarely if ever permits himself the luxury of a laugh. He has had his ration for one morning. But on this occasion he allows himself the faintest of smiles.

"Let us say that I neither affirm nor deny what you have just said. The truth must remain hidden in deference to my brother's reputation."

There is another decent interval of silence before Arnolfini puts his next question.

"How long did you work on *The Mystic Lamb?*"

"You could say, 'too long!' But that is easy to calculate. I have been working since my brother's death in 1426."

He looks critically at the paper on the easel before continuing.

"But I have had serious interruptions for great Missions abroad on the Duke's business. Let me see. You may relax for a minute."

Van Eyck walks over to a wallet hanging from a peg on the wall and consults a small book.

"Ah, here we are. My brother died in September. Yes. I worked on the Lamb from October until the following October, then from February, 1428, until October of that year. Then nothing for over a year as I went off to Portugal. I resumed my task in January, 1430, and worked without interruption until I finished and the work was consecrated on St. John's Day, 6th May, 1432. So that's about four and a quarter years of solid painting, if my calculations are correct."

He emits something akin to a sigh and strides back to his easel where he picks up his crayon.

"Let us continue. Please assume your pose once again."

Giovanni makes a minute adjustment of his head before speaking.

"I am astonished, Master, at your industry but having seen

the finished work, I can well comprehend the enormity of your task. But tell me, sir, what exactly does the inscription on the picture mean?"

"It means what it says."

"Remind me, if you would be so gracious, of what it does say."

Van Eyck thinks for a moment.

"The inscription is in Latin which I will translate for you. It goes something like this:"

The painter Hubert van Eyck, who has no superior, began the great work which Jan, his inferior in art, has completed; the work has been paid for by Joos Vidt

Van Eyck works in silence for about a minute before adding one last comment.

"And finally there is a chronogram inviting you to contemplate the work on 6th May, 1432."

Arnolfini mulls over the inscription in his mind. He is tempted to ask van Eyck if he was the author of these words, but realises that it is so obvious that he was that it would be grossly impertinent to enquire. Accordingly, he says nothing.

The two men fall silent.

Giovanni's mind flits from silks to dogs, from cod and salmon lying on a marble slab to the Blessed Virgin receiving the Annunciation, from the tree-lined ramparts of Lucca to his beautiful Giovanna walking thereon. As always, his face betrays no emotion.

Jan van Eyck is busy capturing on a small piece of paper not only the outward lineaments of Arnolfini's face, but also his inner soul. That is the skill of his artistry, the nature of his genius. He is totally absorbed in his work.

The only sounds are the scratching of the artist's crayon, the muffled cry of a baby downstairs and the chiming of the half hour from some distant church.

Chapter 20

May, 1995

"Here you are at last. I was just saying to Bill, he'll be here at any minute. Wasn't I, Bill? Welcome, welcome. Down, Mr Chips, get down, get down, boy! Bill, take him into the kitchen. He's just so pleased to see you. Normally, he's a very well behaved chappie, aren't you, my darling? Bill, make sure he doesn't get the meat. On the table. Under that cloth. I'm so sorry, how do you do, I'm Heather Hepton, please call me Heather. John, I can't tell you what a pleasure it is to come face to face with you after all our telephone conversations and little notes flying between us."

She lets go of his hand at last. Heather is a handsome woman with a well-endowed body, dressed in clothes which proclaim taste, money and a certain flamboyance. Beneath a sharp, sensuous face with slightly too much make-up on it and an aquiline nose, her body movements proclaim authority, self-assurance and efficiency. Heather leads John through the hall and into the sitting room.

"Come into the lounge and meet the Thorntons. Edward, Peggy, let me introduce John Arnold."

The Thorntons turn out to be a nice but unmemorable couple. They live locally, actually just in Devon, "place called Uplyme – you won't have heard of it," explains Edward Thornton over drinks. "I retired seven years ago and we looked for a house down in the west country. Love this neck of the woods. Actually, although we live in Devon, our postal address is Dorset. Funny, isn't it?"

John does not think it is funny in the slightest. He smiles bleakly at Mr Thornton, a thin, watery smile. People who say 'actually' in every third sentence do not deserve his attention. He

159

turns to study a large framed watercolour on the wall. Mrs Thornton joins him – John is hopeless at names, he has just been told the Thornton woman's name and he hasn't the foggiest what it is. He has a vague idea that it begins with M. Or P. Mind you, if it is any comfort to John, unbeknown to him, neither has Peggy Thornton the faintest what this other man is called. Doesn't matter.

They begin to discuss Golden Cap, Thorncombe Beacon, Stonebarrow and other landmarks on the coastline which is what the picture depicts. They agree that it is a good watercolour, that the coastline is incomparable and that, yes, they must walk its length one day. Two more sips of Amontillado and they have gone through the motions of what constitutes polite conversation between middle-class English strangers. Boring. Unemotional. Uncontroversial. Apolitical. Trivial.

There are certain subjects which are taboo at drinks parties of this sort. "I cannot say," thinks John, "that I believe in God and the Life hereafter or that I lust after my hostess; that I shall vote Labour hereafter; that I am not very well off and that I need a hernia operation." That reminds him. Surreptitiously he slides his hand into his pocket and eases the situation.

He finds himself talking to Bill. About dogs. About one dog in particular. Mr Chips. Just his luck to be stuck with a dog fanatic. Fond as he is of animals in general, he takes little interest in other people's pets.

In the course of duty John has met bores before, golf bores, cooking bores, gardening bores but never a dog bore. Bill is doing his best to make up for lost time. He is clearly a specialist in the subject whose themes are inexhaustible. What fascinates and amazes John is the fact that Bill appears to be blissfully ignorant of the profound lack of interest that he, John, has for anything to do with Mr Chips.

Ten minutes of desultory conversation, or to be more precise a monologue from Bill largely uninterrupted except for the occasional grunt from John, and two glasses of Amontillado pass when Heather emerges from the direction of the kitchen and peremptorily summons John to her 'Den', as she insists on calling it. There they are to discuss the afternoon's arrangements.

160

"Bring your glass, John, just along this passage, and down three rather nasty steps. It's very dark, here, let me hold your hand. We don't want you coming to any harm, do we?"

The hand-holding episode ('h'm, promising,' thinks John) leads to nothing. Heather's 'Den" turns out to be a minute room containing her desk with an Amstrad PC on it and a leather armchair alongside.

"Sit you down there, John, and I'll ensconce myself here."

She manages to imply by 'ensconce' if not a coronation, at the very least a Bishop's enthronement.

John eases himself into the deep leather chair and finds himself looking up at Heather. The last time he was in such a position was when he lay full length and looked up at Miss Simkins, his dentist, who said, "Open wide, please, Mr Arnold" and he had made a detailed study of Miss Simkins's magnificent eyebrows while she probed and drilled.

To John's slight disappointment, Heather is extremely business-like and professional. The interview is conducted briskly. Heather elicits from John a brief C.V. which she quickly assimilates. She explains the business side of the meeting. There follows a technical discussion about the projector, John's slides, the screen, the pointer and the throat mike.

"We like to pride ourselves here in Beaminster that our N.A.D.F.A.S. is one of the best attended, well organised and most cultured in the west country. I think you'll be impressed, my dear," and she leans forward and gives his arm an affectionate squeeze. John finds himself looking up at a pair of very dark, lustrous eyes, heavily accentuated with dark blue mascara. H'm, tempting, he thinks, though van Eyck has immediate priority. For the first time he notices what magnificent eyebrows Heather possesses. Images of Miss Simkins swim into his subconscious and he has to restrain himself from opening his mouth wide for her inspection. Was it only two summers ago that he had played vicarage tennis with Monica Simkins?

He decides to serve up a juicy lob.

"Did you know, Heather," adopting the conspiratorial tone which Heather is using and leaning forward in his chair to get within petting range, "did you know that in the 15th century, when van Eyck painted his women, there were no bosoms?"

He pauses for effect. Heather looks interested, by no means shocked.

"What do you mean precisely, John?" she asks, a trifle huskily.

"I mean that bosoms were unfashionable. Women had their breasts bound up tightly and their waists came up just below their breasts. The important thing, as I'll show this afternoon in my slides, was to have a long neck and a tiny waist. The longer and the tinier the better."

There is a pause. Mascaraed eyes look deep into hornrimmed spectacles. It is an uneven contest. There is no way that mascara, not even when laid on good and thick, can get past Vienna Line heat-resistant trifocals.

For three long seconds they look at each other. Suddenly Heather lets rip with an almost girlish laugh, grabs John's arm and yanks him out of his chair with a "well, with my shape I was clearly not born in the 15th century. Let's go and have some lunch." Still holding his arm, she guides him skilfully up the three dangerous steps back to the sitting room or 'lounge' as she calls it.

"Luncheon, everybody follow me. Bill, get the plates, please, and don't let Mr Chips out. Tell him he'll get his dindins soon. And he's to be a good boy. Now (with an expansive gesture), how have I seated you? Bill sits at the head of the table of course. Peggy, would you sit on his right? Edward, you're on my left, and John darling, you're on my right. Everybody sit while I get the food."

In Heather's absence, John finds himself talking to Peggy Thornton. Trivialities are exchanged. "No, we've always wanted to live in Devon. The opportunity occurred when Edward retired. Before that as a matter of fact we lived in Berkshire. But we love it down here – all those deep sunk lanes and thatched cottages." Peggy goes on for another two minutes of what John considers a monologue before he is suddenly asked his profession and where he lives. For one blinding moment, staring at Peggy Thornton, he pictures her with a moustache and three stripes barking out,

"Name, rank and number, sonny." He can still say it without thinking. "Arnold, Private, 19196003, sir." And that must be forty years ago. He snapped out of his reverie.

"Oh sorry, what do I do? I'm a schoolmaster or to be more precise, was."

For a few moments he reminisces about his career before Peggy Thornton becomes bored and takes up the running. She talks boringly about Dorset. Every third sentence is predictable, every second trite.

When his turn comes, John explains that he went to prep school in Langton Matravers on the isle of Purbeck, between Corfe Castle and Swanage.

Peggy Thornton says she knows where he means. John can tell from her expression that she doesn't have the faintest idea. And doesn't care. He hopes his audience this afternoon will not be so obtuse.

He finds himself reminiscing about what he refrains from calling 'the happiest days of my life.'

"Yes, we used to run every Tuesday and Thursday mornings down to the Dancing Ledge and swim in a pool which had been blasted out of the rock there. In the nude. It was a magic place. Not because we were nude of course."

He laughs nervously and Peggy Thornton joins in. Suddenly, there is a braying sound on his right.

"What have you been doing in the nude, John? I hope you're not giving your lecture like that. What I might call bare-faced cheek!" Again the bray.

"No, Heather, I was just telling Peggy here how I learnt to swim in those distant, halcyon days."

"What was halcyon about them?"

"Oh, the innocence. What Wordsworth calls 'the visionary gleam'."

"Yes, well I lost my innocence a good few years ago. Do start, everyone."

John looks down at an avocado mousse with prawns which has appeared from nowhere. Bill has filled one of his glasses with what he takes to be Hock. Heather raises her glass.

"Well, here's to what I am sure is going to be a very

successful lecture. Cheers."

Everybody embarks on individual conversations. John can hear Edward having an animated discussion with Bill about alternative routes from the M3 through Dorset to Beaminster. He thought he caught the word Shaftesbury. He certainly heard Blandford Forum mentioned. Funny how you pick up certain individual words. Peggy then nattered on to Edward about an exciting exhibition of raffia work in some local gallery. John feels himself drowning as waves of intense boredom wash over him.

John comes to his senses as he finds he has to bear the full brunt of a Heather tête-à-tête. It's funny how avocado acts as a mild aphrodisiac.

"So tell me, John dear," says Heather provocatively, a tiny sliver of prawn hanging seductively from the edge of her mouth, "tell me about your BayeuxTapestry lecture. You know, I'm sure I told you, my committee looked long and hard at your programme. We very nearly chose that. Did we make an awful mistake?"

Only she doesn't say 'awful'. The word comes out as 'nawful'. North country, thinks John.

"Well, Heather, I think you made the right choice. Van Eyck and more particularly Arnolfini is a gripping story which I hope your audience will find fascinating. I know I do. It's a picture I have been fascinated by since I was, oo let me think, since I was thirteen."

"Really?"

This is said as encouragement to elaborate. The mascara says, 'gimme more."

"Yes, I can remember the precise moment I first met Arnolfini. I was sitting in a classroom, trying to write an essay on some boring topic, I've forgotten the subject, and I didn't have an idea in my head until I looked round the classroom in desperation and saw Arnolfini hanging on a wall and I wrote about that. Won a prize, too, for my effort."

"Really?"

This 'really' is different from the previous 'really'. It's more breathy, more intense, more redolent of profound and genuine fascination with the subject. John decides that Heather in her time has taken part in much amateur dramatics and been rather good at it.

"I've been fascinated by dear old Arno ever since and have researched him, his life, and everything I could lay my hands on. And you know what, Heather?"

"What?"

"I'm still finding out things about him and his bride. Every time I look at the picture I discover something new. I bet you that this afternoon during the course of my lecture I shall think of something new to say about the picture."

"Really."

Ah, this 'really' was quite different from the others. It carried the clear signal – 'this subject has gone on quite long enough; I am getting bored'. John winds up the subject as he downs the last morsel of avocado.

"The dear old Bayeux Tapestry of course would have gone down well too. As did this avocado," he adds graciously as his plate is cleared.

Roast lamb makes its triumphal entry with mint jelly, carrots, sprouts and leeks in a sauce, duchesse potatoes and gravy. He passes plates and everyone is served handsomely. Bill pours a Chambertin into his other glass.

Bill is now going on about the relative merits of Safeway, Waitrose and Sainsbury. Peggy seems to find that conversation stimulating, God knows why, and the three at the top of the table happily play the game of pushing their laden trolleys around bulging aisles.

Heather and John, on the other hand, opt firmly for culture. The current exhibition of Dutch Flowers in the 17th century at the Dulwich Art Gallery is discussed, described and lauded. The benefits of being a Friend of the Royal Academy are agreed to outweigh the horrors of getting up to London.

"And they serve jolly good coffee in the Friends' Room. Did you see by the way the recent Picasso exhibition at the Tate?"

"No, but I did get to the Mantegna at the Royal Academy."

"Ah, I thought the West of England Summer Exhibition in

165

Bristol far better than the summer show at the R.A."

"I agree. Have you ever seen the Monets at the Marmottan in Paris?"

Table-top tiddleywinks with a lot of nudging, squidging, flicking and hopping. It all means nothing at all. Except the number of points each participant scores. But the food was excellent. And the wine.

"No, honestly, Heather, I couldn't, delicious as it was. That was a really sumptuous meal. No, Bill, I've got to drive – and give a lecture. No more, thank you."

And so to a decent little apple tart with lashings of clotted cream which left nobody accepting a very respectable cheese tray supported by Dorset Knobs. Heather's laconic, "well, shall we join Mr Chips in the lounge for a quick coffee?" gets everyone moving. Mr Chips is ecstatically pleased to see everyone and over-zealous in his attention. John approves of dogs – at a distance.

Coffee is quickly drunk. Suddenly it is ten to two and time to head for the Arts Centre, "a mere five minutes away in my car," as Heather assures him.

"Bill, you bring the Thorntons in your own time. I'll go ahead with John to set things up."

Heather's car is a sporty-looking B.M.W. in an ostentatious red. She proves an expert driver. Her backing out of her driveway into a Beaminster side street is casually fast and efficient. They speed along Acacia Avenue, turn left, then right, across the High Street and there they are. Only once during that short journey did Heather's hand brush against John's arm as she changed gear. An accident? John wonders.

They get out of the car with John carrying his carousel of slides and move inexorably towards the Arts Centre. Heather says something faintly absurd.

"Do you know, John dear," she says, looking portentous in her mauve presidential suit, "whenever I think of Arnolfini and imagine myself saying, 'Mr Arnold is going to talk about Arnolfini,' I always find myself getting his name wrong."

"Why?" asks John, sweating slightly as he struggles to keep up with an exuberant Heather, "what do you say?"

166

"I don't know why," answers Heather, "but I always find myself saying, 'Mr Arnold is going to talk about Arnold Scharwzenneger!" and, as she opens the Arts Centre doors, she bursts into a high girlish laugh.

Where has John heard that giggle before? For a moment he is nonplussed. Then he remembers. Of course. In the 'Den'.

Chapter 21

1st May, 1434

On the door of a house in Sint Gillis Nieuw Straat there is a knocker in the shape of a silver dolphin. This dolphin has watched a small party leave the house and wend its way towards the church at the end of the street. It is Saturday, the first of May, 1434, and a baptism is taking place in St. Gillis Kerk in the fair city of Bruges.

Gathered around the font, the small group of parents and godparents listen to the priest who reminds his congregation of the origins and significance of the sacrament of baptism. To their attentive ears his first prayer sounds strangely old-fashioned.

Almighty and everlasting God, which of Thy justice didst destroy by floods of water the whole world for sin, except eight persons, whom of Thy mercy (at the same time) Thou didst save in the Ark: and when Thou didst drown in the Red Sea wicked King Pharaoh with all his army, yet (at the same time) Thou didst lead Thy people the children of Israel safely through the midst thereof: whereby Thou didst figure the washing of Thy Holy Baptism: and by the Baptism of Thy well-beloved Son Jesus Christ, Thou didst sanctify the flood Jordan, and all other waters to this mystical washing away of sin: We beseech Thee (for Thy infinite mercies) that Thou wilt mercifully look upon this child, and sanctify him with Thy Holy Ghost, that by this wholesome laver of regeneration, whatsoever sin is in him, may be washed clean away, that he, being delivered from Thy wrath, may be received into the ark of Christ's church, and so saved from perishing: and being fervent in spirit, steadfast in faith, joyful through hope, rooted in charity, may ever serve Thee: And finally attain to everlasting life, with all Thy holy and chosen people. This grant us we beseech Thee, for Jesus Christ's sake

Our Lord.

The priest looks down at the placid baby cradled in his surpliced arms and accords it the gracious benefit of a smile.

So far, so good. The infant to be christened has not made a murmur. A mere three days old, the baby is wearing a long white christening robe, made of finest Bruges lace. The garment is called a chrisom-cloth. Until he is one month old, the child will be called a chrisom-child. Should the child have the misfortune to die in the next three weeks of its life, this garment will become its shroud. Birth and Death are potentially present in one cloth.

Happily this baby seems healthy and alert as he stares up at the strange man holding him. The priest asks a man standing beside him what name the child is to bear.

"Philip," replies Sir Peter de Beaufremont, Lord of Charny, in a firm, clear voice. Sir Peter is wearing a beautiful red woollen tunic, slit at the sides and trimmed with fur. His scarlet hose is set off by pointed felt shoes with gold tips at the toes and heels. He looks and is aristocratic.

But, truth to tell, despite his fine clothes and high standing in society, he is not the godfather. He is here standing proxy for Philip, Duke of Burgundy, whose affairs of state sadly preclude his presence. Naturally, the child is to be named Philip after his distinguished godfather and naturally he is christened on 1st May, the Feast Day of Philip the Apostle and name day of his godfather.

The priest dips his silver dish shaped like a scallop shell (to remind us that we become in baptism Pilgrims of Christ) in the consecrated water and pours some on the babe's forehead and on his chest saying, *Receive the sign of the Holy Cross* (here he makes a cross with his finger on Philip's forehead and chest) *both in thy forehead, and in thy breast, in token that thou shalt not be ashamed to confess thy faith in Christ crucified, and manfully to fight under His banner against sin, the world, and the devil, and to continue His faithful soldier and servant unto thy life's end.*

"Amen," says Sir Peter firmly.

"Amen," echo the other godparents.

"Amen," say the proud parents of Philip.

"Sniffle, sniffle," whimpers Philip, the newly baptised soldier of Christ. But the tears are withheld as bravely he faces the world.

Briefly the priest exhorts the godparents to remember that they are sureties for the child and have promised that he will forsake the devil and all his works and constantly to believe God's holy words and obediently to keep His commandments. The Lord's Prayer is said, a blessing pronounced and the service is concluded.

Later that month, Jan and Margaretha van Eyck, for they are the parents, will receive six handsome silver cups, a christening present from the Duke. The cups which weigh 12 marks and cost an astonishing 96 lions and 12 shillings, have been made by Jean Peutin, the celebrated Bruges goldsmith. It is a singular distinction and almost unprecedented mark of favour.

Outside, in Sint Gillis Kerk Straat, the sun is shining brightly as the party stroll towards the van Eycks' house in Sint Gillis Nieuw Straat for a christening luncheon.

Jan van Eyck walks proudly beside his young wife, hopeful that one day his son will become a great painter like his brother (and Philip's uncle), Hubert.

Margaretha who carries the baby is more practical. She wants to get home as quickly as possible and change Philip out of his chrisom-cloth. She considers that wearing it is a bad omen.

And Philip? He suddenly decides that he is hungry and begins to wail.

Sir Peter de Beaufremont has just remarked that he is hungry too. The timing of Philip's tears strikes everyone as felicitous and a good omen. There is laughter in the air as the company reach the van Eycks' house and enter past the silver dolphin door knocker.

The door shuts fast once everyone is inside the house. The laughter continues unabated. Outside the dolphin resumes his quiet vigil. Was it van Eyck's fertile imagination or did the dolphin really wink at him as he returned from the christening? Maybe.

170

Chapter 22

May, 1995

Tap. Tap. Tap.

"Goo – goo – good – phoo – phoo – phoo."

Much tapping of the microphone. Much blowing into the microphone. It seems to be working.

"Good afternoon, ladies and gentlemen, can you all hear me?"

"Yeeeeeeeeeeeeeeeeeeeeeeeeeeees."

The chorus of assenting voices stridently proclaim their faith in the amplification system. Standing on the stage behind Heather clutching her microphone, John observes that the audience is predominantly female and elderly at that. Heather has warned him that at least five per cent of the audience will fall asleep during the course of the lecture, however brilliant it may be.

"Not an insult to you, dear boy, merely a combination of senility and fatigue. They generally wake up in time to applaud you at the end."

In the old-fashioned hall which calls itself rather grandly the Beaminster Arts Centre, there are seven rows of red seats, six each side of a centre aisle, with three rows of cinema tip-up seats at the back on a rake. Almost all the seats are occupied.

Running right round three sides of the hall is a cream-coloured balcony where there is a further good turnout. Above the stage and the audience are gantries of stage lighting. In the central aisle a projector stands, its carousel loaded with his precious Flemish slides. He hopes fervently that Brian who helped him load his slides will get the focus right. There is nothing worse than looking at slides which are fractionally out of focus. Or even worse, upside down!

From the projector, cables run up to the stage. All that John has to do is press a button and hey presto! the slide changes. The cables have been fixed to the floor with yellow tape so that the old dears will not trip over them, break all their bones, sue W.D.D.F.A.S. and thereby close the Society for good.

He has also been armed by Francis, the hall's general factotum, with a throat mike ("Don't cough too loudly, John, or we shall all have our ear drums pierced," Heather warned him at lunch) and a Red Dot Pointer ("We had a lecturer last month who waved the red dot all over every slide and it made us all feel sick. Use it sparingly, John dear, there's a good boy," Heather urged him before the lecture, putting an admonitory hand on John's arm. Clearly she had forgotten that she had already warned him about this hazard in her first letter).

Heather stands there in front of him, exuding authority. She is quintessentially the Chairman. Over their pre-prandial drinks, they had discussed 'Chairwoman' and even worse 'Chairperson'; Heather had reacted with horror to both appelations. "I am the Chairman, dear, and what was good enough for my predecessors is good enough for me. Besides, 'man' in this context does not carry the connotation of masculinity but rather of authority. That is what has been invested in me as Chairman. Don't you agree?" And then she had shut up as if she had realised that she was becoming rather pompous.

The talking in the hall gradually subsides. Heather has their attention and starts again.

"Good afternoon. Welcome to our monthly meeting. It is very gratifying to see such a good turnout. May I welcome you all in general on this beautiful summer's day and express a very warm welcome in particular to our new members who are joining us for the first time this afternoon.

Before I introduce our speaker, whose talk we are so looking forward to (here a backward smirk at John), I have a few notices to give out. The Membership Secretary, who is sitting in the front row (here a gracious nod to Peggy Thornton) tells me that that there are still a few subscriptions outstanding. Please see Peggy after the meeting and pay up. Otherwise, we shall have to devise some mediaeval torture to make you conform.

172

And we don't want that, do we?" A ripple of laughter testifies that Heather's jokes, though macabre, are usually appreciated.

"I hope you've all picked up your copy of the N.A.D.F.A.S. magazine with its wealth of information, its fascinating articles on Church Restoration, Stately Homes, Repairing China and Carpet Weaving, plus a grand crossword with generous prizes. It would be so nice if some clever person from here were to win the competition. So the message from your committee, in the immortal words of Wilfred Pickles, is 'Have a go'.

Now next month, on the 18th to be precise, we are going to Hampton Court for the day. Sewards coach will leave the Beaminster car park at 7.30. That's 7.30 a.m., I'm sorry to say. We plan to have a guided tour of the State Apartments with all their lovely furniture and pictures. Then there are a series of optional tours. You can see the Mantegnas in the Orangerie if you like – Charles the First acquired them for the nation, you know. They are quite magnificent. I do recommend a visit."

John is pretty sure that most of the audience do not know about Charles the First and the Mantegnas. Heather has definitely scored a cultural point here.

"Or." Here Heather rescues her glasses which are resting on her bosom, attached by a gold chain around her neck. 'Lucky glasses,' thinks John as he studies his notes.

"Or you could walk round the magnificent gardens, or have a guided tour of the Royal Kitchens, or visit the Maze and get lost like the three men in a boat. Or…"

Here she pauses dramatically. There is no question that Heather likes her 'ors'.

"Or you could visit the Real Tennis Court where legend has it that Henry VIII was playing tennis when he heard about the execution of poor Anne Boleyn (Heather makes Anne Boleyn sound like a relative) and hear a short lecture on how to play the game from Jack there who is a member. Thank you, Jack." Here another smirk and gracious nod.

"Built in 1536, I believe. Is that right, Jack?"

"1530, Madam Chairman," comes the firm reply from Jack in the third row.

"I stand corrected."

173

The cliché produces another general titter.

"So all that on June 18th for £18 which includes the coach fare and the price of entry. Pretty good value for money I would have thought. Anyway, if you would like to go and there are still a few tickets left, please see Alison Butler afterwards."

It is at this point that John finds his attention wandering from the matter in hand. As Heather's voice recedes to a murmur, he finds himself wondering what he is doing here at all. How on earth did he get here at all?

Suddenly the picture of a classroom swims into his sub-consciousness. He is on the Isle of Purbeck all those years ago, desperately trying to write an essay. He remembers how he had found the Arnolfini portrait on the wall and written that silly essay. What was the title? *Curiosity*. Something like that. That had been the seed which dear old TS at his Public School had germinated. Good old TS! Nice man and admirable art teacher. What then? Of course, he had been teaching Chaucer one winter's afternoon and had become bored with *The Clerk's Tale*. On the spur of the moment, he had whipped out his projector, put up the slide of the van Eyck on the wall and started talking about Arnolfini. And he realised that the more he had spoken about it, the more there was to find out. It was a picture which you could never stop exploring. He had started visiting the National Gallery every month, sometimes more often, invariably spending some considerable time in front of the Arnolfini and finding something new each time. Yes, he is now what you might call an Arnolfini nut. One of his pupils, a very intelligent and immensely tall girl, had once said to him, "You're obsessed with this picture, aren't you, sir. Come on, own up!" And John had laughed and said, "Nonsense, Ali, of course I'm not." Then he had reflected for a moment and had the courage to change his mind. "All right, Ali, I admit it. On second thoughts I suppose you're right." This had been said with a rueful smile though really he was rather proud of himself.

John becomes aware of a murmur continuing in front of him.

With a shock he returns to the present and the scene before him. He sees serried rows of N.A.D.F.A.S. ladies, a few men and

Heather spouting. She seems to be finishing.

"Finally, ladies and gentlemen, may I remind you that our next meeting will be the AGM, when I and most of the committee will be standing for re-election. The AGM starts at 2 o'clock precisely so please come then if you want to attend and not at 2.30 when our regular meeting will begin as usual. That concludes the business side of the meeting."

Heather raises both her arms as if she is about to bless the congregation.

But on this occasion she is not the Pope.

Carefully she removes her gold-rimmed half spectacles from her nose and lays them reverentially, as on an altar, on her bosom.

"Oh, God," thinks John, "here we go. Stand firm in the ranks, men, steady the Buffs, don't fire until you can see the whites of their eyes."

"And now it gives me very great pleasure to introduce our speaker, John Arnold, who is going to talk to us about Flemish painting with particular reference to Jan van Eyck. John who comes from the Home Counties is a retired schoolmaster. He tells me that one of his many hobbies is fly fishing. So I hope we shall take the bait and be well and truly hooked by John's line on these Flemish artists. John Arnold."

Heather steps briskly down the three steps from the stage. As the perfunctory polite applause dies down, John finds his dry throat producing noises.

"Thank you, Heather. First of all, ladies and gentlemen, can you all hear me?"

Murmurs of assent.

"Good. Before we have the first slide, a few brief remarks about the artist.

"Nothing is known about the life of Jan van Eyck before 1422. We may conjecture from various clues that he was probably born about 1390. He would have received a formal training as an artist. From 1415 to 1417 he was almost certainly working at The Hague for William VI, Count of Holland, Zeeland and Hainault.

Perhaps he is the author of one of the miniatures in *The*

Turin Book of Hours which depicts William VI on horseback. Possibly he painted another miniature called '*The Kiss of Judas*'. He may even have painted a drawing of this period, tinted with watercolour, entitled '*Fishing Party at the Court of William VI*'. But all of this is conjecture.

"What is certain is that by 22nd October, 1422, he had become attached to the Palace at The Hague of Count John of Bavaria, brother of William VI, as the official painter and 'varlet de chambre', whatever that may mean. He had been commissioned to decorate the palace. It is a task which will occupy him until 11th September, 1424. He was paid, incidentally, at the rate of eight lions a day, while his assistants each received two lions a day.

"By the time he has finished his formal education, still only in his twenties, Jan van Eyck has arrived. His enormous talent is about to blossom. When Count John dies on 5th January, 1425, and civil war erupts, Jan seeks refuge in Flanders.

"He moves to Bruges where all his masterpieces will be painted. That is where our story of Arnolfini takes place and that is where I hope to solve *A Mystery*.

Can we have the lights out, please?"

Darkness.

"Thank you."

Click!

The first slide appears.

"Let's start with the simple facts about this very well known painting, facts which are incontrovertible. Very well. What do we know and what do we see? The picture hangs in the Sainsbury Wing of the National Gallery which I am sure all of you have visited. It is usually called the *Arnolfini Wedding Portrait* or the *Arnolfini Marriage*. It is painted in oils on a wood panel by Jan van Eyck in 1434, probably in Bruges where van Eyck lived. The panel measures 32 $^{1/4}$ x 23 $^{1/2}$ inches, quite a small, intimate picture by National Gallery standards. If more than two people stand in front, it is a crowd.

Van Eyck has been inaccurately described as the inventor of oil painting. What is certain is that he was one of the first painters to use oil paint to achieve such glowing colours and microscopic details. He is a very important figure in the Early Netherlandish or Flemish school of painting whose influence was felt not only throughout Flanders but also across the Alps into Italy.

Now what we see in front of us (here John begins to pick out details with his red pointer, being careful not to keep the dot on too long or waggle it too vigorously) are two people and a dog in what appears to be a bedroom. The couple are painted full length – incidentally, the first full length double portrait in the history of painting – and they are holding hands. At the top of the picture we can see a chandelier, below that a signature on the wall, beneath that a convex mirror. All of these features we shall examine in some detail in a minute. As we look more closely, we notice fruit behind the man on the left, a pair of shoes kicked off carelessly in the bottom, another pair under the mirror on the floor, some glass beads beside the mirror, a little dog standing patiently at the couple's feet, a brush hanging from the bed. And those colours. I hope your chromatic senses are being ravished by the gorgeous green of the lady's dress and the sumptuous scarlet of the bed coverlet and the red of the prie-dieu at the far end of the room. The whole ambience of the room denotes wealth, from the five layers of lace on the lady's head to the rich Turkish carpet on the floor. And of course this couple must be rich to be able to afford imported oranges. I think we cannot help observing and asking ourselves the question, "Is this lady pregnant?" Be patient. I shall try to solve all these mysteries in the next half hour.

Click!

We are looking at a detail in the picture, the head and shoulders of the man. How solemn he looks, those strange, heavily-lidded eyes, the curious ears, that huge and expensive beaver hat, the fur-trimmed gown, the raised right hand. His name is Giovanni di Arrigo Arnolfini, a rich banker from Lucca in Italy. He lives and works in Bruges.

Click!

And now for the lady. Like Giovanni she is also Italian, from the same town, Lucca. She is Giovanni's wife, of that there can be no doubt. Her maiden name was Giovanna Cenami, daughter of an Italian merchant who also came from Lucca. Her father worked in Paris which is where Giovanna must have met her future husband.

Now is she pregnant, I hear you ask. The answer is, of course not. Let me explain how I can be so dogmatic. Giovanna is wearing a very fashionable, immensely expensive, green woollen gown, undoubtedly woven in Bruges. When the Royal School of Needlework decided to reconstruct this dress for an exhibition in the National Gallery they had to use thirty-five yards of material to make the dress. The gown is edged with fur and has elaborate embroidery on the sleeves. She is holding up the front of her dress to allow herself to pose with her husband, as was the fashion. She is certainly not pregnant. But of course the artist by that gracious curve of the dress has suggested that she will be pregnant once the marriage has been consummated in the bed on the right.

Click!

A chandelier, partially gleaming from the daylight which comes from the window on the left. In it burns one candle. Why one candle, when it is broad daylight? Is it a wedding candle or even a candle used when one takes an oath? We shall see.

Beneath the chandelier, in legal calligraphy, is the inscription *Johannes de Eyck fuit hic* and then the date written in Flemish – 1434, set between two tiny crosses. Jan van Eyck was here in 1434. So the artist has signed the picture in this unusual fashion. Why? Does this suggest that he was one of the men in the mirror, a witness to the wedding? This is one of the many problems which must be solved in this fascinating picture.

Click!

The mirror and the beads. Here we have van Eyck's technique displayed for us at its best in all his dazzling virtuosity – geometrical purity, miniature painting of the highest skill and glittering lustre. In the mirror we can see the backs of the married couple, the rest of the room and two men standing in the doorway. Around the mirror are ten tiny scenes from the Passion of Our Lord – you can see the Crucifixion at the top. Hanging on a nail are crystal prayer beads, an early form of rosary.

Click!

The dog, the first realistic dog ever painted. I am told by the experts at Crufts that he is a Belgian or Brussels terrier. He is every bit as well groomed as his mistress. He looks up straight at us and I swear that you can see his tail wagging. Look at that wet nose! Do you think he is planning an outrage? Anyway, what he is doing is standing (literally) for marital fidelity. Dogs in the 15th century were well known symbols of fidelity. Look at mediaeval tombs in our cathedrals and churches with the effigy of a knight in full armour lying on his tomb with a dog at his feet, faithful unto death.

The word symbol perhaps triggers in us a response as we begin to realise that the *Arnolfini Marriage* picture is packed with symbols, all painted with astonishing realism. Not just the dog but the colours, the chandelier, the mirror, the beads, the shoes, the bed, the carvings, the fruit, the signature, the two main figures, the carpet, the shutters, the scale of the two figures, the signature, even the light.

But now it is time to come off the fence and be a little more dogmatic. Let's look at the picture again in more detail and see if we can determine precisely what is happening.

So I go back to the first slide, the whole picture."
Click!

Chapter 23

June, 1434

It is hot, very hot. For the past ten days, Bruges has been sweltering in a heat wave. From the Bishop down to the humblest beggar, from merchant to mariner, housewife to harvester, all are suffering. For none is there relief, not even the Duke in his palace.

But wait, there is one exception. The small boys can find solace. After school they run out of the City down to the river bank where they strip off and plunge in. The pure water is wonderfully refreshing as it embraces their naked bodies. Never having been taught to swim, instinctively they employ the dog stroke, paddling about happily in the shadows as they splash and duck each other. They do not venture out into midstream where the current is strong. Last year one of their fellow pupils drowned at this spot. Though his name is never mentioned, the memory lingers; his shadow darkens the corners of their lives, prompting vigilance.

Nor can the haymakers find any shelter from the blazing sun. The grass in the fields outside the City walls is ready for the scythe. The men have put on long shirts which cover their bodies loosely down to the thighs. With bare feet and a straw hat to save them from sunstroke, they are ready for a long day's work in the fields. The sun actually rises at 4.43 am on the longest day of the year. By 5 o'clock it is light enough to work and their task begins, even though the dew is still on the grass. Funnily enough, that dampness helps them to cut through the crop. Not that they find it amusing. On they go, minute by minute, hour after hour, pausing only every fifteen minutes or so to whet their scythes. The whispering note which sings in the hard sunshine as they scythe through the grass is replaced sporadically by the whistling tone of the whetstone.

On they go, establishing a rhythm which never varies. Fifteen minutes of hard scything, five minutes of whetstoning, row after row, swish and cut, swish and cut, swish and cut.

There are three men, one dressed in a red shirt, one in white, the third in blue. They work as a team, scything in unison. This rhythm helps their concentration, keeps their rows straight and gives them the impetus to continue what becomes by the end of the day a backbreaking, even suffocating task.

Together they swish, swish, swish in time all the way up the row. Each swish demands a complete turn of the body. The scythe is taken right back behind the body until the two arms are straight; then it is brought round a full one hundred and eighty degrees, cutting through the stubble. Three steps forward and the process is repeated. Each row takes at least eight minutes to cut. At the end they permit themselves the luxury of taking off their hats and wiping their foreheads with their shifts which are soon wringing wet. Thirty seconds' rest and they are off again. At the top end of the field, after they have cut four rows, the solemn business of sharpening the scythe begins. Each side of the blade gets some twenty or so strokes of the whetstone before it is deemed to have recovered its pristine sharpness.

Once all three men are ready for the next row, they line up. They say nothing. In this heat conversation is both a luxury and an effort. White and blue shirts take their time from red shirt. Red shirt draws his scythe back at the top of the new row and, sensing that the other two are ready, begins his sweeping movement all over again. The baked, red earth absorbs silently the drops of sweat which fall freely from their brows.

Every twenty rows or so, – ten up and ten down – liquid refreshment is taken on board. Each man holds the earthenware jug by the handle, balancing it on his raised forearm and allowing the lukewarm wine to slurp down his throat until his thirst has been partially slaked. The wine has little effect on the men. Twenty rows later most of it will have come out of their bodies in the form of sweat.

While the men scythe, two women are raking up the cut grass into small shocks. They are dressed in loose-fitting blue gowns over white petticoats with long sleeves. They too have no shoes on their feet. One of them has tied a kerchief over her hair, the other has a long white linen cloth protecting both her head and the back of her neck from the fierce sun. The first woman rakes the hay into small bundles which the other picks up with a two-pronged pitchfork to create a row of hay shocks. They too say little or nothing. It is not that they do not have plenty of town gossip and tittle-tattle to communicate. Their feminine presence in a picturesque meadow may look idyllic. In reality the work is hot, unromantic and cumbersome. But it has to be done. For a long steamy day's work, they will be paid a pittance, enough maybe to buy one loaf of bread for their family's supper.

Seven hours after they have started, they hear the bell of St. Donatian chiming noon. Men and women gratefully stop work. They saunter down to the river's bank to find shade under a pollarded willow. Here they break their fast with a simple meal of coarse bread and cheese washed down with some more wine. After the meal, for half an hour they permit themselves the luxury of a siesta before haymaking begins again. It will be ten o'clock before they finish, too tired to do anything but tumble into bed. Tomorrow they will all have to start again with the next meadow. Life is indeed hard.

Meanwhile, the Duke who is entertaining foreign dignitaries in his cool Palace, could, if he so wishes, observe the haymakers' labours. Mind you, he would have to climb the winding stone staircase up to the top of a turret from which he could gain extensive views of all his territories in that part of the world, including the fields which are having their hay cut.

But he is too busy for such frivolities. More serious matters occupy his ducal attention. The weighty question being debated is, 'Shall we go hawking tomorrow?' With him is the Ambassador from Spain.

Now that the harvest has begun, there will be plenty of activity from birds and rabbits, hares, deer, foxes and other game. From that point of view the omens are auspicious. Duke Philip has consulted his head Falconer and reports his opinions to the ambassador.

"Excellency, my Falconer, I believe he's called Charles,

tells me that this confounded heatwave is playing havoc with my hawks. They simply won't hunt; the heat makes them lethargic. He is inclined to think that it will be a waste of time. But of course I am entirely at your disposal. Excellency, what do you think?"

His Excellency is not prepared to express an opinion one way or the other. He leaves the decision to the good judgment of his Grace, the Duke. That is why His Excellency is an Ambassador. It is his job to sit on the fence, something which he does supremely well.

But let us leave this council of war. It does not matter whether they go hawking or not. They are merely playing a game. Haymaking is for real and must be done. Swish, swish, swish go the blades silently through the compliant grass.

And the day gets hotter as the Duke's hawks and falcons mope and fret in the mews.

For no good reason, one of the haymakers suddenly starts singing. It is the woman with the kerchief. She sings in a high reedy voice whose passion and conviction more than compensate for any lack of musicality.

I sing of a maiden
That is matchless:
King of all kings
To be her son she chose.

He came also still
Where his mother was,
As dew in April
That falleth on the grass.

He came also still
To his mother's bower,
As dew in April
That falleth on the flower.

He came also still
Where his mother lay,
As dew in April
That falleth on the spray.

Mother and maiden
Was never none but she:
Well may such a lady
God's mother be.

The men and the other woman join in softly the refrain of the last two lines of each verse. When they finish, there is a moment's silence and reflection. Perhaps a prayer is said. As St. Donatian's softly chimes 6 o'clock in the evening, their Angelus Domini has been sung.

The Duke does not hear it in his ivory tower as he worries about his hawks. Nor does Margaretha van Eyck sponging her new baby Philip with water to cool him down. Nor does Arnolfini negotiating business deals with his fellow bankers. Nor does Giovanna Cenami, standing on a dais, posing for her portrait. Nor does Jan van Eyck as he works on Giovanna's face. Her left eyebrow is coming on well. He is almost satisfied with his work.

Chapter 24

May, 1995

Click!

"So here we are, ladies and gentlemen, back with the oh-so-solemn Giovanni Arnolfini and his bride-to-be Giovanna Cenami gazing submissively at him. All the critics suggest that we are looking at a wedding. Let's see if they are right.

Before I start, it might help if I pose a few questions, prompted by a quick scrutiny of the work. The moment we begin to ask these questions, we shall begin to see immediately that there are obvious problems.

Why on earth is the ceremony taking place in what appears to be a bedroom? And why is there a dog present? Where is the priest? Why is there only one candle lit in the chandelier? Is she pregnant? It certainly looks like it. Why has he got his hat on and his shoes off? Are those apples or oranges on the chest behind him? (John's red dot pointer is busy). Why are there beads and a brush hanging on the back wall? Why has van Eyck signed the painting in such an unorthodox manner? What's that figure above the joined hands of Giovanna and Arnolfini?

More importantly, who is in the mirror?

And perhaps, above all, is the ceremony taking place at this moment or has it already occurred? Or, to put it another way, are we to treat the picture as a wedding certificate, or is it merely a souvenir like all those photos that get taken at the church door after the wedding ceremony? Is it necessarily a wedding at all? Could it be something entirely different?

Finally, can we deduce from the numerous clues in the picture the supposed time of the year when the event is taking place?

Those are quite enough questions. The answers must be

attempted if we are to understand this picture which has fascinated and intrigued its admirers ever since it was painted.

Now for a secular wedding to take place in the 15th century not in a church three criteria had to be fulfilled. Vows had to be exchanged, there must be witnesses and the marriage must be consummated. Clearly Giovanni with his right hand seems to be making some sort of declaration. With his left hand he supports Giovanna's right hand, a gesture which in the 15th century would be taken to be one of submission by the woman to the man.

Click!

Who are the witnesses to this unusual event? In the mirror we can just make out two people, standing facing us between the backs of the couple. One is in blue, the other in red; both wear chaperons. Behind them we can just make out a spot of light from the front door of the house which has presumably been left open. Perhaps it is a hot day, summertime maybe and they need a draught inside to stir up the air. After all the two major participants are wearing pretty heavy clothing.

But the man in blue and the man in red in the mirror are not the only witnesses. There is also the artist himself, Jan van Eyck. Where is he? I suggest tentatively that he is not necessarily one of the two men reflected in the mirror. But van Eyck certainly painted the picture and, as was his custom, he signed the double portrait.

Click!

If you look above the mirror, you can see the elaborate piece of calligraphy, suitable for a legal document – Johannes de Eyck fuit hic – 1434. Jan van Eyck <u>was</u> here. Not you notice Jan van Eyck <u>is</u> here or even, I painted this picture.

In fact van Eyck signed five of his paintings on the frame in this distinctive and unique way:

JOHES. DE. EYCK. ME. FECIT. 1437

or

JOHES. DE. EYCK. ME. FECIT. ANO. MCCCC. 33. 21. OCTOBRIS

He also signed the portrait of his wife, Margaretha, thus:

ALS IXH XAN

which is Flemish for 'as well as I can', but may also be

translated, if we accept the pun on **IXH**, 'As well as I, van **Eyck**, can paint.'

What is striking about the signature on the Arnolfini portrait is that it is unlike any other autograph that the artist ever used. Why is that? Perhaps it is because van Eyck is not signing the picture; he is acting as a notary, a legal representative of the church, witnessing formally by his artistic skills an event which has already taken place. I would submit that vows have already been made by Giovanna and that Giovanni is in his turn making his oath, witnessed by the two men in the mirror and by the artist who confirms the fact by his contractual statement by signing the picture with a legal flourish in his elegant calligraphy.

Click!

And of course that brings us to the chandelier above the signature and the mirror immediately below. In the chandelier, if you look very closely (red pointer) there is evidence of two candles, the lit one on the left and some traces of wax here in one of the three holders on the right.

The extinguished candle or *la chandelle éteinte* as it was known alludes to the contemporary adjudication of claims by fire. In the 15th century, when a document was being drafted or a legal agreement drawn up, a candle was lit. When the candle burnt out or was blown out, the legal aspects of the act were deemed to be binding. It was also customary to light a candle when an oath was being made.

If we agree that a legal event has taken place in this room which has been independently witnessed, with both parties to the contract exchanging binding legal vows, all of which has been legally corroborated and transcribed by a notary, then the Arnolfini so-called Wedding Portrait begins to lose some of its mystique. A man and a woman have made solemn oaths in the presence of God and of witnesses. The event has been signed and sealed. The picture is living proof of that event.

We have studied the chandelier and signature. If we want to find God in the picture, it is time to look in more detail at the mirror."

Click!

"This is the focal point of the whole picture, around which

everything seems to turn. Indeed you could almost liken it to a cog wheel which motivates the rest of the machinery in the picture. Around it revolve the dramas of the people and artefacts in that room.

What can we see in the mirror and how far can we trust what we see?

If you walk into Exeter Cathedral, the magnificence of Bishop Grandisson's Decorated Gothic building will immediately catch your eye. You will find yourself admiring and being astonished at the vault which runs uninterrupted from the west front to the high altar and beyond, a distance of a hundred yards. Its multiplicity of ribs is locked together with carved and painted bosses, of which there are more than five hundred."

Click!

"In the nave, one boss in particular will catch your eye. It is in the last bay but one before the Norman transepts. It shows the murder in 1170 of Thomas à Becket, Archbishop of Canterbury. This was a subject of particular interest to Bishop Grandisson for it was one of his predecessors, Bishop Bartholomew, who had led the ecclesiastical enquiry into the murder, and Grandisson himself had written a biography of Becket.

The boss, almost a yard wide, is well worth studying in detail. We want to go on looking at it but as we gaze up, so the crick in our necks gets worse. Ah! But the kind Dean and Chapter have thought of our problem and come to our rescue. There is a sort of wheeled trolley for our use which contains a large flat mirror on top. We wheel it down the central aisle of the nave, rather like an air hostess dispensing drinks or duty-free, until it is positioned directly below Becket. Then we can gaze down (instead of up) into the mirror and can study the assassination in comfort.

What we can see is Becket kneeling before a small altar. He raises his arms to ward off the fatal blow. In doing so, he stretches open his chasuble to reveal a white rochet. His mitre has fallen on the floor. Behind the altar we can make out a shelf with communion vessels, chalices and a pyx. By Becket's side stands an attendant cross-bearer, vainly trying to ward off the dreadful blow aimed at the Archbishop's head. And the four

188

knights, in full armour, crowd in to perform their murderous task. Fitzurse with his bear's head badge on his shield gives the first blow. It is all there in vivid reality on a three-foot round boss fifty feet above our head in Exeter Cathedral.

But wait! What we are looking at is an illusion, a representation of reality. Even if we leave the mirror and crane upwards to gaze at the boss, that too is a representation of a real event. Like the people in Plato's cave, looking at the shadows on the wall, we are twice removed from the truth."

Chapter 25

20th July, 1434

It is 7 o'clock in the morning on the morning of Tuesday, 20th July, in the year of Our Lord, 1434. It is going to be hot again. Very hot indeed in Bruges.

Already the stallholders are setting out their wares. By now the streets are thronged. People are favouring the shady side of the street. Shutters and windows are being flung wide. Like the dogs lying lethargically on the streets, the city is beginning to pant. "Yes, brother," says one stall-holder to another, "it's going to be 'ot today and no mistake. Mark my words, I reckon it'll be a roaster today." His companion is not inclined to disagree. Besides it's too hot to argue. As he spreads his wares, ripe cherries, along his stall, he watches two ladies hurry by jabbering in some strange language.

But then he is used to that. In this day and age, the 1430s, Bruges has become a very cosmopolitan city. Bloody foreigners! The city is bursting with them, all taking trade away from decent, honest, Flemish men, "born and bred 'ere. What's more, worked 'ere all our lives."

Walk down Bredelstraat towards the central square once a day for a week and you would in all probability meet Venetians, Genoese, Florentines, Pisans, Catalans, Portuguese, Burgundians, Bretons, Moravians, "Turks" (that is traders – Armenians, Persians and others besides Turks – from the Near East), Slavs (mostly Dalmatians), Bavarians, English ("they're the worst"), a few Scots, the odd Lucchese, some Savoyards, a smattering of Danes, a Greek or two and the rest from God knows where.

"I'll tell you something, brother, what is true. Cross my 'eart and 'ope to die if it isn't."

190

"What's that?"

"The Duke's a good man. No question of that. But I don't 'old with all them foreigners being allowed to settle 'ere and take the bread out of our very mouths. I mean it's not fair, innit?"

His companion listens to this diatribe impassively while selecting another bunch of cherries – geans he calls them – six of which he stuffs into his mouth. He nods in affirmation.

A fat black cat is curled asleep on a nearby doorstep. The stall-holder spits his six pips carefully one after the other at the cat. The first five missiles miss. Number six scores a direct hit eliciting a scalded squeal of indignation and an undignified exit through an open window. "Even that Tom's probably imported from some foreign land," he asserts by way of corroboration, helping himself to some more geans.

A Bruges housewife hoves in sight and pauses at his stall.

'Yes, mevrouw, 'ow can I help you? They're delicious." He holds up a bunch of his geans to tempt her. They glitter in the sunlight. The serious business of clearing his crop of cherries begins with his first sale.

Meanwhile the two women who have hurried by speaking some incomprehensible language are nearing their destination. The language is French. They have been to Mass in Saint Gillis church on this, the Feast Day of Saint Margaret, the patron saint of childbirth.

How appropriate that one of the women is called Margaretha, named after the Virgin Martyr. Margaretha van Eyck has been telling her companion, Giovanna Cenami, how and why Saint Margaret is so very special in the Christian church.

"She was the daughter of Diocletian," explains Margaretha as they hurry along Gouden Handstraat.

"Dio who?"

"cletian."

"When did she live?" asks Giovanna.

"Oh, hundreds of years ago. Let's just say a long time ago. Before you were born. Or me," adds Margaretha rather lamely.

Gales of giggles.

"And where did she live?"

191

"In Antioch."

"And where's that?"

"Oh, over there," replies Margaretha, waving her hand vaguely in the general direction of the east.

More laughter.

"So what's special about her?" asks Giovanna when she has recovered her composure.

"Well, a very important man called Olybrius wanted to marry her but she rejected his advances."

More giggling.

"So Olybrius denounced her as a Christian whereupon Satan disguised himself as a dragon and swallowed her."

Giovanna considers this improbable story for a moment before accepting it. In the 15th century simple faith is perhaps easier to achieve than it would be six hundred years later. Scepticism, let alone cynicism, has not yet polluted religion.

They have arrived at the door of their house. Today is Giovanna's matrimonial day. The bride-to-be pauses on the top step before going inside.

"Well, I'm not going to reject my man and be turned into a dragon," announces Giovanna meekly but firmly as she faces a bustling Bruges.

"Of course you're not," says Margaretha, gently propelling the younger woman into the house. "You're going to be married today and have lots of children and make your husband very happy. And I am going to have the privilege and pleasure of preparing you for your wedding."

She takes Giovanna's two hands and presses them gently whilst looking into her eyes.

"Now tell me, have you dismissed all your maid servants?"

"Yes," replies Giovanna, squeezing Margaretha's hands in affectionate response, "I have sent them all below stairs. And, dear Margaretha, it is exceedingly gracious of you to help me with my pre-nuptial preparations on this, your name day. I want you to know that I am extremely conscious of the great honour you bestow upon me. I could not have endured the last six months in Bruges, waiting to be married, without your friendship and companionship. For me it has been a period of trial and tribulation as my Giovanni has argued with the authorities over where and when we were to be married. Without you I should have been lost."

Margaretha says nothing but there is a suspicion of a tear in her eye as she embraces Giovanna in the hall.

"May God bless you and your marriage and may you be as happy in yours as assuredly I am in mine."

Another squeeze, another hug and the front door shuts behind the two women who make their way upstairs.

On the first floor they go into a reception room which exudes luxury, good taste and money. A large bed stands on a dais with 'scarlet' covers and curtains. On the bed are laid out a number of items – a fine green woollen dress trimmed with fur with an immensely long train and long sleeves with elaborate dagging. There is a blue underdress made of damask also trimmed with fur, a leather belt with gold decorations, a white linen veil, gold bracelets, a gold chain, and a pair of red leather pattens decorated with brass studs.

Beside the bed stands a high-backed oak chair with finials, one of which depicts St. Margaret with a dragon at her feet, another a woodwose, a third a lion. The ceiling has a beam running across the middle of the ceiling. Near the back wall hangs a handsome brass chandelier. The floor, surprisingly, has bare boards with just the one carpet beside the bed. There are two windows in the room, both of which are glazed in the upper parts with clear bull's-eye glass and red, blue and green stained glass; the lower halves are open with six shutters on each. Because there is no fireplace, this room is used only in summertime.

In front of the second window stands a wedding cassone or chest with five oranges on it which must have cost a fortune. There is also an apple on the window sill, not cheap but far less exotic than the oranges which have been imported all the way from Portugal.

On the back wall hangs a large circular mirror which Margaretha now takes down and hangs on one of the shutters of the second window. On the cassone a servant has placed a tub containing hot water spiced with herbs. Beside it lies a slab of soap and two towels. We are ready for our pre-nuptial ablutions.

But first there must be a last look at the world outside, busily oblivious of the events taking place in this room today. From the first floor window of the brick house, the two women can see the tops of the cherry trees with their abundant crop waiting to be picked. Beyond the trees the gabled roofs and spires of Bruges make a familiar and comforting backcloth.

Margaretha offers Giovanna an orange and takes one herself. As they peel and eat them, they gaze at the view. Somehow the unfamiliar sharp taste of the oranges matches their emotions. The pristine purity of the early morning light, the sense of wonder and deep spiritual satisfaction they feel at having been to Mass on this St. Margaret's Day, their affection for each other, the solemn events that lie ahead this very day, the innate feeling that their especial innocence, mutual confidence and support will somehow be shattered or at least changed this day, all these complex emotions turn them into very solemn, serious and even sad persons. The time for giggling is over. They have finished their oranges and throw the peel out of the window into the street below. They dip their hands in the tub and dry them on the towels. Instinctively they hold hands as they look out at an indifferent world. They sigh and turn to the business in hand.

One of them starts to undress.

***

Below stairs, the unprecedented events surrounding another bath on the same day in the same house are being recounted.

"So what 'appened next?"

"Go on, Pieter, you kin tell us!"

Pieter grins sheepishly and takes another pull at his flagon of ale. It is a bribe, a blatant bait to induce him to describe what has occurred. He wipes his mouth with the back of his sleeve, spits on the sawdust floor and pushes the pewter mug towards Anna with a sly smile. Should he divulge what the Master has made him do? He can't see any harm. This is a golden opportunity. The cook and all his helpers are out in the market

194

buying the food for a big dinner upstairs tonight. The great gloomy kitchen down in the basement is empty, save for Pieter and the two scullery maids, Anna and Joop. Dressed in coarse brown linen, the girls have covered their heads and dresses with white linen. Grease, fat and wood ash have left their indelible marks on the women's clothes. Their aprons are filthy from continual tending of the fire which smokes fitfully and reddens their eyes.

Still young and buxom, already they are showing incipient signs of wear and tear. The bloom is beginning to fade. Pieter will have to hurry if he wants to catch them in the first flush of youth. As a matter of fact, he is considering just that. Yes, he will definitely 'pull' one of them tonight. "Which one? Doesn't really matter. They're both equally ugly. Trouble is, you 'ave to look at the mantelpiece when you pokes the fire. I dunno. Might give myself a treat and do both. See 'ow I feel."

For Anna and Joop, blissfully unaware of Pieter's seduction plans, this is an adventure, to capture Pieter all to themselves and to hear about the strange goings on above stairs, a place which they never ever visit. After all, there is little enough excitement in their lives. The work is hard, drab and boring. Endless, mindless kitchen preparations – tending the fire, turning the spit for hours at a time, peeling vegetables, washing dishes, stirring pots, scrubbing pans, receiving constant abuse and filthy innuendoes from the male staff, this is their lot. They accept it because they have known no other life and there is no alternative.

Anna comes back to the long table in the middle of the kitchen, a wooden table scored all over with knife marks and sets down the full pewter mug in front of Pieter. She sits down beside him on the bench. Joop leans forward provocatively across the table. Her great floppy breasts practically spill out of the top of her dress. She stares brazenly up at Pieter.

"Go on now, Pieter, you be a good boy an' tell us everyfink. Us'll keep it a secret. You kin trust us. An' there might be something in it for you, know what I mean?"

Very slowly she lets her tongue lick her top lip from right to left; then does the same thing with her bottom lip, only this time, for variation the other way round.

That does it. Pieter decides here and now that there are further rich pickings to be gained. Tonight. In the attic.

He starts to tell his story.

"Well, it's quite simple really, it were like this. Master gave me a right royal bollocking last week because I 'ad let Hendrik 'ave a run in the town. Mind you, I reckon he'd 'ad a super dooper time. He'd 'ad a dip in the canal, been to the market, fed 'imself up on all sorts of scraps, met several other interesting dogs and done you know what but I can't mention 'ere in polite society, rolled in some 'orse shit, and to cut a long story short, thoroughly enjoyed 'iself."

Pieter pauses to increase the tension.

"Go on, Pieter," urges Joop breathlessly.

"Yes, do go on," seconds Anna.

Pieter takes another swig and continues in his own sweet time. He likes milking the situation.

"When 'e come back, I'd be the first to admit 'e didn't look exactly clean or pretty. 'E were in a nawful state. 'E were covered in horse mess, 'is fur were all matted, 'e 'ad fleas and smelt like a bog after a long, hard winter if you know what I mean. Master were furious."

Pieter does a very fair imitation of his master's voice.

"Get that dog cleaned up, Pieter," 'e thundered at me. "And I mean clean. Give him a bath, wash him from head to tail, dry him, comb his fur, brush him and present him to me again as immaculate as a new born baby."

Pieter adds a post script to this description after a moment's reflection.

"You know what, I've never seen the Master proper angry before. E's normally such a gentle, quiet, even-tempered sort of bloke. Never raises his voice. Not normally."

Anna is amazed.

"Bath 'im?" she exclaims incredulously. "Put 'im in a bath? Wiv 'ot water? And soap 'im? Why, that's not decent. Even us 'umans don't 'ave to do a fing like that!"

Joop adds her quarter groat's worth.

"I feel for 'im, I do, I'm sorry but I 'ave to say it, I don't care who 'ears, that's no way to treat a poor dumb animal," she says gazing up wide-eyed at Pieter and helping herself unasked to a swig from Pieter's pot. "Did you do it, Pieter?"

"Course I did. You know that old copper bath in the stables? Well, I 'eated up lots of pans of water on a fire in the stable yard, not that that made me very popular with the ostlers. Anyway, I filled the bath with 'ot water. I think 'Endry must 'ave 'ad some inkling what I were going to do cos I 'ad the divil of a job to find 'im. He were 'iding from me, you see, under a table in one of the rooms. I dragged 'im out and took 'im out to the stable yard. I lowered 'im ever so gently into the bath until he were standing wiv just 'is neck and head above water. Looked ever so funny 'e did. Then I got to work with a bar of soap and lathered 'im all over. You know what, I fink 'e rather liked it. After a bit. I mean 'e complained like merry 'ell at first but bit by bit 'e settled down and by the end 'e were standing ever so still and rather enjoying 'imself, know what I mean?"

"Yes."

"Anyway, I gets 'im really clean – what the Master called immabulate, or some word like that – and lifts 'im out of the bath and then 'e did a terrible fing."

"What?" cries Joop breathlessly.

"What was it? Do tell us?" implores Anna simultaneously.

Pieter indulges himself with a dramatic pause to increase the tension before replying.

"'E stood right there in front of me, cool as brass, and suddenly shook 'imself so violently I got covered wiv water."

Shrieks of laughter.

"It were no laughing matter, I can tell you," says Pieter when the laughter subsides. "I were soaking wet. Any road, I grabbed 'old of 'Endry, wrapped 'im in a big towel I 'ad ready, and dried 'im all over. When 'e were really dry, I carried 'im to the Great Hall, sat 'im on my knees in front of the fire and started to comb 'is coat which were terrible matted like. I done a good job on 'im, mind you, though I do say it meself. It did take the best part of two hours but at the end 'e looked smashing. Then I brushed 'im to make his 'air stand up on end and I stood back and looked at 'im. Booful, that's what 'e were, booful, though I do say it meself. Then I took 'im up to the Master. Master didn't say much. Mind you, I could tell 'e were pleased. 'E looked at 'Endrik very critical-like from all angles, then 'e grunted and told me to 'ave 'im ready in the afternoon cos 'e were taking 'im to the Arnolfini 'ousehold. An' that's what I done. Here endeth me story."

Pieter takes another swig at his ale and looks pleased with himself. The kitchen maids are enchanted with the tale. For a dog to have a bath is the funniest thing that has so far happened to them in their uneventful lives.

The return of the cook and his army of minions from the market place laden with provisions heralds the end of leisure. For Pieter it is time to attend to his Master; for Anna and Joop two hours of steady peeling lie ahead; for Hendrik the beautiful there is a special function that afternoon in a specific room in front of two special people. With witnesses.

Chapter 26

May, 1995

Click!

"Now let's get to our mirror. It is concave – flat mirrors were very rare in the 15th century – surrounded by a circlet of red and blue, the red echoing the prie-dieu and the bed, the blue the under-dress that Giovanna is wearing. Then round the exterior of the mirror are ten tiny rondels depicting the Passion of Our Lord. Finally the outside shape of the mirror has suggestions of the artist's palette.

Of course many artists subsequently have used mirrors in their paintings. Most famously Velázquez copied van Eyck in *Las Meninas*, and even in the *Rokeby Venus*. But van Eyck is almost certainly the first to paint a mirror's reflection.

A perfect mirror is a well-known representation of the Blessed Virgin Mary, *speculum sine macula*, a spotless glass. I want to suggest to you that the pose of Giovanna Cenami is strongly reminiscent of the way in which Flemish artists depicted the Blessed Virgin Mary. I am thinking of such painters as Geertgen tot Sint Jans, Jan Gossaert (also known as Mabuse), Gerard David, Hans Memlinc and Robert Campin. We have not time right now to look at examples but you can easily find them in the Sainsbury wing of the National Gallery.

The mirror with its scenes of Christ's last hours, if we can trust its veracity, appears to act as a proof that a marriage has taken place. The illusion is the reflection in the mirror; the reality is Christ, depicted in the top rondel, who died to redeem us all.

In the Cathedral at Lucca there is a much cherished and worshipped carving of the crucified Christ. According to legend, this wooden sculpture was miraculously found on the Tuscan

199

coast in the eighth century and then made its way to Lucca. This larger-than-life carving has always been an object of particular veneration in Lucca. In 1369 the Lucchese business community in Bruges signed a statute which governed their business activities, laid down a code of conduct for families living abroad and pledged devotion to *Volto Santo*, the Holy Face, Lucca's cherished carving. Giovanni Arnolfini was undoubtedly a member of this community. The *Volto Santo* would have been something very precious to him.

So there we have a reflection of a room in which two people stand under the Crucifixion which is itself under the signature of the artist whom we can perhaps see reflected in the door. He is the little figure in red (his favourite colour) standing behind another witness in blue.

I would suggest that the picture is both a portrait and a legal document, proving that the Arnolfinis have been legally married. The two candles, one lit, one burnt out, the Lucchese symbol of the *Volto Santo*, the formal signature on the back wall and the back view of the couple in the mirror all prove that there has been a marriage.

But above all, the mirror, exceptionally large for its time, with its expanding view of the room, its two witnesses facing us, its blue and red circlet, its hint of a palette and the Crucifixion placed so prominently between the calligraphy and the mirror reflection corroborate all the evidence.

There has been a wedding at which vows have been exchanged. The mirror is placed exactly to show us where the priest would stand at a wedding if he were marrying a couple. The mirror is the priest and when we stand in front of the picture, we are standing exactly where the priest would have stood to marry the Arnolfinis."

Click!

"Oh yes, ladies and gentlemen, there has been a wedding. Of that there can be no shadow of a doubt. And what is more, I think we can say with reasonable certainty when exactly it took place. Look, please, at the top of the elaborately carved chair, immediately to the left of Giovanna's head-dress. You will see a lady and in front of her a winged lion in profile, the lion of St.

Mark of course whose Feast Day is 25th April. I submit that the Arnolfinis were married in Bruges on 25th April, 1434, in this very room."

John pauses a moment. His throat is getting parched. He is feeling nervous tension and is sweating freely. But he does not think it would be circumspect to wipe his brow. Instead he takes a long drink of water before continuing.

He has been going now for three-quarters of an hour. He has arrived at the crux of his lecture, the controversial bit. He is about to go over the top and can sense the Boche machine-gunners flexing their trigger fingers.

"Excuse me. Let me now try to pull together the different theories into one coherent whole.

The critics all seem to agree that the picture is a wedding portrait. I both agree and disagree with them. Of course Giovanni and Giovanna were married to each other. I have suggested that the date was 25th April, 1434, St. Mark's Day. As I have said, the mirror has acted as the priest; the witnesses to the wedding are the two men reflected in the mirror, the candle signifies the legality of the ceremony, and van Eyck's elaborate signature testifies to Jan being the legal representative.

But this picture, like so many great paintings (for example, Holbein's *Ambassadors*), is capable of sustaining more than one interpretation. It shows a wedding, yes, but also a divorce!"

John pauses for a second to allow the full weight of this amazing statement to sink in. He detects a faint stirring in the audience. He can see an old dear in the second row being nudged awake by her neighbour.

"I repeat, a divorce. I know, I know, it is shocking. One always wants great pictures to be somehow comforting, for *The Hay Wain* for example to roll gently through an idealised Suffolk landscape in which Constable seems oblivious of all the appalling rural poverty prevalent at that time. Let's see what the evidence is for such a controversial statement as I have just made.

Well, the Arnolfinis were married in April. Let us now conjecture what may have happened. Some time in the next four months Giovanna committed adultery. I think it is plain that she is pregnant. The fulsome curve of her gown over her womb is clear enough proof.

Now look once again where my red pointer is, there, just above the touching hands of the two Arnolfinis. I'll give you a larger slide."

Click!

"This is the most prominent place in the whole painting, the focal point.

What do we see?

Carved on the end of the arm of the chair is a finial of a hideous figure with some sort of hat. It is a woodwose or wild man of the woods representing carnal desire. Around the mirror we have scenes of the divine passion of Our Lord. Above the married couple, hovering menacingly directly over their clasped hands, is another form of passion, in a word, lust. And look at all that red in the picture. Yes, the red of the prie-dieu, it is true, echoes the sacred passion around the mirror. But, above all, look at that scarlet bed, just crying out for sex. *'Tis a consummation devoutly to be wished.'*

I'm sorry. I've shocked you but facts are facts and the obvious must be stated. Van Eyck is telling us that the couple were married but that she committed adultery, almost certainly in this very bedroom where she became pregnant.

The woodwose over their hands is the die or what the Chinese call the 'Chop', the handle one grasps when one applies the die and seals a document. The mirror is the seal, the woodwose the handle.

And look at all the other clues which van Eyck has kindly scattered so liberally all over the picture so that there can be no misunderstanding.

Behind Arnolfini, there is an apple on the window sill. Why? Because, like Eve, Giovanna has been tempted and fallen. She has eaten of the forbidden fruit of the Tree of Knowledge.

And the little dog at her feet, what's he doing there? You can forget Crufts and all your own dear little pets. Dogs in the 15th century were scavengers and thieves. Legend has it that Judas Iscariot, the arch betrayer, kept a dog as a pet. The dog was an attribute in that age of envy, one of the Seven Deadly

Sins. And of course we all remember Bill Sikes and Bullseye who betrayed him. This little dog, standing so patiently at the feet of Giovanna, is announcing emblematically that she is not to be trusted.

Now what about the single candle in the chandelier? In Holy Week, candles were lit for Matins and Lauds and gradually extinguished one by one, until finally only one candle, that held by the priest, was left alight. When last of all he put his one out, the congregation took it as an allusion to the Apostles' desertion of Christ at the time of his Betrayal, Trial and Crucifixion. Incidentally, they still perform this ritual in the Greek Orthodox church at Easter.

Similarly, we can say that Giovanna has deserted her husband and, as I have explained, her candle or *chandelle éteinte* is well and truly extinguished.

And the mirror is not only a symbol of the Virgin Mary, or if you like the virgin Giovanna that Giovanni married back in April; it also represents the naked truth because a mirror does not lie. The mirror shows in one of the rondels the Betrayal of Christ in the Garden of Gethsemane. And in the mirror's reflection we can see a pregnant and shamed Giovanna being divorced by her husband whom she has betrayed.

That is the case for the prosecution."

Again John pauses dramatically; again he takes a sip of water. He is feeling strangely elated, drunk with his oratorical power over his audience. He finds himself almost floating behind the podium on the rostrum.

The audience appears to be still listening. Indeed he flatters himself that they are mildly intrigued by his theory and in the palm of his hand. Palm of his hand? God! How John hates clichés – at the end of the day, having said that, all things considered, *tout bien considéré* – how can people be so lazy? The French phrase reminds him of a rather good meal he had recently at a bistro in the Rue du Bac. Talking of meals, he finds himself wondering what he is going to eat for supper. That woman in the third row appears to be asleep. The journey home should be a piece of cake. Whoops! Piece of cake. There goes another cliché. The M25 shouldn't be too bad. When's the rush hour? It's always rush hour on the bloody M25.

John suddenly becomes aware that he is standing in front of a predominantly female audience of N.A.D.F.A.S., all of whom have paid good money to hear him lecture and that he is saying absolutely nothing. How long has been silent, for Pete's sake? He begins again hurriedly, without first collecting his thoughts.

"The M25 is usually extremely crowded in the rush hour."

He stops. The audience seems bemused.

"I'm sorry. Please ignore that. I'll start again."

As a diversionary tactic he blows his nose. The throat mike picks it all up and amplifies it to the audience. At the back of the hall it must sound disgusting, like a rhinoceros vomiting.

"Excuse me. Let me now attempt, ladies and gentlemen, to tie the whole picture together. Here are a few final titbits for you."

Click!

"If we look at the whole picture once again, we are perhaps struck by the strong vertical lines. Framed by the two Arnolfinis, there is a bold vertical line running from top to bottom of the picture. I hope you can all see my red pointer. At the top, the chandelier with its single candle. Then the signature which contains a number of strong verticals, then the mirror – there are many verticals in it – then his and her hands surmounted by the woodwose, then down the line of the prie-dieu, along the edge of the carpet and the floorboards, past the white zigzag of the hem of her dress all the way at last to the dog who acts as a sort of wicket-keeper or long stop, if you know your cricket, ladies, which I am sure you do."

Flattery, thinks John, it always works, especially with women.

"Now let's talk briefly about the colours. Red, the colour red or scarlet. Did you know by the way that this colour was produced from the female bodies of kermes insects which feed on the kermes oak found in Spain and the Levant? You didn't? Never mind, don't let it bother you. If it's any consolation, I didn't either until quite recently.

Did you know that it was the colour used in the Middle Ages to decorate the front of pawnbrokers' shops? You didn't?

I'm not surprised. I didn't either until I began my researches on this picture. How appropriate that red should be used as a colour for Arnolfini, the international financier.

And green, that other predominant colour in the painting. Giovanna Arnolfini, *née* Cenami, wears a sumptuous green woollen robe. We are meant to take notice of that colour. In the 15th century green was the colour of the cloth that members of the Arte del Cambio, the Florentine Guild of Bankers and Money Changers, were required to place on the tables they used as their 'Banks'. So you see, when this picture was painted. both red and green stand for money. Now let's take another look around the room for ostentatious signs of wealth."

Click!

Chapter 27

20th July, 1434

Hendrik is exhausted, as well as being humiliated. He has never been so clean in his life. Lathered and scrubbed, dried and brushed, combed and clipped, pampered and perfumed, he feels disgustingly clean. It is not natural. He cannot any more with advantage scratch or bite any part of his body. Even the fleas have drowned. Hendrik feels that none of his friends in the market will speak to him again. They certainly won't recognise him. And what is worse Mistress seems preoccupied. It is all very unfair. There is nothing for it but to turn round three times, curl up and go to sleep. Sweet doggy dreams!

Mistress is indeed busy. She has divested herself of all her clothes which have been piled in an untidy heap in the far corner of the room. Laid out tidily on the bed are Giovanna's wedding garments.

Beside the bed Margaretha van Eyck watches over the operations with a keen eye. She is there at her husband's request and of her own volition to assist Giovanna in her pre-marital ritual ablutions and investing.

Although there are still seven hours to go before the ceremony will take place, Jan van Eyck has asked his wife to have Giovanna ready by noon. Then he and his servant Pieter will prepare this room for the ceremony which will take place at two o'clock in the afternoon. When Margaretha asks her husband who the witnesses will be, he replies somewhat curtly and enigmatically that he will be one and the other is a man that he knows will be coming. From where he is not prepared to say. He does add one piece of gratuitous information. The second witness, who will arrive only at the last moment, will be dressed in blue.

So there stands Giovanna, stark naked. Mind you, meek and submissive as she generally is, on this occasion she has protested bitterly about this unwarrantable intrusion into her privacy, to say nothing of the quite unnecessary activity of bathing herself all over before she can get married. Who ever heard of such a thing? What other woman has ever done so outrageous and unconventional a thing as this?

It just so happens that Margaretha van Eyck, standing by the bed, enjoying the spectacle of Hendrik twitching in his doggy sleep and Giovanna soaping her sweet young body, can answer that.

"Bathsheba."

"Who?" demands Giovanna working a soapy flannel vigorously on her knees.

"Bathsheba," repeats Margaretha. "We had a sermon about her last week in church. It seems that David, King of Israel, was walking one evening on the roof of his palace in Jerusalem. You know how bored kings get sometimes. And from the roof of his palace he saw something."

"Saw? What?"

"A young woman washing herself. Just like you."

A smile from Giovanna, now working on her ankles.

"And the Book of Samuel where the story is recounted goes on to speak of David finding the woman 'very beautiful to look upon.' Just like you, in fact."

"Pooh, what nonsense," says Giovanna, pleased all the same with the compliment. "I'm not beautiful."

But she is. Indeed, the more Margaretha contemplates Giovanna, the more comely she finds her. There is something almost Eve-like about her straightforward, innocent, uncomplicated beauty. The apple standing on the window ledge beside the mirror merely serves to underline the comparison.

The fact is that Giovanna by any standards of the 15th century is very handsome indeed.

She has long brown hair, never cut since birth, which at the moment hangs down her back. This hair must be combed and brushed and braided and put into two cornettes enmeshed in red nets. Surrounding the horns will be small plaits. Most of her head will be covered by a fine white linen coiffe of five layers with fluted edges which will frame her pretty face.

This operation alone will take the best part of two hours of patient, laborious, painstaking work which Margaretha will joyfully undertake.

Giovanna has a lovely high forehead, always a good feature in a woman. It seems to express so much desirability, accessibility and purity in her.

Then her nose swoops down from her slender eyebrows like a peregrine falcon stooping on its prey. A pair of pinched nostrils, sweet, adorable lips, a tiny chin, high cheekbones, soft, dark-brown, almond-shaped eyes, a gloriously white complexion and a tall neck complement each other and complete a compellingly lovely head.

But the body, ah, the body! How Margaretha would have liked to possess such a voluptuous body, just made for sensuality. High, soft, small breasts, a tiny waist, long arms ending in extraordinarily long fingers and thumbs, very good wrists, admirable ankles, lovely legs.

"Turn around, Giovanna, please."

Giovanna does so.

Margaretha appraises her back keenly. It more than passes muster.

"Here, let me soap your back."

Margaretha jumps off the bed where she has been sitting, soaps the cloth in the hot water and vigorously rubs Giovanna's back and neck, taking care with her left hand to hold Giovanna's hair well away from her body.

While this ritual is taking place, Giovanna examines her back critically in the mirror on the window sill. She seems satisfied with what she sees.

"Now wash your private parts and we are finished. I'll dry you."

Discreetly Margaretha turns her back on Giovanna and busies herself with preparing the clothes while Giovanna completes her toilet.

When every part of Giovanna's body has received its ritualistic ablution from the herbal waters, Margaretha pronounces herself satisfied. Giovanna's pristine body is now dried from top to toe.

For the next three hours, the bride-to-be is perfumed, coiffeured, dressed and bejewelled. It is a very private and personal performance. Although we have been permitted to glimpse the ceremony of the pre-nuptial bath, it would be impertinent and an unwarrantable intrusion into her privacy and the intimate secrets of her charm to watch Giovanna getting dressed.

Let us contemplate her when she is finally accoutred and adorned. Under her immense, green, woollen, richly embroidered gown, trimmed and lined with white fur called miniver, culled from the bellies of squirrels, she wears a deep blue damask petycote, also trimmed with fur. Beneath that her breasts are tightly bound, her legs sheathed in silk stockings.

For jewellery she wears a two-stranded gold necklace, gold bracelets with pink braid on her wrists; her high waist is held by a pink belt of dyed leather with golden decorations of dots and lozenges with a small blue dot at the centre of each lozenge. On her feet are pattens covered in red leather and straps decorated with brass studs and buckles.

At the ceremony this afternoon her husband ('how strange that word sounds,' she thinks to herself) will place two rings on her left hand ('I hope they will fit. He would not let me try them on in case it brought bad luck'). She will make her vows, Giovanni will reciprocate, there will be witnesses, there will be a wedding feast in the evening, and then the marriage will be consummated in this very bed.

Margaretha, busy tidying the room, who misses nothing, intercepts and interprets Giovanna's glance. Silently she puts down the clothes which Giovanna has discarded and folds her in a long embrace. It is a warm and loving clasp, expressing friendship, companionship and knowledge of those intimate secrets known only to women.

"There is nothing to be afraid of. You will be very happy. May St. Donatian bless you and make your marriage a long and fruitful one."

As if on cue, the great bell of St. Donatian's begins its

solemn task of striking the twelve strokes of noon. Hendrik wakes up and decides that he must do something to earn his keep. He hears approaching footsteps and gives two sharp yaps. As commanded by his master, Pieter has arrived to prepare the room.

The two women leave the room, arm in arm. Ahead of them goes Hendrik, tail working feverishly. It reminds Giovanna of an enthusiastic acolyte she saw this morning at Mass who swung his thurible with similar zest. She imparts her memory to Margaretha. Both women laugh. This laughter triggers Hendrik who starts to bark joyfully.

The omens augur well. It is going to be a beautiful day. And a memorable one.

***

The Confraternity of the Dry Tree in Bruges usually meets on Tuesdays. Membership of its organisation is restricted to Italian merchants, resident here in Bruges. Its principal members and co-founders are Sebastiano Guistiniani, Vittore Lomellini and Giovanni di Arrigo Arnolfini.

Guistiniani from Padua is President, Lomellini of Verona is Secretary, Arnolfini from Lucca its Treasurer. Guistiniani likes Lomellini but does not trust him. He dislikes Arnolfini but needs him as a business associate. Lomellini admires Arnolfini but thinks he is a crook. He both likes and trusts Guistiniani. Arnolfini trusts no one.

Behind Arnolfini's cautious, mistrustful expression with the permanently curled lip and small, suspicious bluish-grey eyes, there lies a cold, calculating brain. Though he likes neither of his fellow countrymen, he needs them. The silk trade is a cut-throat business. There is so much competition from elsewhere, particularly France. The cocoons of course are spun in China, Bukhara, Afghanistan, Cashmere, Persia, Southern Russia, Turkey, Egypt and Algeria. There is one crop annually of the golden yellow or white silk.

Sebastiano Guistiniani is the acknowledged expert on the international trade and its ramifications. He has travelled extensively throughout most of these countries, buying, advising, cajoling, wrangling. Vittore Lomellini has picked up some useful knowledge about the variety of diseases to which silkworms are vulnerable – Flacherie, Pébrine, Guttine, Grasserie – any one of which could strike arbitrarily, without warning or apparent cause, to wipe out a whole batch of valuable cocoons. Yes, Guistiniani and Lomellini are too useful and knowledgeable to be jettisoned. Arnolfini understands the actual silk process of *Bombyx mori* from the larva to the chrysalis. His mind is full of silk minutiae: the mulberry tree, *Morus alba*, battage brushes, reelers, raw silk being spun to make the warp, spun silk creating the weft, hanks of the final product ready for the international market.

The Dry Tree is indeed a genuine confraternity. Brother needs brother. No single member would survive long without mutual assistance.

On a bright Tuesday morning in July, 1434, they are meeting in Sebastiano's house. It is 8 o'clock in the morning. Giovanni is dressed in an olive-green tabard or heuque, trimmed with brown fur which is probably sable, fitting close at the neck with an upturned collar also of fur. On his head he wears a hat made of plaited straw which has been dyed black. The ring on the little finger of his left hand indicates that he is a fully paid-up, working member of the Dry Tree.

Business is discussed, prices agreed, and technicalities ironed out. Of small talk there is none. Sebastiano for example does not mention that his daughter is going to have a baby. Vittore does not think it of sufficient interest to say that his mother died recently. Giovanni is certainly not going to tell them that he is getting married later that day, to an Italian girl. And not in church.

For six months, soon after he had visited Canon van der Paele last December, Arnolfini has been brooding over that edict proclaimed in January. The church has not sanctioned his wedding in St. Donatian's. It has all been explained to him very gently, very patiently but irrevocably by Canon van der Paele on his second meeting with the Canon after the latter had consulted his Bishop.

Apparently non-Flemish citizens of Bruges, by which Arnolfini understood van der Paele to mean Italians, were not entitled to be married in church, however long they had been resident in the parish. This was the law of Flanders, a law which Canon van der Paele in his dotage had forgotten. No amount of Arnolfini's silken money can circumvent the church's adamantine decision.

"But my dear sir," the Canon announces triumphantly in his second interview with Arnolfini, "all is not lost. Be of good cheer, O ye of little faith. I have discovered a solution, a way out of the impasse. You want to be married in Bruges; in Bruges you shall be wed."

Out come the spectacles, out comes the book. After much grunting, wheezing and peering, an explication is forthcoming in the shape of a mini-sermon.

"Pope Alexander III – a very good Pope, incidentally, – in the twelfth century, more than two hundred and fifty years ago, promulgated during his Pontificate a Canon Law which recognises throughout Catholic Europe as a valid marriage those individuals who have freely exchanged vows with one another in the presence of witnesses. Provided that betrothal has the authority of witnesses and is followed by intercourse, the marriage is deemed to be legal and consummated. Voilà. *Avec de la patience, on arrive à tout.*" The Canon's fluent French is marred by his execrable accent. The book is shut with a triumphant snap and the old face splits into the broadest of broad smiles.

Once Arnolfini realised the situation last January, he discussed the whole business with the one man whom he really trusted in Bruges, Jan van Eyck. The painter suggested that Arnolfini and his bride should be married straightaway in a secular marriage. But Arnolfini immediately pointed out three stumbling blocks. Giovanna's dowry had first to arrive from Lucca, her trousseau must be woven and a new brick house built for the wedded couple. All of this would take time, probably as long as six months. The wedding is tentatively fixed for July.

But in addition van Eyck thought of a brilliant and original idea. Why does he not paint their picture, a full length wedding portrait, in their new home, in the presence of witnesses, with certain symbolic items in the room suggestive of the sacrament of marriage? Then the picture would be at one and the same time both a memorial of their wedding and proof that they had been and were legally married.

At first Arnolfini dislikes the idea intensely. It smacks too ı of ostentation, something which he abhors. But gradually Eyck wins him over. The whole situation is discussed at minable length, again and again. Both parties put forward estions, some practical and sensible to be taken on board, others ludicrous and quickly abandoned. Giovanna of course is also frequently consulted. At first embarrassed by the idea, she has been gently persuaded by her fiancé and by Margaretha van Eyck. Indeed she herself has made several interesting suggestions, including the tentative and daring proposal that there should be a mirror somewhere in the picture. Jan van Eyck has promised to consider the idea.

And so it has been agreed. Both Giovanni and Giovanna have paid regular and separate visits for the past five months to van Eyck's studio to have their portraits painted. Now in July the double portrait is finished (or almost); Giovanna's dowry has arrived from Lucca, her wedding gown with its thirty-five yards of fine green wool has been woven in one of the best workshops in Bruges, their handsome house has been built on St. Jacobsplein. Only the wedding remains to take place.

His business done in less than an hour, Arnolfini takes his leave of his associates and makes his way across the city towards the western side. He is seeking the workshop of a celebrated goldsmith who has something for him.

Jean Peutin resides in Noordzandstraat in a poky little workshop, full of shining treasures. His workbench, set in the window of his shop through which the local children love to gawp and make faces, is covered with the bric-à-brac of his trade. There lie a pair of portable scales, a set of weights, pincers, a crucible, tongs, files, a magnifying glass, a magnificent gold chalice finely chased, several nuggets of gold, a small oval mirror, a pyx, a glass dish, papers, gold coins, all scattered about in what appears to be careless confusion.

Peutin himself is a big man with huge hands which look incapable of any finesse but which are in fact extremely adept at his craft. His work, widely respected and known throughout Bruges, can be seen on many tables of rich burghers and the high altar of the Cathedral.

His greeting to Arnolfini is perfunctory, little more than a glance and a grunt. He is a man of few words; his gold does the talking. Arnolfini's business with Peutin is soon concluded. Two gold rings, destined for Giovanna's fingers, have been crafted by the goldsmith and placed in a velvet purse tied with a blue ribbon. Arnolfini checks that the rings are what he has ordered and pays for them on the spot with gold lions which he extracts from the purse at his waist. Peutin would have liked to have seen the bride and measured her fingers. But that was forbidden.

"It would bring bad luck," he is told peremptorily. He has been assured by Arnolfini that Giovanna possesses exceptionally slender fingers. "But how slender is slender?" he asks his wife that evening over supper. "Besides, these fancy foreign merchants always exaggerate."

"You're right, my dear," says his wife, passing him a wooden platter of meat with a hunk of black bread on the side, "you can trust them about as far as you can throw that loaf."

"What I say is that if he wants small rings, he has got small rings. I've made them one third less than the normal size. That should fit the fingers of his beloved bride."

"Of course they'll fit, my dear. Your rings would fit a queen. Shall we start?"

And they bow their heads and clasp their hands in prayer as Peutin says Grace.

But as Arnolfini will find out later today, he has exaggerated the slimness of his wife's fingers and Peutin has taken his orders too literally. The two rings will not fit. The one on the little finger of Giovanna's left hand will go over the first knuckle but not over the second, however hard she tries. The ring on her second finger sticks when she tries to get past the first knuckle joint. Arnolfini will be very cross indeed; Giovanna will be considerably upset; and Jan van Eyck will faithfully record the misfit when he paints in the two rings in the finished portrait. As for Peutin, he would observe, "I told you so," if he dared. As it is, he says nothing when the rings are eventually returned for refitting, But the look which he gives Arnolfini says it all. And that night at supper, there is no shortage of conversation with his wife, Irene.

Meanwhile the morning is nearly over, the wedding is in a mere two hours' time and Arnolfini must return home to get dressed. He splashes through the streets of Bruges. It has rained heavily last night with violent thunderstorms though by now there is merely a fine drizzle.

Arnolfini's fine new pair of wooden pattens rapidly become spattered with mud.

With thoughts of his beloved ever uppermost in his mind, Arnolfini walks briskly towards his new house. As he approaches, it stops raining and the sun comes out.

Chapter 28

May, 1995 / 20th July, 1434

"So here we are, ladies and gentlemen, back with the whole picture. If you look round the room, you are confronted with and can hardly miss blatant signs of wealth. I have already mentioned oranges. Perhaps Arnolfini has provided his bride with her ostentatiously expensive green gown with the blue undergarment. But she in her turn has brought him a very handsome dowry. To be horribly pecunious for a moment, there is a double bed, a carved chair, a prie-dieu, a pair of silk slippers, prayer beads, a Turkey carpet, an extravagant mirror and a superb chandelier, all luxuries which must have cost a small fortune.

Behind Arnolfini in his expensive, furred tabard and straw hat which testifies eloquently to his wealth, there stands a 'cassone' or wedding chest, doubtless containing many more rich offerings. Yes, there's no doubt that Arnolfini has married someone who is well endowed, not merely in physical beauty.

1434 was the year in which Duke Philip the Good reformed the Burgundian currency which was thereby unified and stabilised. Some of that stability is self-evident in this room. Two years earlier van Eyck's first child had been christened with the Duke as his Godfather. Affairs of state had meant that someone else had stood proxy at the font for the Duke. Perhaps the Duke should have been present at this wedding too but doubtless pressing fiscal reform kept him away and Jan van Eyck stood proxy for the Duke. We shall never know for certain but it is a tempting theory.

Meanwhile some of the urgency which Arnolfini must have felt is shown in the bottom left hand corner of the picture. In his haste to get married, he has come into the room and carelessly kicked off his mud-stained wooden pattens. There's a man who knows what he wants.

So for the last time, let us look at the room and see if we have missed anything. Funnily enough, although it is so small, the mirror shows us more than the frontal view does. So back we go to the mirror."

Click!

And then something extraordinary happens. At least John thought it was extraordinary.

It's hard to describe.

When the senses become fuddled through fear, drink, anaesthetics or some extra-sensory perception, whilst what is happening is frighteningly clear at that particular moment, afterwards it all becomes a blur.

Thus, when John had hit black ice on Watling Street one frozen January day, all that he could recall was the car slowly revolving in circles at forty miles per hour as he and the passenger screamed and the car proceeded in a straight line whilst turning round and round for several hundred yards before stopping in a ditch. The whole event must have lasted a mere twenty seconds; in retrospect and at the time it seemed more like twenty minutes.

On another occasion when John had gone into theatre for a new hip, the anaesthetist had asked him to count to ten. He could remember clearly that he had got to four before he went out. Those four seconds lasted a long time.

John still does not properly understand what happened to him during that lecture. He has of course discussed it fully with his doctor but remains baffled.

That he is in full possession of his faculties is incontrovertible. He is not unduly tired, stone cold sober (two glasses of Bill Hepton's excellent wine was all that he had drunk, oh and one glass of sherry), he is giving what he prides himself is a good lecture which is going well, and he believes in neither the supernatural nor the occult.

And yet, and yet, something happens.

He has been talking for just over an hour. He is winding up his lecture, getting ready for the applause and the questions, the plaudits and the vote of thanks, the obligatory cup of tea with the fawning sycophant asking ludicrous questions that he has already answered in his lecture, the farewells and the drive home with the fat cheque nestling in his breast pocket. His mother would ask polite questions and contrive platitudes about 'I'm sure the audience loved you, darling,' and 'it must have gone very well' and even 'it must have been very nice'. Very nice, indeed. He had heard them all a hundred times and like stale Weetabix they were nourishing but not very palatable. Supper would be at the Fleet Service Station on the M3 with a cursory glance at the papers before heading home.

That is what should have happened. That is what John expects is going to happen. That is what does not happen.

He remembers that he has just been talking about the colours in the Arnolfini portrait and the signs of wealth. He wants the audience to have one last look at the detail of the mirror in huge detail.

You must appreciate that the screen at Beaminster is twelve feet square. He is standing beside it, in the semi-darkness, with only the glare from it illuminating him. From where he stands the screen, which he can see at an oblique angle, is vast. Inside the ten rondels, the mirror shows the reflection of a room. It is a huge room. It is Brobdingnagian. Like Gulliver, he feels that he can step into another world. Like Alice, he has no fear of mirrors.

John takes a hesitant and tentative step forward.

He takes another.

He can see people in the room.

He wants to join them. He is intensely curious to know what is going on.

He feels that he knows the room intimately – its dimensions, its perspective, its inhabitants.

He steps forward, through a door, past the hall and joins someone else in a room. He can remember vividly the slight feeling of guilt he experiences that he has left the door ajar.

He is surprised. He had expected to come into this room from the other end, to see the backs of the couple in front of him. But it is the other way round. He has entered through the door and the couple are facing him.

Idiot! He thinks to himself. You don't come into a room through a mirror. You're not Alice, you come in through a door.

The man next to him who is wearing a red costume makes no acknowledgment of his presence. He seems to be staring intently into the room. Because John cannot see properly, he edges past the other man to get a better look.

"Careful," murmurs the man beside John. Surprised, John instinctively looks down to see what the danger is. There they are, right in front of his feet! He is almost stepping on them. A pair of wooden pattens, somewhat muddy, carelessly kicked off by their owner.

There are two other people in the room, a man and a woman. They have their backs to John and the man in red. They are kneeling together on the prie-dieu at the far end of the room under the mirror. He is wearing a fur-trimmed brown robe and a large black hat, she is dressed in a huge green robe and white coiffe. On the bed, curled up asleep, is a small dog.

Whilst the couple at the far end continue to pray, John finds himself staring at a room which he thought he knew intimately. How wrong he was! It is much bigger than he imagined.

There are two sets of windows through which the soft light of Bruges floods. As the room is on the first floor, at the level of the tops of cherry trees, he can see the gabled skyline of the city, punctuated by the spires and towers of churches.

He looks around the room. Yes, there on the far window sill is the apple and on the cassone the three oranges. He can see and admire the whole of the Turkish carpet, usually hidden by Giovanna, and the bed and far wall on the right, completely invisible in the National Gallery picture. A painting hangs on that wall, a very small Madonna and Child in an ornate frame. Who painted it, John wonders. Robert Campin perhaps. It's his style. Surely not van Eyck.

The glint from the brass chandelier as the sunlight hits it and the single candle burning in one of its six sconces catches his eye. What a splendid object!

There is silence in the room broken only by a very faint murmuring from the couple at their devotions and the clicking of

219

a rosary. The little dog gives a slight whimper in his doggy dreams. A skein of geese fly over the house making that curious creaking noise suggesting that their wings need oiling. A laden cart rumbles by somewhere outside; distant voices can just be heard from the nearest street. Sint Gillis chimes the quarter hour.

There is a stirring. The couple stand up. John notices that Arnolfini has been using the glass beads which he now hangs back on the wall to the left of the mirror. He thinks it is curious that he had not noticed its absence even though he knows the room and its contents so well.

Arnolfini turns round and comes towards John, stopping just short of his pattens on the floor. John stares at him in astonishment and disbelieving recognition. It can't be but it is! The nose, the eyes, the ears, all are the same, unmistakable. It is his father! The man whom he has not seen for nearly fifty years.

John stares and stares at Arnolfini, hungry for recognition, acknowledgment of his presence, some sign that explanations will follow. But nothing happens. Arnolfini stares impassively past him, his face expressionless. He is waiting for his bride.

Giovanna for her part gathers up in front of her the immense folds of her glorious green dress and picks up the dog from the bed. She comes down to her husband to be and puts Hendrik down on the floor in front of her, his tail towards Arnolfini. She murmurs a few endearments and gentle commands to him in French as she bends over him.

He takes up his position, standing stock still. Proud, erect, alert and mischievous, he earns 'tu es vraiment un bon chien. Sois gentil, mon p'tit,' from Giovanna.

She turns and faces Arnolfini with a quick smile. As she gazes at her bridegroom, the light from the first window on John's left catches the delicate alabaster white of her complexion, her slender hands with their long, pointed fingers and her snowy coiffe.

God! She is beautiful, thinks John. Why have I never noticed that before?

Arnolfini looks at the man on John's right, gets a nod and the ceremony begins.

He holds out his left hand, graciously inviting Giovanna to

place her right hand in his. She does so timidly.

With immense solemnity Arnolfini raises his right hand, the palm pointing towards Giovanna.

As John watches, the man who looks so like his missing father pronounces very slowly and very solemnly, in what John takes to be Latin, his marriage vows. Though the face is familiar, John finds the accent strange. When Arnolfini has finished, he brings his right hand down and places it on top of the lady's right hand which is resting on his left hand.

For a moment or two the three hands remain interlocked. Then Arnolfini removes both his. Giovanna raises her right hand and in a clear, childish treble reiterates her vows. She looks straight at John. Arnolfini for his part gazes at her. When she finishes speaking, there is silence for the space of a moment or so. Then Arnolfini takes her right hand again and the pair look at each other.

John finds intensely moving the look of adoration that she bestows on him. His gaze is more enigmatic but equally capable of being interpreted as love.

Because John has left the outside door open, the single candle in the chandelier starts flickering. The little dog, a mere four feet in front of him, suddenly begins to wag his tail vigorously. They are being made welcome.

The ceremony is over.

The man beside John makes a tiny noise in his throat, a cross between a grunt and a cough. John looks at him. The warm, brown, intelligent eyes flick once to the left. They tell him to follow. When he does so, he finds outside the room a vestibule where there is a table and chair.

Giovanna has put on her red slippers which she has left by the prie-dieu; Giovanni has slipped on his wooden pattens. Holding hands, the newly-wed signor and signora Arnolfini come out into the hall.

With a gracious gesture the man in red invites Arnolfini to sit and sign the book. John realises that it is a Wedding Register.

He watches Arnolfini sign but cannot read his handwriting. It looks very inelegant, one might almost say scruffy, minuscule letters, very hard to read. He remembers that his father had almost illegible handwriting, perhaps because he was left-handed, like John. Funny, what a coincidence! John notices that Arnolfini is left-handed also.

Now it is Giovanna's turn to sign. It is quite a performance for her to sit down but she achieves it in the end. Hers is a much more legible signature.

The man in red invites John to sign the Register. John is surprised but sits down, dips the quill in the ink and signs his name. He regrets that his handwriting is so awful.

Finally it is the turn of the man in red. John can see quite easily over his shoulder what he writes. In a very elegant script he inscribes:

JOHES. DE. EYCK. FUIT. HIC. MCCCC. 34. 30. JULIUS.

The penny drops. There are moments in one's life when one marvels at one's own stupidity. This was such a moment.

How could John have been unaware that he was in the presence of Jan van Eyck? He has spent much of his life obsessed with one painter, with one picture painted by that man. Now when he finds himself in his presence, it does not register with him.

John remembers in retrospect that at this supreme moment in his life (like stout Cortez, 'silent upon a peak in Darien') his overwhelming emotion was not astonishment or excitement but rather anger at his own blindness.

But there is no time for these thoughts. With a grave bow of the head, the newly-weds go back into the room where the wedding took place, Arnolfini firmly closing the door behind him. John wonders if they are going to consummate the marriage then and there. He has looked for the last time at the face of Arnolfini, so astonishingly like his father, received not a flicker of recognition in reply, and been left standing baffled by the table in the vestibule. He gives an involuntary sigh and a slight shrug of the shoulders.

Jan van Eyck catches the sound and the movement, smiles at John and invites him with a gesture to follow him. Off he goes busily with John following in his wake. Outside there is a perron with a double staircase. John follows van Eyck as best he can down the left-hand staircase, somewhat handicapped by the wooden clogs which he finds he is wearing.

In silence they walk through the sunlit streets of Bruges, in silence they arrive at van Eyck's house in Sint Gillis Nieuw Straat, somewhere in the house a baby in crying. In silence they climb the four flights of stairs to his studio at the top of the house, in silence they enter.

There it is!

Chapter 29

20th July, 1434

St. Donatian's starts to toll the hour.

"One last thing, Pieter – when I tell you, get a ladder and place one candle in the chandelier. Just the one. In the first bracket on the left, there!"

Van Eyck points.

"Then light it."

"Yes, Master, and shall I.."

But what he was going to say we shall never know.

At that moment, there is a heavy knocking at the front door. When Pieter opens it, two people come into the room.

There is also a dog.

Van Eyck welcomes the couple with a gracious bow. The man who acknowledges the painter's presence with an inclination of the head proceeds to slip off his wooden pattens. The woman gives him a shy smile.

Familiar as he is with their physiognomies, for he has been painting their portraits (separately) over the past six months, van Eyck is yet surprised at their appearance. It is the first time that he has seen them, dressed as they are, together. The man is wearing a close-fitting tabard known as a *heuque*. It is made of silk velvet edged with crimson-purple sable, a colour which the artist has had difficulty in accurately copying. He has used red lake, ultramarine, black and white pigments. Even so, he is not entirely satisfied with the end result.

Beneath the *heuque* Arnolfini is wearing a satin damask fabric with a design of arabesques and leaves which van Eyck has painted dark grey on black with shadows of a purplish colour. This is a garment which has caused much less trouble for the artist who has also enjoyed painting Arnolfini's cuffs at his

224

wrists which are made of silver braid on a purple base. Arnolfini has wrapped around his right wrist a scarlet lace with silver tips which Jan van Eyck has taken much delight in copying. When he asked Giovanni Arnolfini the purpose of such a lace, Arnolfini gave such a convoluted and enigmatic answer to do with business dealings, the Confraternity of the Dry Tree, whatever that is, the *Volto Santo* and the lace industry in Bruges that van Eyck remained baffled. Never mind, he has enjoyed painting accurately such a minute detail.

To complete the ensemble, Arnolfini is wearing purple hose and a pair of silk socks for indoor use after he has discarded his somewhat well-worn and muddy wooden pattens. He has a gold ring on the index finger of his right hand which sets off his long, delicate fingers, the nails of which have (surprisingly) a quantity of dirt under them, acquired by his repeated handling and inspection of bales of cloth. All of this has been faithfully recorded in the double portrait.

Under his enormous black hat which casts such sinister shadows, Arnolfini's mysterious face – the hooded eyelids, the swooping nose, the cleft chin, the extraordinary ears – gives him an ethereal appearance which van Eyck hopes he has captured in paint.

Giovanna is breathtakingly beautiful. Jan van Eyck's wife, Margaretha, has done a magnificent job in presenting the bride beautifully adorned for her bridegroom. From the top of her elaborate huvé to her petite feet, invisible under the sumptuous green gown, she is perfection. Her porcelain complexion contrasts with her husband-to-be's much ruddier and closely shaved face. Her dress which has thirty-five yards of finest Bruges wool in it is trimmed and lined with the most expensive and softest fur, known as pure miniver, obtained from the bellies of red squirrels (and from no other part of their bodies). The ends of the long sleeves are decorated with elaborate dagging, cut into the shape of Maltese crosses, the edges pinked to prevent fraying. Her underdress is virgin blue damask, trimmed at the hem with white fur. At her wrists she has bands of gold and pink braid. Around her minuscule, high waist she wears a pink leather belt. But all this finery is merely a frame to set off her high forehead, delicate eyebrows, warm brown eyes, tiny chin, oh so long neck, elegant fingers and petite body.

Gravely and graciously Jan van Eyck greets them.

"Signor Arnolfini, signorina Cenami, I bid you a warm and felicitous welcome. May the God of Abraham, the God of Isaac and the God of Jacob bless you both and sow the seed of eternal life in your hearts."

Arnolfini replies in Italian, one of the many languages which van Eyck has learnt on his diplomatic travels.

Meanwhile the exquisite Giovanna Cenami, soon to become Sighora Arnolfini, has picked up her dog, a Brussels griffon, and placed him on the bed where, after a little gentle encouragement from her, he settles down to watch proceedings with one eye whilst pretending to be asleep.

Arnolfini and van Eyck exchange a few remarks about the procedure of the imminent ceremony. Van Eyck explains what is going to happen. Arnolfini is concerned about there being only one witness at the moment. He is assured by van Eyck that another will appear at the right moment.

Behind that enigmatic mask there is a trace of scepticism. Diplomatically he holds his peace.

While all this has been going on, Pieter has lit the right-hand candle; the one on the left stays unlit, as ordered. That done, he has quietly left the room. The short candle on the right of the chandelier will now burn for perhaps one hour. When it goes out, the marriage contract between the two consenting parties will be legal. Both will have made their vows and signed the register; the extinguished candle, the so-called *chandelle éteinte*, will be visible proof of the new treaty.

Meanwhile, as has been agreed beforehand, the couple now have an opportunity for prayer. There is an hour before the legal document must be signed, two hours before the second witness will arrive and the marriage vows can be exchanged.

"May God sanctify and bless you both in your marriage," van Eyck murmurs as he leaves the room, closing the door behind him.

The couple turn and walk hand in hand towards the red prie-dieu on the back wall underneath the mirror. Giovanna removes her red slippers and kneels down. Arnolfini takes off the wall a set of glass prayer beads hanging from a nail beside the mirror. They are made of amber strung on a green cord with a tassel at both ends. There are twenty-nine beads on the paternoster. With this *aide-memoire*, Giovanni and his bride-to-be will study on their knees the scenes of the Passion depicted in the ten tiny rondels around the mirror. For each rondel, they will say a prayer.

Here are the ten scenes and their prayers:-

At the very bottom of the mirror the first picture shows Christ's Agony in the Garden of Gethsemane by the brook Cedron. Click goes a bead. They remember Christ's prayer whilst the disciples slept, "not my will but Thine be done."

The second rondel depicts Christ being betrayed by one of his disciples, Judas Iscariot, and another disciple, Peter, impulsively cutting off the ear of the High Priest's servant. They pray that they may learn to emulate Christ's capacity for forgiveness and His gift of healing.

Click goes another bead. Now Christ is standing before Pilate, just as they too will soon be standing before God as they exchange their marriage vows. They pray for humility and a right judgment in all things.

Click. Now Christ is being scourged and mocked at the column by the Roman soldiers. "Father, forgive them, for they know not what they do." They pray for patience, fortitude and tolerance.

Click. Christ carries his Cross up the Via Dolorosa towards his Crucifixion and agonisingly slow death. "I am the Resurrection and the Life." They pray that they may read, mark and learn in Holy Scriptures of the life of Christ.

Click. The sixth bead takes them to the top of the mirror. Christ is crucified. "Eli, Eli, Lama sabachthani?" Perhaps, thinks Arnolfini, the most terrible words ever uttered. "My God, my God, why hast Thou forsaken me?" For this couple, kneeling before the rondel, the Cross has a particular significance, reminding them not only of Christ's Redemption of their sins by His supreme sacrifice, but also of their own unique and venerated crucifix, carved by Nicodemus, the *Volto Santo*,

227

hanging in their beloved Cathedral back in Lucca. They pray for Christ's blessing on their marriage and on their homes back in Lucca

Click. The seventh bead shows the Deposition from the Cross and Pietà. This causes them to remember the love of their parents and friends. "Honour thy father and thy mother; that thy days may be long upon the land which the Lord thy God giveth thee."

Click. Christ is laid in the Tomb. "O Death, where is thy sting? O grave, where is thy victory?" They remember all those who have gone before them and pray for the repose of their souls.

Click. Christ descends into Hell. "For this corruptible must put on incorruption, and this mortal must put on immortality." They ask God's blessing on those less fortunate than they are.

Click. The Resurrection. Christ is carried triumphantly up into Heaven. "The third day He ascended into Heaven and sitteth on the right hand of God." They give thanks for the blessed assurance of their own redemption through Christ's supreme sacrifice and the inestimable joy which this affords.

Ten beads have gone; nineteen remain.

Twelve of them are used to pray to the twelve apostles, each of whom has a special attribute and a personal gift to bestow.

The final seven remind them of the Seven Cardinal Virtues, the Seven Sorrows of the Virgin and the Seven sacraments.

St. Donatian is striking half past one before they have finished and van Eyck returns.

***

Meanwhile, while Giovanni and Giovanna have been at their devotions, for his part Jan van Eyck has been taking a turn around the fair city of Bruges. And fair it certainly is. The streets are moderately clean, the citizens well clothed and fed, the buildings along the numerous canals elegant, imposing and handsome.

The day also happens to be particularly beautiful. True,

228

there was a brief shower early this morning. But now it is pleasantly warm (not blazing hot as it should be in the dog days of July) under blue, cloudless skies. A gentle breeze does just enough to flutter the blue lion on the flags of Brabant which hang from all the public buildings.

The artist strolls along beside one of the canals and watches children at play outside St. Janshospitaal. He thinks it would make an interesting genre picture, but does not have the time to throw away his talent on something so frivolous. Anyway, he has too many commissions.

In the fish market he buys a pair of young herrings caught that morning in the North Sea. He eats them raw, chucking their heads in the canal. Delicious! He and the fishwife exchange pleasantries. She is a interesting woman with a charming sense of humour, albeit a bit earthy. If the truth were told, he did not really want any fish. He merely wanted to share a joke with the fishwife!

In the Burg he indulges himself with a glass of wine for the herrings have made him thirsty. He strolls along to the imposing Stadhuis where he collects from a fussy official the documents necessary for the wedding. Refusing to be flustered by this bureaucratic minion, he completes the formalities and returns home as St. Donatian is striking the half hour.

Here he finds that the couple have said their prayers. In the small ante-chamber or vestibule where there is a table and chair, both sign the legal documents which are then sealed. In the main chamber the candle extinguishes itself. The marriage contract is now law.

All that remains for the marriage to be sanctified, apart from consummation, is the exchange of vows between the betrothed in the presence of two witnesses. Van Eyck will be one, the other is coming any minute now. How van Eyck knows that is not understood and it would be impertinent to ask him for details.

"Would you like to say a final prayer while we wait?" suggests van Eyck. "The other witness will be here in two minutes."

Without questioning his percipience, Arnolfini and his

bride-to-be return to the prie-dieu where the silence of the room is broken only by the faint murmur of their prayers.

The artist fetches Pieter who has been waiting outside to light the left-hand candle in the chandelier. This he does deftly and immediately leaves the room.

Van Eyck returns to his position by the door where he stands patiently. He is confident that he will not have to wait long. Sure enough, soon he hears the clacking of wooden pattens labouring up the stone staircase, the outside door being opened and left open (he can feel the breeze on his neck) and someone crossing the ante-chamber and drawing close. Another moment and John Arnold is standing beside him.

At this solemn and significant moment van Eyck makes no acknowledgment of Arnold's presence. He contents himself with staring into the room, checking every last detail. Because John Arnold cannot see properly as van Eyck is somewhat blocking the way, he edges past him.

"Careful," murmurs van Eyck. Arnold looks down and sees that he is almost standing on a pair of wooden pattens which someone has carelessly discarded. They look muddy.

Arnold seems familiar with the room. Van Eyck notices that he is looking intently around him, as though searching to see if everything is there. He observes that Arnold is staring intently at the Madonna which Robert Campin painted and, as an act of homage, presented to van Eyck to hang on his wall. It is a beautiful picture which van Eyck admires very much and which he has presented to the Arnolfinis as a wedding present. Early on he decided that it was too important and too difficult to reproduce accurately in his painting. Besides, the presence of the Madonna at a wedding would complicate the elaborate and inherent symbolism which is lying latent just below the surface all over the picture. For these and other reasons van Eyck has placed the painting on the right hand wall where it features neither in his painting of the room nor in the reflection in the mirror.

In the chamber there is silence broken only by a very faint murmur from the couple as they recite their prayers. Other sounds are the sporadic clicking of the beads, an occasional whimper from the dog on the bed as he dreams his doggy dreams, the creaking sound of a skein of geese as they fly over and the usual distant noises of a city at work. A cart rumbles by outside, the driver shouting imprecations at his recalcitrant beast. Sint Gillis chimes the quarter hour.

The couple stand up. Arnolfini carefully hangs the rosary back on its nail to the left of the mirror.

When he turns round and faces the new arrival, van Eyck cannot fail to notice the astonishment on Arnold's face. It is patently obvious that he seems to know Arnolfini. For his part, there is no flicker of recognition on Arnolfini's face.

Giovanna gathers up in front of her the immense folds of her green gown which immediately creates the impression that she is pregnant. She picks up the little dog from the bed. With a few words of encouragement, she induces him to pose in front of her and Arnolfini.

Satisfied that he will behave himself, she turns, faces Arnolfini and flashes him a quick smile. Van Eyck catches Arnold admiring her delicate, porcelain beauty.

Arnolfini looks at the two witnesses; the man in red gives a nod and the ceremony begins.

Giovanni Arnolfini holds out his left hand, graciously inviting Giovanna to place her right hand in his which she does. Very solemnly he raises his right hand, stares at a crucifix which is hanging on the back wall beyond Arnold's right shoulder and affirms in Latin his marriage vows. When he has finished, he slowly brings his hand down and places it on top of Giovanna's right hand resting on his left.

For a magic moment or so the three hands remain firmly embraced. Then Arnolfini removes his. Giovanna Cenami raises her right hand and reiterates her vows She looks straight at her husband who in his turn gazes back at her. When she has finished, he takes her right hand and looks lovingly at her.

For her part the look which she bestows upon her brand new husband seems close to adoration.

When Arnold first came into the room, he left the outside door open. The slight breeze causes the single candle in the chandelier to flicker. The little dog senses that the ceremony is over. He wags his tail furiously.

The artist makes a tiny noise in his throat which attracts Arnold's attention. Arnold looks at van Eyck who indicates with his eyes that Arnold should follow him out into the vestibule. Out they go and stand beside the table and chair.

Immediately they are joined by the newly-weds, who have put on their shoes. Responding to an invitation from van Eyck Arnolfini sits down at the table and signs the Register. Giovanna follows suit. Van Eyck invites Arnold to emulate him which he does, dipping the quill in the ink pot and nervously inscribing his name with several blots. Van Eyck cannot but help notice how execrable is Arnold's handwriting. After them van Eyck appends his signature in his customary, meticulous fashion.

Van Eyck bows formally to the couple. With a slight nod of his head he indicates to John Arnold that he should follow him.

Out of the vestibule they go, down the double staircase and along the streets of Bruges in the bright sunlight. They do not say a word. When they reach the artist's house in Sint Gillis Nieuw Straet, they climb the stairs in a silence broken only by the clacking of his pattens, and the distant sound of a baby crying. In silence they enter the artist's studio.

There is an easel in the middle of the room with a picture on it. Not a very large painting. Arnold stares at it in astonishment. From the look of recognition on his face van Eyck can tell that Arnold is familiar with the painting. Arnold for his part stands transfixed for several minutes. He says nothing.

But van Eyck does not mind. He lets the wedding portrait of Giovanni Arnolfini and Giovanna Cenami do the talking. It has plenty to say.

Chapter 30

June, 1995

My dear Heather,

I write to you in haste, gratitude and trepidation. In haste because I want to explain as quickly as I can what happened to me during that extraordinary lecture; in gratitude for your outstanding hospitality, the friendliness of your audience and the understanding you showed to me during my eccentric behaviour; and in trepidation because I am not quite sure what occurred during my 'blackout' on the stage nor indeed how long it lasted.

But I do feel that I owe you and your members the courtesy of an explanation. So here goes.

You will remember that I was coming to the end of my lecture and starting to wind up. On the screen I had projected a large detail of the mirror in the Arnolfini picture. From where I was standing beside the screen, it looked enormous. I remember that because as I wanted to see some detail the better, I moved towards the screen until I was standing a few inches from the mirror.

How can I explain what happened next without seeming deranged or hallucinatory? I am neither mad nor given to extra-sensory manifestations. I am in reasonable, not to say, rude health. Apart from the usual childish illnesses and one artificial hip, I have never been unwell in my life.

After my experience in Beaminster, I went straight round to my doctor for a check-up. Dr Andrew Llewelyn ran his rule over me from head to foot and pronounced me A1. There was absolutely nothing wrong with me. And yet, and yet, I had had an 'experience'.

233

Heather, have you read *A Passage To India* by E.M.Forster? I am sure you have or, at the very least, seen David Lean's film. You will remember that, during that disastrous picnic arranged by the well-meaning but incompetent Dr Aziz, one of his guests, Mrs Moore, had some sort of hallucination in the caves of Chandrapore.

Well, that is what happened to me at Beaminster. It is so extraordinary that I have written an account of my 'experience' and herewith send you a copy. Please read it and feel free to comment if you would like. The only thing I would ask is that you do not show it to any one else but treat it as confidential.

By the way, I have called it an 'experience' with acknowledgment to the Misses Mobberley who saw extraordinary 18th century events and people when they visited the gardens of Versailles in the early part of this century.

I send you my 'Experience" with renewed thanks for your marvellous hospitality and my best wishes to your husband and Mr. Chips.

Much love,

John

encl/-

P.S. I do hope I get invited back to Beaminster. I would very much like to give another lecture, this time on the subject of Dutch Genre Pictures in the second half of the 17th Century.

An Experience
by John Arnold

I am a retired schoolmaster, aged sixty-eight, who from time to time, gives lectures on art. In May, 1995, I was lecturing the West Dorset N.A.D.F.A.S. at Beaminster. My subject was the Arnolfini Wedding Portrait by Jan van Eyck which hangs in the National Gallery. I had been talking for over an hour and was beginning to wind up my talk. On the huge screen I had projected a giant detail from the picture, the convex mirror

234

which hangs on the back wall of the room in which the Arnolfinis are standing.

Because there was a big audience in the auditorium and little ventilation, the room had become rather hot. I was sweating somewhat freely but otherwise felt very healthy.

I should explain that I have been obsessed with the Arnolfini portrait for a long time. I have seen it repeatedly, read numerous books about it and am even contemplating writing one myself on the subject. Whenever I am in London, I make a beeline for the Sainsbury Wing of the National Gallery where it hangs in Room fifty-six. The picture never fails to fascinate me and to reveal some new feature which I have never before noticed.

On the occasion of my Beaminster lecture, I approached the screen with its huge projection of the mirror the better to look at it. To my surprise I suddenly spotted something new. In the mirror you can see the reflection of the couple. They are standing with their backs to us and between them there should be a little dog. But it isn't there! And it should be! Why not? I had never noticed this discrepancy before. And to make absolutely certain, I leant forward and stared intently at the screen. I still wasn't quite sure. I moved even closer to get a better view and then felt myself falling.

To tell the truth, it was rather a pleasant sensation. That is to say, I didn't experience any fear. I knew I was quite safe and that I would land safely somewhere. And I was right. I fell into that room reflected in the mirror!

I remember thinking that I should be standing behind Arnolfini and his bride. But somehow I arrived at the other end of the room where a man in a red chaperon and robe was already standing by the door. As I pushed by him, he murmured "careful." I descended two steps into the room, looked down and there they were! At my feet, rather mud-stained, a pair of wooden pattens. Where had I seen them before?

And then I noticed a little dog right in front of me, not more than six feet away, standing there looking so bright and intelligent. Behind him (the dog must be male, he looks so masculine) stand Giovanni Arnolfini and Giovanna Cenami. I

235

find myself witnessing their wedding or whatever it is that they are doing.

The word 'witness' as I use it here has two meanings and I intend deliberate ambivalence. I find myself acting as a witness at a ceremony and I am looking at the couple performing in that ceremony.

Words are spoken and vows exchanged. Arnolfini puts his right hand on top of Giovanna's right hand which he is supporting with his left. Giovanna raises her right hand and in a childish treble repeats a vow. Then it's all over. The little dog acts like a timekeeper. "Finished, that's it, we can all relax now," he says and jumps up on to the bed to be petted. Oh, yes, and a single candle in the gleaming chandelier flickers. I have but a few seconds to glance round the room which I feel I know so well. Yes, there are the three oranges on the cassone with one on the windowsill. Or are they apples? The scarlet of the bed catches my eye, contrasting with the red of the prie-dieu. For a second I stare at a picture on the right-hand wall, not visible in van Eyck's picture. I have time to register that it is a small, beautiful painting of the Madonna in a domestic interior by Robert Campin perhaps or Rogier van der Weyden. Could it be by Petrus Christus? Possibly.

I catch a glimpse of myself (with some surprise) in the mirror on the back wall. I appear to be wearing a long blue gown and blue chaperon with what I later discover is a long cornette. Curiously enough, I find my outfit very comfortable.

If I were to mention at this juncture that the man standing bang in front of me, Giovanni Arnolfini, bears a striking resemblance to my father, who left my mother when I was a little boy, that would only complicate a situation which, heaven knows, is complex enough.

The man in red just behind me makes a small noise in his throat, catches my eye when I turn and invites me to go with him into the ante-room. I follow him to find a book on a table. Arnolfini sits down at the table, picks up the quill pen and writes with a flourish. Then it is the turn of Giovanna who signs quickly and neatly. When my turn comes, I dip the quill in the silver ink-well and scratch my name on the vellum in what I freely admit is pretty wretched handwriting. The man in red then writes his name with amazing calligraphic skill and speed. I have no difficulty in reading what he has written. In the most elegant script he has inscribed:

JOHES. DE. EYCK. FUIT. HIC. MCCCC. 34. 30. JULIUS.

The penny drops. I am standing in the presence of Jan van Eyck, Flemish painter extraordinary, *primus inter pares*, up there in the Pantheon of great painters alongside Raphael, Velázquez, Rembrandt, Titian, Holbein and no more than half a dozen others.

But there is no time to assimilate the enormity of the occasion. The mundane takes precedence over the historicity of the occasion. I watch in a sort of stupefied amazement as van Eyck sprinkles sand over the four signatures, bows his head slightly to the couple and with his eye invites me to follow him.

A polite inclination of my head to the Arnolfinis and I am clacking my way out of the front door, down a double staircase and striding along in the footsteps of my guide. Not a word is spoken. In my bemused state, I cannot do justice to the mediaeval city of Bruges which is where I presume that I am.

But I do have certain hazy memories of that walk – of tall, handsome houses surrounded everywhere by water. I had not realised what a plethora of canals Bruges enjoyed. But I do remember the sharp stench of open sewers prevalent in the streets, the sound of church bells tolling deeply and a street vendor who was peddling black cherries making persistent efforts to sell some to me.

So as we enter Sint Gillis Nieuw Straet whose name I saw painted on a wall, I find myself admiring the gabled houses even as I finish eating a handful of cherries which the persistent vendor has thrust upon me. Very good they are too! My only problem as we go into the fourth house on the right is what to do with the stones.

I clack my way up four flights of stairs behind van Eyck, desperately looking for a pocket in my outfit where I may conceal my stones. Halfway up the stairs I can hear a baby crying. At the top of the house we enter a room which I immediately recognise to be the artist's studio. The tools of his

237

trade are scattered all around the room. In the middle of the studio stands an easel with a picture on it. I stare at it with astonishment and delight. It is 'my' picture. Jan van Eyck, the man in red, is looking intently at me; he seems satisfied with my reaction. But he says nothing.

And I am content to say nothing too. I let the wedding portrait of Giovanna and Giovanni Arnolfini, whom I have just seen going through some sort of ceremony, do all the talking. I find that the picture has plenty to say. I am transfixed as I stare at it. I become oblivious of my surroundings, of the painter's presence, of the strange clothes that I am wearing, of the pips still in my mouth. All I can do is gaze at the portrait and marvel at the familiarly strange and the strangely familiar.

When Wordsworth revisited Tintern Abbey, he wrote his poem which carries the long title of *Lines Written a Few Miles above Tintern Abbey, on Revisiting the Banks of the Wye during a Tour, July 13, 1798*, usually abbreviated to *Tintern Abbey*. He felt a *'tranquil restoration'* and talked of experiencing

> *In hours of weariness, sensations sweet*
> *Felt in the blood, and felt along the heart,*
> *And passing even into my purer mind*
> *With tranquil restoration.*

I simply could not express my sensations and emotions better than Wordsworth did. For me there was at that moment *tranquil restoration*

> *While, with an eye made quiet by the power*
> *Of harmony and the deep power of joy*
> *We see into the life of things.*

For I find I am looking at the Arnolfini Wedding portrait, freshly painted (mind you, it always looks freshly painted), in the studio where it was painted, in the presence of Jan van Eyck who has just spent the last six months painting it. That sentence is so surprising, so outrageously improbable and incredible that I shall repeat it the better to revel in its ineffable beauty. Jan van Eyck in July, 1434, is showing me in his studio in Bruges his latest picture, the so-called Wedding portrait of Giovanni Arnolfini and Giovanna Cenami.

That is what holds my attention, riveting my eyes on

Giovanni's serious face, on Giovanna's benign beauty, on the mirror, the dog, the light, yes, above all the light. I glance to my left in Jan's studio. Of course! High up on the wall is a large window pouring in the daylight of Bruges. That is the actual window which must have illuminated the right cheek of Arnolfini and the whole face of Giovanna, lit the chandelier, made the oranges glow and cast all those delectable and intriguing shadows. I find myself looking with great attention at the way the artist has painted the light hitting the fur on the right side of Arnolfini's gown (his right, our left as we look at him). It is a wonderfully accurate and perceptive piece of observation which I have never noticed before.

How fresh, how clean, how pristine the picture looks! Yet, in all conscience, it does not really appear any different from that with which I am so familiar in the Sainsbury Wing of the National Gallery. It's the same picture about which I have just been lecturing. Suddenly I feel convinced that everything I have been saying in Beaminster is uninformed, superficial, just plain wrong.

For what seems an eternity Jan and I stare at the picture. Not a word is said. The reality is the picture, we are the illusion. But the truth, where is that? Perhaps Jan will tell me.

I turn towards Jan in his red gown. He has discarded his chaperon. He stares at me impassively, the suspicion of one eyebrow raised, as though in interrogation.

At last he speaks.

"Well?"

Chapter 31

June, 1995

<u>An Experience</u>
(continued)

"Marvellous!" I breathe, through a mouthful of cherry stones.

Immediately I realise the inadequacy of speech and of that particular epithet. The picture is not marvellous, not miraculous, not wonderful, it is incredibly skilfully painted. That is quite another matter.

Jan comes over to me and holds out his cupped hand. With his artist's eye of acute observation, he has spotted that my mouth is full of cherry stones. As decorously as I can, I spit out the stones. Jan gives me the ghost of a smile before depositing them in a china dish standing on a trestle table. He wipes his hands on a towel and returns with two folding chairs which he opens and places in front of the easel. With an imperative gesture, he invites me to occupy one of them as he sits in the other. We settle down in front of the picture and look intently at it.

For a few minutes nothing is said. At last Jan breaks the silence.

"I thank you for coming to my studio and looking at my latest work. Study it carefully for as long as you like and then tell me what you see."

What an invitation! For some reason I think of Gulliver being invited in the same courteous way by the King of Brobdingnag to give an exact account of the Government of England and wishing for the tongue of Demosthenes or Cicero. And I recall how eloquently Gulliver spoke in defence of all the institutions in England that he admired but all to no avail. The

King's response at the end of Gulliver's discourse was comprehensively damning.

"*I cannot but conclude the Bulk of your Natives, to be the most pernicious Race of little odious Vermin that Nature ever suffered to crawl upon the Surface of the Earth.*"

What will be Jan's response when I have finished? Can I possibly do justice to such a masterpiece? Where to begin? There is so much to say, so much that is obvious, so much obscure or allusive. Of one thing I am sure, I must beware of revealing to Jan that I am familiar with the picture. I must talk as though I have never set eyes on it until this moment.

"Well, Master, I can see two people and a dog standing in a room, two people indeed that I saw an hour ago in that very room."

Jan interrupts me.

"Correction. You did not see them. You witnessed them, quite another matter."

"I stand corrected, Master. I presume in that case that they are getting married, though why they are marrying in a room and not in church I have no idea. The man looks very solemn and raises his right hand to make the vows. She gazes at him submissively."

"Good. Let me say that what you witnessed an hour ago in that room may have been a wedding. Equally well it may have been the exchange of vows on the couple becoming affianced. Or it could have been something else. Let us move on. We will return to that question later."

"May I then respectfully ask you, Master, who the two people are?"

"Certainly. He is Giovanni di Arrigo Arnolfini, merchant banker of Bruges. You saw him signing his name in the book."

"Indeed."

"She is called Giovanna Philippa Cenami. They are Italian and both come from Lucca, a town north west of Florence."

"I see."

"He is a rich business man who has resided in this city for some considerable time. She is a wealthy heiress whose parents live in Paris. So much for introductions. Now, tell me, can you

241

see any signs of wealth?"

I look hard at the picture. This, I think, is going to be an easy one to answer. There are signs of opulence everywhere.

"Yes, I can, Master. Everywhere I look. I can see the rich gown that she is wearing, the layers of lace on her head, her gold necklace, her blue silk undergarment, her gold belt, the mirror, the four oranges, his fur gown, the carpet and of course I can hardly fail to notice the magnificent chandelier."

I feel pleased with myself, fairly sure that I have missed very little. But I am wrong. Jan van Eyck gives something approaching a sigh. When he speaks, he shows patience and tolerance of my fumbling ineptitude.

"Yes, that is very good, sir, but I am bound to say that you have missed a great deal. Eyes have you but you see not, as St Paul says. By the way, that is not lace she is wearing, but linen, the finest that Bruges can weave, five layers to signify the five senses."

"Of course it's linen, Master. How stupid of me! The senses you say? But where is Hearing, Master?"

"Arnolfini has just repeated his vows. She has just heard them, we have witnessed them," explains Jan patiently. "Sight is what is held in the mirror. Touch is her hand resting in his. Smell is the dog. Taste are the oranges."

"Yes, I see."

"Oranges which are imported from Castile in Spain are extremely expensive. That is an apple, by the way, on the window sill, not an orange. It is a rare variety called *gaudium Paradisi*, very difficult to obtain, extremely expensive. It is not the first time that I have put it in one of my paintings. I used it when I was working with my brother, Hubert, on The Mystic Lamb. I was painting Eve at the time and naturally I made her hold an apple as a reminder of the Fall. And here's the same apple again."

"Very interesting," I murmur, as my brain calls up a picture of Adam and Eve in The Mystic Lamb. Yes, she is holding an apple. Let me think. Which hand? The right surely. Yes, that's it, Eve with her huge forehead and strangely swollen stomach. Shy, solemn, mysterious Eve, our grandparent, holding that fatal apple which betrayed us all and introduced sin into the world.

It is my turn to sigh. There is silence for a moment or so, a silence which is not in the least oppressive or embarrassing until Jan breaks it with his next gentle question.

"Tell me, sir, do you know why oranges are an indication of wealth?"

"I would have thought, Master, because oranges are difficult to obtain and therefore expensive?"

"You are partially right. Yes, they are very costly because they come all the way from Spain and Portugal. But they are also traditionally the fruit of kings. By placing three oranges on the chest, I am hinting at the majesty of marriage, the richness of the sacrament, even the three gifts that the Magi presented to the Christ Child in Bethlehem."

"I see. And the apple?"

"Ah, that is a gentle reminder, as if we need one, that Man is fallible, that we are all born with original Sin in us. Eve tempted Adam with the fruit of the forbidden tree and he did eat. That apple sitting so invitingly by the window which Arnolfini will see when he turns round and which is called *gaudium Paradisi*, the joy of Paradise, in reality brings only sorrow. When I painted Eve many years ago, I put an apple in her hand, the same fruit as I have used here. I am not saying that Giovanna will be unfaithful to her husband. I am merely reminding the viewer that she is the daughter of Eve, the traditional and original temptress."

"Of course."

"But I could also be saying that Giovanna is Venus or Aphrodite if you prefer to whom Paris awarded the apple in his famous Judgment on Mount Ida. So that would make Giovanni the personification of Paris who fell in love with Helen and we all know what that led to! Take your pick."

"I think I prefer Giovanna as Eve, Master."

Van Eyck gives a little chuckle in the back of his throat.

"So do I. Now tell me, have you noticed something else on the window sill? I have given the apple here a reflection which you can see if you look at the bottom of the window casement."

I look very carefully where he has indicated and there, sure enough, is a delicate reflection of the apple, a faint red blush on the windowsill.

"I see it, Master, now that you point it out. And what does that signify?"

"Oh, lots of things – that I am a clever painter!"

Jan's eyes twinkle as he speaks.

"That the apple is round, that there is a back side to the apple, that sin is all-embracing, that like the mirror which shows another point of view, the reflection of the apple enables us to see that which without the image would be invisible, that there is more to life in general and this painting in particular than meets the superficial eye. Oh and lots more."

He smiles triumphantly and I take pleasure in sharing his victory.

"Can you see any more fruit, cherries or grapes, for example?"

That question really surprises me. I thought I knew the picture. I look hard but fail miserably.

Jan smiles.

"Try looking out of the window."

I do so and immediately spot them. How blind I have been!

"Those cherries which you see growing so profusely on that tree just outside the house I put into the picture as a means of dating the painting and because they are there! I like to paint reality. It is the month of July and that cherry tree is bearing a very good crop, as you can see. Our market is at the present time full of cherries for sale, as you very well know."

Again that little warm smile.

"But if you want the cherries to represent something, they are the fruit of Paradise and a reward for virtuousness. And like virtue, they are clearly visible but slightly inaccessible, hard to achieve without some effort in climbing the tree. Did you enjoy them, by the way?"

"I did indeed, Master. They were very tasty. I should like some more."

"You shall have some when we dine. By the way, if you are interested, I believe these cherries are called Mahaleb, a rare and late strain."

He pauses for breath, gives a short little laugh, curiously high pitched, and produces a linen kerchief with which he fastidiously wipes his fingers. Toilet done, he addresses me again.

"Can you see any other fruit?"

I know what I am going to say long before I say it. In vain I look all around the picture. Not a fruit in sight.

"No, Master."

"If you look just to the left of the bed, you will see an elaborately carved headboard. Just to the right of the brush hanging from the top of the headboard you will find a bunch of grapes. There, do you see them?"

He points with his maul stick.

"Yes, I can see them. Why did you put them in?"

"Well, they make a satisfactory decoration. But countless classical authors have used grapes to indicate marital fidelity. They augur well for this marriage and its consummation in this bed."

"Ah yes, the bed. I take it we are in a bedroom."

"No, that is not correct. We are in a room which we call the thalamus, that is to say an inner room specifically reserved for a woman's apartment. If you look on the right-hand side of the painting, everything around Giovanna is feminine – the bed, the brush hanging from the chair, Giovanna herself, her silk slippers, the Anatolian carpet, St Margaret carved on top of the chair, and of course Giovanna's magnificent gown with its rich dagging."

"What is dagging, please?"

"It is the elaborate embroidery in the form of Maltese Crosses on the end of her sleeves."

"I see."

"Then if you look on the left we observe the masculine – Arnolfini in his dark brown gown trimmed with fur, his huge straw hat which I can assure you cost a great deal of money, his wooden pattens, the oranges sitting on the cassone."

"The what?"

"Cassone. A wedding chest or elaborate wooden container packed with linen and other fabrics, an important part of the bridegroom's dowry. By the marriage, she brings him valuable possessions and wealth from Paris and Lucca. He provides the house and some of the furnishings."

"Will you tell me about the house, please?"

"Certainly. If you look out of the window, you can see that the house is made of brick. That is a sure sign of wealth. Most of the houses in Bruges today are built of wood; only the very rich can afford brick. And the windows have clear bull's-eye glass in the top with blue, red and green stained glass. That's another sign of wealth. As is the custom, the lower part is not glazed but covered, when needed, with shutters.

"How do the shutters work? I assume you shut all the left hand ones first and then close the right hand ones. Is that right?"

"Not quite. A good shot but wide of the mark. What you do is close the top left shutter, then the bottom left, then the middle left. Follow that with the top right, then the bottom right and finally, lock all the shutters by closing the middle right. It may sound complicated but really it is quite simple."

It was my turn to laugh.

"So Giovanni Arnolfini has provided a solid house built of brick with windows glazed at the top and shuttered below. He has brought his bride a rich cassone. Then look at the floorboards, good solid planking, nicely laid with all the nails well and truly hammered in. I should know because I've painted them all and put the grain in the timber. But that's enough about the floorboards. Let us raise our eyes higher. What can you tell me about the chandelier?"

"Ah, Master, I thought the chandelier would be next on the agenda. I presume you want me to try and explain to you why there is a single candle burning in the chandelier."

"If you would be so kind, that would interest me enormously."

"I'll try, Master. Give me a moment to think."

246

Chapter 32

June, 1995

"If I may say so, Master, the chandelier is absolutely brilliant. I find my eyes continually drawn back to it. I do congratulate you on your painting of it."

"Thank you."

A slight bow of the head and the merest twinkle in those blue eyes convey unmistakably to me that Jan van Eyck is pleased with the compliment.

"Tell me, please, Master, before I attempt to answer your question about the single candle, a little about this magnificent chandelier. I presume that it is expensive."

"Yes, very costly. Brass is not an easy metal to manufacture. There are chandeliers in some of our grander churches. To find such a chandelier as this six-branched specimen in a private home is rare. It denotes wealth. By the way we call it a *kroon*, which simply means crown. It is also sometimes called a *lichtkroon* or *kroonluchter*, a lightcrown or crown lighter."

"Why is that?"

"Oh, simply because when a person or couple stand beneath the chandelier, they are crowned by the light."

"I see, Master. Thank you for the explanation. Now let me attempt to understand the single candle. I think the candle represents the presence of God in the room. Just as we light candles and place them on the altar to show that God is with us during the divine service, so I should imagine this candle tells us that God is visibly present here."

"I agree."

"Then I would think that it signifies a legal contract. She has made her vows and her candle is extinguished. At least I think I can see the remains of a candle in the chandelier on her side. He is making his vows and his candle still burns brightly."

Jan seems pleased with my answer.

"Good. Very good. Quite perceptive in fact. But you have only nibbled at the biscuit, as we say. There is so much more to digest and understand. Explore it! Think! Don't be satisfied with just the two answers. My picture is complex and multi-layered. Try again."

All of this is said in the friendliest of tones but with an intensity that is almost frightening. I think hard for a moment.

"It's a wedding candle, lit in honour of their marriage. Like candles lit in church for any sacrament."

"Yes, and?"

"Um..it represents the fleetingness of human life perhaps?"

I sound more tentative than I really am. After all I have read Panofsky and many other commentators on this painting. I am particularly *au fait* with the National Gallery Catalogues, especially Lorne Campbell's sumptuous *The 15th Century Netherlandish Schools* which contains his detailed and expert analysis of the Arnolfini portrait.

"Correct, but you still have not fully explored its significance. Let me explain. See if you can follow. The candle represents many aspects of life. Like life itself, it is multi-faceted. Like life itself, it illumines briefly our short lives."

"Yes."

"Well, first and foremost, as you correctly said, the candle is the spirit of God, what you may call God's all-seeing eye. Everything in the room is observed by Him. The picture after all is about sight above everything else. We look at the picture and everyone in the picture looks back at us. Giovanni and Giovanna are looking at us, as we can see in the mirror. So is the dog. We in our turn as witnesses look back at them. But God, with His universal gaze which embraces everything, can see every facet of the room. I have hinted at the panoramic breadth of vision with the reflection of the apple, the mirror which sees everything, the light on the chandelier, and the way the light hits the individual rondels around the mirror in different ways."

Layer after layer of meaning in the picture seems to be unfolding before my very eyes.

Van Eyck continues his exposition.

"So the candle signifies the presence of God, the presence of the Christ-Priest. It is also the Marriage Candle as you rightly said. It shows the single choice which the couple have made. So it is the candle which is carried in the wedding procession, the very same candle which is placed in the nuptial chamber, there to burn until the marriage has been consummated. You probably know that a lit candle denotes an untouched bed or a marriage as yet consummated."

I nod my head gravely. So much fresh knowledge is pouring into my brain that I have forgotten how much I already know.

"Then again as you hinted it is the *chandelle éteinte*, a candle used in oath-taking or the signing of legal contracts. It remains alight until the vows have been made or the contract signed and sealed. When the candle has been extinguished or burnt itself out, the legal character of the act is deemed binding."

Jan van Eyck pauses to let his words sink in. He goes to a small table at one side of his studio, pours two glasses of wine from a decanter and returns back to his seat. He proffers one glass to me. Gravely we salute each other, glass held up to the level of the nose before we take a sip. The wine is delicious. Both the bouquet and the taste are unfamiliar to me yet instantly attractive. Jan gives me a warm smile of encouragement before continuing.

"Then again a candle is a simple timepiece which expresses the fleeting nature of human life, the transient affairs of this world."

I nod.

"At Candlemas it is a symbol of the light of faith personified. And in Holy Week at Matins and Lauds twelve lit candles are gradually removed one by one from the Sanctuary until all are gone, signifying the Apostles' desertion of Christ. This act is called Tenebrae. The church remains in darkness until the glorious Resurrection on Easter Sunday when all the candles can be relit."

Jan pauses for breath. I think it is impolitic to say anything. All I can do is marvel at the complexity of the symbolism.

"I suppose I should mention the obvious, that here in Flanders candles are very expensive items which we use sparingly. Did you know for example that tallow costs a very great deal in Bruges? The price of tallow (which is far less desirable for candles than wax because of its sooty smoke and unpleasant smell) is roughly four times the price of meat. So that a single candle represents in effect the price of four good meals. It is, therefore, an obvious luxury to have one burning in a room, especially in broad daylight when it is not needed. Of course the Arnolfinis could have lit all the candles in the chandelier, all six, but that would have been sheer ostentation and wastefulness. No, a single candle lit to welcome the visitors shows some degree of wealth as well as decent bourgeois thriftiness! Moreover, it reinforces all the other objects in the room which stand for luxury and wealth."

"Indeed."

"Here I might mention something that is of rather a delicate nature. Please tell me at once if you find it offensive. A single candle can be taken, indeed it has been taken by some, the less prudish that is, to stand for sexual passion. I hasten to add that I had no such thought when I painted it."

It was the nearest that I had seen Jan come to being embarrassed. I laughed politely to indicate my indifference to the subject.

"I think it is time to leave the subject. A single candle has been lit to welcome the visitors and to stand for all the things we have mentioned. The more you think about it, the more complex an object and symbol it becomes."

"I see," I murmur.

"Ah, but that's where you are wrong," said Jan with the hint of a smile, "you do not see. Look again at the chandelier. What do you notice about the light?"

I stare hard at the chandelier. It seems to me that I have never really looked at it before. The brass glitters in the sunlight streaming through the window. I stare at its polished luminosity in wonder.

Sometimes the truth is so obvious that you cannot remark it even when it is staring you in the face. But suddenly the penny drops, I have seen it!

"Of course, master! His side of the chandelier is brightly lit, hers is in relative darkness."

"Good. You are very observant. What does that tell you?"

"That she has made her vows and so her candle is extinguished. And because he is still making his vows, his side of the chandelier is brightly lit."

"Precisely," murmurs Jan. "And tell me, please, why are there fleur de lis and strawberry motifs on the chandelier?"

I stare hard at the chandelier, realising that although I have often looked at it in a perfunctory manner, I have never accorded it the detailed examination it deserves. Yes, there are the fleur de lis, four of them, with an abundance of strawberry leaves beneath them and the six sconces. I think hard.

"I'm not familiar with fleur de lis, Master. I associate them with the French monarchy."

"You are quite right. It was, I believe, Clovis who first adopted the fleur de lis. As you will doubtless remember, Clovis was a Merovingian King of the Franks about a thousand years ago. He defeated the Burgundians and the West Goths and fixed his court in Paris where he chose the emblem of the fleur de lis as the symbol of his purification by baptism when he embraced Christianity. The lily symbolises purity. So the fleur de lis symbolise Giovanni's purity and Giovanna's chastity."

"Of course. And the strawberry leaves?"

"They pronounce fecundity."

"I understand," I say and I do. Milton had prayed to his Heavenly Muse, the Holy Spirit that

What in me is dark illumine.

I feel that what has hitherto been dark has been for me illumined. But of course there is still much light to be thrown on dark corners, much unravelling to be done.

There is a long silence as I explore the whorls and curlicues of the chandelier. When I look at the candle once more, I swear that it starts to flicker!

It is Jan who at length breaks the silence. He has been fiddling with the purse at his waist from which eventually he extracts two gold coins. He hands them to me to examine.

Both are gold and in pristine condition. I guess that they are freshly minted. The first shows on the obverse a knight in full armour charging recklessly and on the reverse a shield with fleur de lis and lions in the quarters. The second coin has the same crest on one side and an ornate cross with two lions and two fleur de lis in the quarters on the other. Both coins are very handsome and surprisingly heavy,

"They're beautiful," I say, "What are they?"

"They are the new unified coinage. Our Duke, Philip the Good, has issued new coinage to commemorate the unification of Burgundy and Flanders. A marriage, you might say, like the Arnolfinis!"

We both laugh.

"It is very beautiful, as you say. The first coin which you examined is a rijder, minted last year in Ghent. It has the arms of Burgundy on one side and on the other the ornate cross with two lions and two lis in the quarters and **MONETA NOVA COMITIS FLAND**. inscribed around the edge. In other words, 'New Money of the Count of Flanders' who is also known as the Duke of Burgundy. So you see that fleur de lis and lions are the recurring heraldic motifs of Flanders. Now look at the chandelier again."

I do so. I look hard and can plainly see the fleur de lis. Of lions I can find no trace.

"I'm very sorry, master, but I'm not sure that I can see any lions."

Very patiently, very politely, very carefully, Jan van Eyck takes a maul stick which is leaning against the wall and points with it to the base of the chandelier in the picture. There, staring me in the face, plain as a pikestaff, is a handsome lion with a ring through its nose, looking down on the signature, the mirror, the joined hands, her slippers and the dog. How can I possibly have failed to see it, I who have looked at this picture so many hundreds of times? I marvel at my blindness and wonder at my

252

obtuseness.

Van Eyck explains to me that not only does the fleur de lis denote purity and the lion discreetly emphasises strength and fortitude, but their presence in the picture, riding high over everything else, is also a polite tribute to the Duke. The presence of the fleur de lis and the lion proclaims the provenance of the picture, that it emanates from Flanders, that it is unashamedly Flemish and proud of it.

"So much for the chandelier. What do you observe about the glass beads on the left of the mirror?"

"The beads – I assume they are a rosary – are exquisitely painted if I may say so."

Jan inclines his head to hide a shy smile, pleased with the compliment.

"The more I look at them, the more radiant they become," I add.

For want of something to do, I count them. There are thirteen on the left, sixteen on the right of the nail from which they hang, twenty-nine in all. Surely those numbers cannot be significant. But in the light, how they gleam and glisten!

I recount my observations to Jan and explain my problems with the beads.

Jan assures me that the two numbers are entirely arbitrary, absolutely without significance. They are, as I have suggested, a Paternoster, twenty-nine semi-transparent amber beads, strung on a green cord with green silk tassels at each end. But they are more than just a rosary. They are a wedding present from Giovanni to Giovanna, indicative of the purity and immaculate nature of the bride and the sanctity of the wedding ceremony. They could also be interpreted as a hint to the woman that, like the beads, she should remain quiet and devout!

He continues.

"There's something else about the beads which I should like you to observe. There are two sources of light in that room – the natural light which pours in from the two windows, the window which you can see on the left which lights up the back wall including the mirror and the beads. The second window which is visible in the mirror illuminates his and her faces. That's one source of light. But there's another source of light, the light which comes from the candle and shows that God is present in the room. Now look again very carefully at the beads. You will see a small dot of light on the left of every glass bead, light reflected from the window. But on the right you will observe that there is a very strong source of light, so strong that it casts a shadow. That light comes from the candle, that is light which emanates directly from God."

"I see," I breathe, marvelling at the artist's skill. "I do see it and I think I understand."

Van Eyck looks pleased.

"Next I think we should look at the mirror and any problems that it may pose."

"Ah yes, the mirror," I agree.

But at that moment the great bell of St Donatian's begins to toll the hour. Without being conscious of so doing, I count the hours. One, two, three, four. 4 o'clock. How time flies when one's mind is enthralled. As silence returns to the room, Pieter knocks and comes into the room.

"Dinner, Master," he announces.

So without more ado we go downstairs to eat and drink.

Chapter 33

June, 1995

<u>An Experience</u>
(continued)

We have finished dinner. I am sitting on a cushion upholstered in velvet and damask, staring admiringly at a magnificent tapestry from Arras (so my host tells me) depicting Actaeon and his hounds out hunting at the moment when they encounter Diana bathing. The border of Spring flowers, the startled look on the face of Diana as she tries to hide her naked body from Actaeon's brazen stare and the wild leaping hounds, so soon to devour their master as he turns into a stag, I find very exciting.

The table is set with fine napery. The food has been delicious. I seem to remember that we started with brawn of boar, then a potage of herbs, spices and wine, followed by some sort of roasted bird, possibly guinea fowl, which we broke with our hands; a dowcet of baked meat followed and a leche Lombard which was so delectable that I begged Jan for the recipe. He straightaway summoned his Steward who dictated to Jan the ingredients – pork, eggs, pepper, cloves, currants, dates, sugar all powdered together, boiled in a bladder, cut into strips and served with a rich hot sauce.

What else? Oh yes, there was freshly baked bread, very soft and black inside with a hard crust. For dessert we had oranges, carraways, white apples and, as promised, delectable Mahaleb cherries. This time I had no problem with the stones for a little china spittoon had been provided by my plate! Talking of plates, the food was served on gold. I drank at least three goblets of vintage wine. The goblets were gold also.

I find it difficult when I look back to remember all the details of that room. My abiding memory is of unostentatious but unmistakable signs of wealth all around me, of first class food and wine, of discreet service and gracious hospitality. But above all, I was impressed by my host's conversation. Now what was it that we have been talking about?

You know how it is when you wake up after an especially vivid dream and you clutch despairingly at the memory which slides out of your grasp like the elusive soap in the bath? Well, I cannot now recall much of our conversation. I do remember that we talked of our childhoods. Jan reminisced about his at Maaseyk, of the happy times he had enjoyed with his brothers, especially Lambert. He recounted an incident when he and Lambert had gone fishing one day in the Maas. They had been quite young lads, not much more than four and five. Jan had caught nothing all day while Lambert had landed several handsome trout. Jan had become petulant, even angry. Lambert had said something derogatory about Jan's fishing ability, Jan had lost his temper and swung his fishing rod wildly at Lambert's head. In doing so, he had lost his balance and toppled headfirst into the Maas.

"Now the Maas," as Jan recalled, "was a big river, fast flowing, not to be trifled with and I could not swim. Lambert wasted no time, he was always more sensible and more level-headed than I was. He ran along the bank downstream to where a tree overhung the river, climbed along its lowest branch and as I floated past, grabbed me and brought me considerably waterlogged and the worse for wear out onto the bank where he dried me off. But it was a very close run thing. I very nearly drowned and if I had, you would not have had to endure the exposition of my painting."

"That would have been a terrible loss to the world of art," I ventured.

Jan said nothing but I thought he looked pleased.

He asked me about England and I told him about Devon, its glorious undulating landscape, superb coastlines, pretty towns and villages, rivers, churches and incomparable cathedral.

Then I waxed lyrical about London, about how huge it was, its elegant buildings, noble river, gracious parks and mass of people. Jan listened intently and then astonished me by saying that he too had been to England.

"Yes, I was on a mission for the Duke who sent me to Portugal. We got blown off course and landed on the coast of England, I forget where, and had to spend some weeks waiting for a favourable wind. I took the opportunity of riding up to London. I must confess I was not impressed by the city – so vast, such a muddle of indifferent housing, such a smelly, dangerous and evil place. I had my purse taken straightaway. But there were two buildings I liked. One was the cathedral which stood on a hill with an immense spire, the tallest I think in the whole world. Very, very impressive. You know it of course?"

"Of course. You are referring to St. Paul's."

How could I possibly tell him that old St Paul's had burnt down in the Great Fire of London? I decided silence was the best policy.

"And the other?"

"The other was the parish church of a village across the only bridge, on the south side of the city. I forget its name but I liked its square white tower. I did a sketch of it."

"I think you are talking about St Mary Overie in Southwark."

"Possibly."

He asked me about my childhood. I remember that I told him about one incident, of how I was running across the fields towards the sea and had seen a deer. That was etched so distinctly on my retina that I can even recall the dappled effect of the deer's coat, the two short horns that it sported on its head, its great milky eyes as they gazed blankly at me, the delicate feet and the graceful poise. Jan had liked that. His painter's eye had caught my attention to detail and my observant nature.

I tried to ask him about his brother Hubert but he seemed reluctant to say much. In his turn he cross-examined me about my parents, especially my father. I confessed to him that my father and Giovanni Arnolfini had similar features, might have been mistaken for each other, that I had even thought for a moment as I entered that room this afternoon that Arnolfini was my long lost father.

"It's silly of me. I know it is impossible but there it is. I lost

257

my father and when I walked into that room, I thought for one moment that I had found him."

Jan said nothing but he looked at me and his eyes smiled warmly with sympathy and understanding.

What else did we talk about? I can't remember. That elusive soap has slipped through my fingers. That we conversed, that we had animated conversation on a variety of topics, that it was all fascinating I have no doubt. By mutual agreement we had steered clear of 'that picture', as we had both started calling it. What else we said remains a fog – impenetrable. Such a shame! All I can remember now is the trivial. I feel a bitter sense of loss, like a disciple who was present at the Last Supper and cannot now remember a word that Jesus said.

At the end of our post-prandial conversation, Jan van Eyck leant across the table and picked up his red chaperon which he put back on his head. Suddenly, after those three or four goblets of wine, I felt the strong call of nature. How to convey this to my host? I stirred uncomfortably in my chair. I had reckoned without the exquisite perception and gracious courtesy of the painter.

"You would like to visit the garderobe?" enquired van Eyck.

This was no time for semantic niceties. If the garderobe was what I thought it was, I wanted it. Badly.

"Please," I murmured.

He led me along a passage and showed me a door at the end. I opened it and went in. Shock! Not the surprise of finding a hole in the ground, a very big one too, that was tolerable (after all, I had been in China) but my clothes, how on earth did I get them open enough for me to perform?

It is difficult to describe what I was wearing. I have subsequently been to the V & A to study mediaeval dress so I am *au fait* with the terminology. I now know the technical terms but I can assure you that the actual clothes felt very strange at the time. Let me try to describe what I found I was wearing. I had on a clean linen shirt, somewhat coarser than our modern shirts, liberally endowed with tapes but with no buttons of course. I found myself wearing breeches and a sort of short coat under the outer coat called a petycote. The petycote was scarlet, made of stamell or lynse wolse which is a kind of fine worsted, rather rough to my skin. My breeches were of the pull-up variety, tied with tapes about my waist. Below that I wore what is called a stomacher vampys above my hose. Under everything was a loin cloth, cunningly knotted.

Once when I was in Jaipur I watched a Sikh wind a turban around his head until the twenty-two yards of material became one neat turban. I found myself longing for that Sikh's expertise. It was all those damn tapes and strange knots with which my fumbling fingers were incapable of coping. Anyway, to cut a long story short, I managed eventually after much struggle to undo the requisite strings and 'evacuate my body' as I have since learned is the correct 15th century vernacular, squatting over that enormous hole and wondering what my mother would say if she could see me there.

With great difficulty I did everything up after I had performed. I rejoined Jan at the end of the passage where he had been waiting patiently and we retraced our steps to the studio. Without a word we sat down again and stared at the double portrait.

For some time there is silence, not an awkward silence but the comfortable silence of satisfied bodies and sharp minds encountering the familiar and the strange.

At length Jan speaks.

"I think we agreed that we were going to discuss the mirror."

"Yes, Master."

"Very well. Tell me, please, what you see."

"I see a mirror, Master, which is in my opinion the most spectacular piece of bravado painting in the whole picture. It has an almost hypnotic effect and holds us with its glittering eye. It reminds me of the Cyclops. I think Polyphemus must have had an eye like this."

"How do you know it is a mirror? After all, you cannot see the surface of the mirror. That is something which is impossible to paint."

I hadn't thought of that. I consider the problem for a

259

moment and stare hard at the mirror without finding the answer. Jan decides to help me.

"Look carefully at the ten little pictures around the mirror. How can you tell that they are all covered with glass?"

Again I look hard at the rondels. The penny drops. Of course!

"Because, master, in each of the rondels I can see a reflection of the light coming from the window. So it must be the reflection of the real light that tells me there is glass on each rondel. Only glass reflects the light like that."

I pause triumphantly, rather pleased with myself. I am right too and Jan is generous in his praise.

"Well done, you are most intelligent and perceptive. What you have said is absolutely correct. You cannot paint the surface of a mirror; all you can represent is the reflection on that surface. So the curious fact is that if we can see a reflection in the mirror, we can immediately 'see' the surface of the mirror. No reflection, no surface, it's as simple as that."

"Yes, now you explain it so clearly, I understand."

"Good, now what can you see in the mirror?"

"I can see the room with the backs of Arnolfini and his bride and between them you and me standing in the doorway."

"Yes. And?"

"And I can also see on the right the bed which is the foot of the bed when I come to think of it. Above is the chandelier with the single candle. On the left, below the second window stands the cassone with the three oranges on it and what appears to be a fourth one on the window-sill."

"Good. Except that we agreed that it was an apple."

"Beyond the chest I can just make out a chair and the second window. That is about all that I can see. Oh, and beyond us, the two witnesses, I can see a sort of hall and an open door behind my head."

"Yes, you are very observant. Now tell me, can you see more or less in the mirror than in the reality of the picture?"

"I don't understand."

"Does the picture or the mirror reveal more physical space?"

"Well, now you mention it, I can see more of the room in the mirror than I can in the rest of the picture. Why is that, Master?"

Van Eyck explains gently.

"That is because the reality of the picture is an illusion and the illusion of the mirror is the reality. The mirror is God's all-seeing eye, what someone has called a 'luminous polished eye' and what you imaginatively identified with a Cyclops. Painters and mirror-makers have always worked hand in hand. Perhaps you do not realise that here in Bruges we have a Guild of St Luke to which all artists and mirror-makers belong."

"No, I didn't. Are you a member, Master?"

"Of course. I said all artists are members."

I have been gently admonished. With courtesy and precision the painter continues his exegesis.

"Look again at the reflection. Everything you can see in the mirror is accurate with one exception. All facets of that room exist in reality, the reality of the mirror. With one exception."

"What is the exception, Master?"

"If you look at the foot of the painting you can see the dog. If you now look in the mirror, you will fail to see the dog."

I look and of course he is right. In the painting, there is the dog, but in the reflection which purports to show the room accurately no dog. I am puzzled and admit so to van Eyck who is quick to explain the discrepancy.

"In the mirror a wedding is taking place. Before two witnesses the couple are exchanging vows in the presence of God, symbolised by the candle. So that is the actual wedding which you witnessed a short while ago."

"Indeed."

"But I started to paint this picture more than six months ago. Thus in the painting the wedding is taking place and has taken place, time is both the present and the past. I never painted the dog until the last moment. I did it at the earnest request of Giovanna and I put him in between the couple but long after I had painted the mirror. I did not want to add him into the mirror. So in that respect the mirror is telling an untruth."

Jan smiles at me, relieved to have got that confession off his chest.

"Of course," he adds, " I am very pleased that I did listen to Giovanna and put the dog into my painting, though, Heaven knows, it was beastly hard to paint. I realised that we needed a dog to suggest fidelity and carnal love and benignity and wisdom and melancholy. Yes, all of those characteristics."

"I think the dog is one of the more delightful features of the painting."

"I thank you."

"Tell me, Master, were there any other parts of the painting which you added at the end?"

"Yes, I added Arnolfini's pattens in the bottom left hand corner."

"Why was that, please?"

"I felt that without something there, the picture was unbalanced. Giovanna's green dress with its immense dagging sweeps down to the right hand corner. It needs counterbalancing. Besides, the discarded muddy pattens indicate quite clearly that Arnolfini, the man of business, has come in from the busy city outside."

"I see."

"Then, since you ask, I also added the oranges on the cassone to complement the colour of the bed; to balance the dog at the bottom I added the chandelier at the top. And shall I tell you something else about the mirror? I changed my mind. Originally I was intending it to be octagonal. Indeed I painted it thus in the under-drawing but had second thoughts when I realised that I wanted to put in ten rondels which dictated its final decagonal shape.

Now look at Arnolfini again. Do you see he is standing slightly oblique to us, the witnesses, as is his dog? Have you ever seen in a church the marble effigy of a crusader knight lying in full armour on his tomb with a little dog at his feet?"

"Yes, Master, I have. Often."

"Well, there you are then. Like the effigy of the crusader knight on a tomb with his dog at his feet, Arnolfini stands obliquely to us with his dog at his feet. He is the epitome of the introspective, contemplative, saturnine, gloomy humour, in other

262

words, Melancholy. He is therefore cold and dry. It will be Giovanna's pleasant duty to warm him."

I am enjoying van Eyck's jokes. My smile tells him that he has an appreciative listener.

"So you see the dog is both a personal emblem of Arnolfini, a sort of heraldic device, as well as being a token of the couple's marital fidelity. He is performing a dual function."

"Yes, now you explain it, it is crystal clear. And I notice that he alone is looking straight at us, the witnesses. So I suppose we come into the picture, Master, by encountering his stare."

"Go on," says van Eyck.

"Then Giovanna is looking at her brand new husband who seems to be staring into space, into a corner of the room, perhaps at something which we cannot see. Could it be that Crucifix which I noticed on the wall?"

"Yes, well done, you are right. At the solemn moment when they exchange their vows, Arnolfini is thinking about the redemption of his soul thanks to God's supreme sacrifice. He is looking, as you quite rightly surmise, at the little Crucifix which hangs on the wall at the back of the room and which I chose not to put in the mirror's reflection. Now tell me, who else are looking directly at the married couple?"

I look hard at the painting but fail to find the answer. I shake my head apologetically.

"The mirror unlocks the secrets of that room, it is the mirror that tells the truth. There are two people in the mirror who are looking directly at the married couple. They are of course you and I! We have eye contact also."

"Of course, how unobservant of me."

Van Eyck gives me an encouraging pat on the knee and offers me a glass of wine which I refuse. He pours himself a goblet of wine and takes a sip before his next question.

"Tell me, my friend, what colour are the clothes that you are wearing in the painting? And what colour are my clothes?"

"That's an easy one, Master, mine are blue and yours are red. Why do you ask?"

"Because all the colours in the painting have been carefully chosen to create harmony and to signify different moods,

263

emotions and ideas. For example the red which is so predominant on the bed and the prie-dieu stands for earthly and divine passion. The green of Giovanna's dress is of course fertility and the blue, less prominent but no less significant, represents virginity."

"Yes, and our clothes?"

"You and I, the witnesses, are wearing blue and red as you rightly observe. Now tell me, please, what are the two colours which form a band between the mirror's reflection and the rondels round the mirror?"

"I've never noticed them before. They seem to be blue blocks, interspersed with red bands all round the mirror. Why, I do not know."

"These two colours bear witness to the wedding in the mirror by bonding and binding the mirror and us together."

"I see."

"Incidentally, you might be interested in what I am about to tell you. I was painting the blue blocks one day and had a loaded brush preparatory to filling in one of the blocks on the right when Pieter walked past me in this studio and jogged my arm. I spilled some paint onto the wooden surface. You can see it quite clearly."

I take a look and there it is!

"Why did you leave it in, Master? You could surely have painted it out."

"Oh yes, nothing would have been easier. I left it in because I am a vain man. I strive for perfection and I like to think that some of my paintings get quite close to being reasonably accurate representations of what I am trying to depict. In other words, God has given me the skill, which I share with St Luke, of being able to paint divinely, that is to say to paint what God wants me to represent and to do it with skill, taste, intuition, knowledge, imagination, technique and historical foresight. By leaving that clumsy splodge of paint on the wooden surface of the mirror, I feel that I am showing that I am an ordinary human being who can make mistakes just like everyone else even though I am blessed with some slight ability to paint."

"You are more than just an ordinary painter, Master."

"Maybe. It doesn't matter. But let's get back to our

discussion about the painting. You have seen much and observed well. But tell me where in the picture is there one person above all others who looks down on us miserable and unworthy mortals, the latchet of whose shoes we are unworthy to touch?"

"You mean Christ of course?"

"Yes. Consider the ten rondels, as you call them, surrounding the mirror. What we see in the room, reflected in the mirror, is secular or earthly passion; what is painted in the ten little miniatures is the divine Passion of Our Lord. Please tell me what you see."

"I think I know what each little picture represents but I would be grateful if you would take me through them. Where are we going to start?"

"At the bottom of course, the nadir of Christ's life on earth. He is in the Garden of Gethsemane after the Last Supper. Peter and the two sons of Zebedee are asleep. Christ is agonising over what will happen to Him tomorrow. He prays, 'O my father, if it be possible, let this cup pass from me: nevertheless, not as I will, but as thou wilt." Now tell me, what do you see at the very bottom of this rondel?"

I get up and go up close to the painting, staring hard at the foot of the tiny rondel.

"I'm not sure, Master," I say, returning to my seat. "There appears to be some writing there, maybe Greek or Hebrew. It is so small that I cannot make it out."

"If I tell you that it may be Greek, can you read it?"

I shake my head. Greek School Certificate is a long way behind me.

"Perhaps that is because I did not intend you or anyone else to read it. If it is Greek writing – and I am not saying that it is – then it certainly seems to start with a capital Pi. There are anything from eight to eleven characters, depending on how you read it and how good your eyesight is. So what Greek words beginning with Pi do we have of that length? Let me suggest with diffidence three possibilities:-

Παφητικός
Περιγραπτός
Περίβολοι

265

Παφητικός means Sufferer, a name appropriate to Christ in the Garden. Περιγραπτός means fenced in or enclosed which is what the Garden of Gethsemane is; and finally, οἱ Περίβολοι means the walls around a town or an encirclement, just as Jerusalem is a walled city and Jesus is surrounded by enemies seeking to destroy Him. Now you can take one of these meanings or two or all of them and of course you can, if you so choose, reject them out of hand, in which case those scratches at the foot of the rondel are merely a fence at the bottom of the Garden of Gethsemane into which the secular world will intrude when Judas and the soldiers arrive."

"I like the complexity of your Greek words, Master, and I think I will accept all three interpretations and reject the fence theory. Somehow, I cannot see a Garden like Gethsemane having a fence at the bottom. To me it is too suburban."

Van Eyck smiles and seems pleased with my response. He gives me a quick tour of the rondels proceeding in a clockwise direction.

"Here we have the betrayal by Judas of Christ in the Garden and His arrest. Peter cuts off the ear of the High Priest's servant. So we have Betrayal and Loyalty."

"Yes."

"In the third rondel we see Christ before Pilate, the Deposition and so-called Trial. Judge and Prisoner. In the next Christ is scourged at the column. The Flagellation. The Beaters and the Beaten. Then on the Via Dolorosa, Christ carries His Cross. The Victim and His Executioners. At the top we see the Crucifixion. The Cross and the Mourners."

Diffidently I mention my theory of the *Volto Santo* meaning so much to the citizens of Lucca. Is there any justification in linking that relic to this rondel?

Van Eyck nods his head.

"Possibly. Let's just say that the Crucifixion has a special significance for these Lucchese people getting married but that the Crucifixion also has a universal message which is far more important, the Redemption of our sins through the sacrifice of Our Lord on the Cross – that is the real message, that is what dominates the picture, that is why Christ is at the top of the mirror. Christ's sacrifice for us is permanent, everything else is transitory."

"And what do the last four pictures show?"

"The first on the right shows the Deposition, the Dead and the Living. In the next one we see the Entombment, again the Dead and the Living. In the next Christ is in Hell. The Permanent and the Transitory. Finally, the Resurrection – the Living and the Dead. Like a clock, the ten rondels show us the time, the time of Christ's Passion. And like a clock, each rondel has its own precise little reflection of the true daylight streaming in from the window behind Arnolfini's back You will note that every gleam of light is different. For Christ, time never stands still. Christ is infinitely majestic, mysterious and variable.

And in all the rondels, as in the picture proper, there is stillness and there is movement. Christ is still on the Cross, motionless while praying, stationary at the column. All around Him there is movement, the bustle of Roman soldiers flogging Him, mourners wrapping Him in His shroud, a crowd coming to arrest Him. Only in the top and bottom roundel is there complete stillness. At the bottom the motionless Christ in prayer while the disciples sleep; at the top Christ fixed on the Cross, His mother and John standing still at the foot of the Cross. Then, if you look at the reflection in the mirror, you can see Giovanni and his bride also standing motionless, almost a parody of the Holy Family by the Cross."

"Except that they are not wearing haloes," I say, rather pleased with my wit.

Van Eyck chooses not to acknowledge my remark. Perhaps he finds it offensively flippant. I get the impression that although he likes a good joke, he will not tolerate levity on serious subjects.

Suddenly, he closes the session with a terse announcement.

"But I think we have studied the picture long enough for the moment. Our senses are becoming dulled. Let us have some fresh air and take a little walk. Shall we go?"

Chapter 34

June, 1995

<u>An Experience</u>
(continued)

"I think it is time that we considered the central axis."

The words are spoken gently by van Eyck but with quiet authority. We have been for our walk, enjoyed the sunshine and watched the hustle and the bustle of the market-place. A boatman has taken us for a quiet row along the canals. We haven't talked much but van Eyck has proved an admirable guide with a wonderfully sharp eye for the finer points of the city's architecture. We have eaten another delicious meal – meat, bread, fruit, cheese – all washed down with a tankard of dark-brown bitter beer, very strong, very bitter, very good. Once again we are back in van Eyck's eyrie, his studio at the top of the house, comfortably ensconced in our chairs in front of the painting, comfortably ensconced on its easel.

Looking back on the whole extraordinary episode, I remember now with astonishment that at the time I had no feeling of disorientation, of amazement at my predicament, of worry at how I was going to return to the 20th century. Those things simply did not matter to me. I felt utterly at home in van Eyck's studio. The only pressing subject on my mind at that moment was the central axis of the Arnolfini Wedding Portrait.

My host on my left is staring intently at the double portrait as though seeing it for the first time. From his piercing gaze one would have hardly guessed that he had created the picture.

Jan van Eyck continues his Socratic dialectic.

"We have Arnolfini on our left, his bride on the right. As you will have undoubtedly noticed, everything of significance runs down the middle of the picture. Starting at the top and proceeding down to the foot of the picture, tell me, please, what you can see and what you think each object may represent."

I look at the picture, trying to see it as if for the first time. I think I can feel new vibrations, but I am not sure what they convey. My first words are tentative and banal.

"Well, Master, at the very top we have a wooden ceiling made up of beams and I think I can see in the mirror at least one cross beam."

"Very good. What is the function of the ceiling, please?"

"I don't quite understand."

"What purpose does the ceiling have in the picture? Does it for example establish the upper limits of the room?"

"Yes, it does."

"Very well. Does it suspend the chandelier?"

"Yes."

"Right, so the perimeters of this room are defined by the ceiling at the top, by the window on the left, on the right by the bed and at the foot by the pattens and the dog. Now continue your exploration, if you would not mind, below the ceiling."

"Below the ceiling, hanging from it, I can see the chandelier with its single lighted candle, the wedding candle."

Van Eyck nods briefly.

"Amongst many other things. As we have seen, the single candle is capable of so many different interpretations. We have discussed half a dozen theories as to why there is only one lit candle when there is provision for six. One possibility which you may like to consider is that the candle represents the as yet unconsummated marriage in the as yet untouched bed. You can see quite clearly that the prie-dieu is slightly ruffled; we know that both the participants have discarded their shoes, but the bed is in pristine condition like Giovanna herself."

"I see, Master. You have explained to me how the chandelier carries the fleur de lis and the lion, redolent of Burgundy. Below that there is your autograph. A tremendous calligraphic flourish and then your signature, **Johannes de eyck fuit hic** with the date underneath. I find that hard to read."

"The date is written in Flemish script – *1434*. This year in fact. What do you make of the Latin? Translate, please."

"Johannes de eyck fuit hic, Jan van Eyck was here, or in other words you were here. I take it that you are signing the picture and acknowledging your presence, perhaps in the doorway, which we can see in the reflection in the mirror."

"Good. Very good, in fact. But you have solved only half the puzzle. My flamboyant signature, as you term it, is written in legal calligraphy decorated with cadels and you might say it is an appropriate piece of graffito for such a wall. I painted it with a long narrow brush which had a slight tendency to divide. It proclaims both my authorship of the painting and my presence as a witness to the wedding. I was here. The picture represents a moment in time when God and witnesses were present at a betrothal. That moment no longer exists, except that anyone looking at this painting in the future will also become a witness to the wedding. By reading my signature you have become a witness too. I have performed my duty by witnessing the betrothal and so have you. It will be for others to do the same in the future."

"I see," I breathe. I think I understand what he has just been saying. Van Eyck has dealt with the past and the present. But the picture has been painted before the wedding ceremony has taken place. Somehow I have to comprehend the future while looking at the past.

"Now please continue your downward journey."

"Beneath your signature hangs the mirror and the beads. We talked at length before our meal about the mirror. It broadens our perspective and is the all-seeing eye of God with the scenes of His Passion around the central image."

"Good. The mirror, which was incidentally made for Giovanna Cenami by a leading mirror-maker here in Bruges called Michiel Langhe Jans, is exceptionally large, probably so that it can accommodate the ten little rondels. Normally, such a mirror would have been what we call a *negenoog* or nine-eyes. At any rate, our mirror has the function of representing the Virgin Herself, or Giovanna if you prefer who is a virgin, *speculum sine macula*, or spotless. One final tiny point about the mirror. Have a look at the back of Arnolfini, reflected in the mirror. What do you notice about his hat?"

I take a good look.

"It seems bigger in the mirror than it is in reality, Master."

"Very good. You are most observant. I will leave you to work out the subtle distinction, but I can assure you that it is very subtle indeed. Now what about the beads?"

"Maybe they remind one of a rosary and therefore of prayer. But really are they merely there to suggest purity?"

"Yes, they are an engagement present from Giovanni to Giovanna, indicative of her immaculate nature and perhaps a slight hint that she should remain quiet and devout, like the beads!"

I smile.

"What is on the immediate right of the mirror?"

"Hanging from the bed is what appears to be a brush. Would it be a clothes brush?"

"Exactly. What we call a *kleerbezem*. The brush is placed there as a symbol of domesticity and a strong hint to Giovanna that her primary function, apart from loving her husband and bearing him children, is to manage the home. With the help of lots of servants, I hasten to add."

We both have a good laugh.

"Now what can you see just above the brush?"

"Well, Master, it looks like a carved figure of a saint with a winged lion."

"No, you are right about the saint but wrong about the lion. She is St Margaret of Antioch, very popular amongst women."

"Why, Master?"

"Because she is the patron saint of mothers. My wife who is named after her and Giovanna who is surely going to be a mother soon will both have good reason to pray for safe deliverance of their children to St Margaret."

"What did she do, Master?"

"Legend has it that the devil appeared to her as a dragon when she was being held in a dungeon for refusing to marry since she had dedicated herself to following Christ. When the dragon threatened her, Margaret made the sign of the cross on her breast. The dragon swallowed her whereupon the cross grew bigger and bigger until it split the dragon in two allowing Margaret to escape unharmed."

"That is a charming story. Tell me, Master, I don't wish to appear rude but do you actually believe in such fairy stories?"

"Of course I do! There is no point in having faith unless one exercises it. The story is so fabulous, so improbable that it must be true! No one could possibly have invented such a farrago of lies, it must be true!"

"Say no more, Master, you have completely convinced me."

In my mind I am picturing a delightful painting in The National Gallery by the Spanish painter Zurbaran of St Margaret of Antioch dressed as a shepherdess leading her pet dragon on a lead. It is a picture that I am particularly fond of but I cannot possibly mention it to van Eyck. Zurbaran will not be born for another two hundred and fifty years and the picture will not be painted for three hundred years!

As for my theory that it represents St Mark and the winged lion of Venice, I am ashamed at my obtuseness and keep very quiet about that. I notice that van Eyck is getting excited.

"Now you will observe that I have placed the carved figure very close to the head of Giovanna. That is no accident. Someone as observant as you is meant to be able to connect St Margaret with Giovanna and her wedding day. What is the date of her espousal?"

"Well, it is today, isn't it? Or am I being stupid? I am afraid I do not know what the date is."

"The date today is July 20th and today is the patronal festival of the blessed St Margaret of Antioch."

"So you could say, Master, that you have dated the picture for those that have eyes to see by placing the year under your signature on the back wall and the day and month on the top finial of the bed."

"Exactly!"

I can still hear that cry of triumph, echoing down the years.

The painter now invites me to move down the picture from the figure of St Margaret, past the brush and onto the white fur of Giovanna's dress. Can I see anything on her right sleeve?

I get up and go right up to the painting to get a better look.

There it is! Something which I have never noticed before. Nestling in the fur of her right sleeve there is a bee. I go back to my seat.

"I think I can see a bee on her sleeve. Why is it there, Master?"

"The bee is an attribute of Cupid and the Golden Age. There is an ancient Greek pastoral poet called Theocritus who tells the story of Cupid stealing honey from the hollow of a tree trunk and being stung on the finger. The moral is that pleasure can be transient and even inflict us with sadness and pain."

"Oh dear, how does that apply to Giovanna?"

"That little bee which is almost invisible in her fur is just a gentle reminder to her and to us all that happiness is transient and ephemeral, that there may be a sting in the marriage."

"I don't think many people are going to spot the bee, Master."

"You are probably right. In my experience people are extremely unobservant when they are looking at paintings. Unobservant and impatient. But now let's move down further still to their hands. What can you see?"

"I can see the left hand of Giovanni supporting the right hand of his bride."

"Yes, this is called dextrarum junctio, a well-known attribute of submission. The point is that the taking of a woman's right hand in the man's left has a legal significance. It represents a morganatic marriage, when a man of high status marries a woman of inferior rank. Giovanna may come from a wealthier family but Arnolfini considers himself higher up the social scale. That is what counts.

Now once Arnolfini has made his marriage vows, which he is in the act of doing, he will lower his right hand to enfold Giovanna's right hand in his two hands, as you saw him do this afternoon. This action will symbolise the power of the husband over his wife. She looks submissively at him; he does not look at her. There is no eye contact there. The law of marriage in Lucca promulgates that whereas a widow can claim half of her deceased husband's property, the husband on the other hand can claim no less than two third's of his deceased wife's. Everything is loaded in favour of Arnolfini."

"Perhaps that is why he is looking so pensive," I suggest, "contemplating all that wealth he is going to inherit. The new brick house, the clothes, the bed, the prie-dieu, the carpet, chandelier, cassone, mirror, even a pet dog. It all adds up to quite a tidy sum, eh, Master?"

"Perhaps," says van Eyck in a non-committal manner, "perhaps."

He gets up and leaves the room for a couple of minutes. When he returns, he sits down and says nothing for a space. I have been getting ready to answer questions on the carpet and the dog, so it comes as a surprise when he suddenly springs his next question on me.

"What can you see immediately above the couple's hands?"

I peer at the picture. The woodwose. I must have looked at this picture hundred of times; I have lectured all over England on it; I have read innumerable articles and books. Yet the object in question in one of the most prominent and significant places in the painting has remained unexplored and unobserved by me. True, I have read somewhere that it represents the wild man of the woods and is a symbol for carnal desire. I am sure that I said something like that in my lecture at Beaminster. But I prefer to seek the truth from the Master himself.

Beaminster? The name arouses in me acute feelings of guilt. Here I am in Bruges, hundreds of miles from West Dorset, enjoying myself, while all those nice elderly dear old things will be running round in circles, trying to sort the situation out. What is happening at this precise moment in the Arts Centre at Beaminster? Then I remember. This is 1434. I do not have to give my lecture at Beaminster for another five hundred and sixty-one years. Plenty of time to sort the woodwose out.

But it is all very confusing. I get up and approach very close to the easel. I stare long and hard at the object. So far as I can see (and, remember, it is tiny) there is a little carved figure or rather two of them, back to back. I can see the hairy back of the one facing the wall. The other one, looking out front, has a very ugly face with pointed ears and a sort of cap. It rests menacingly on top of Giovanna's hand with Giovanni's thumb touching its paws. I return to my seat bemused.

"I must confess, Master, that I am hazy. Perhaps you would be kind enough to explain its significance." I have a horrid feeling that once again what I have been saying in my lecture is what my mother would call a load of old toffee.

"What you can see is a woodwose, though some people call it a woodhouse. He is the wild man of the woods and king of the fawns. He is a monster with a grimacing human face, lion's ears and hoofs, not hands. He is dressed in the hairy skin of a lion which he has killed with his bare hands. This lionskin covers everything but his hands and feet. He has fought with and killed wyverns, dragons and knights. He always wins because he is immensely brave. The battle is invariably over some lady whom he covets. He will fight any gentleman, wild animal or heraldic beast for the favour of a lady. He will even assail the Castle of Love. His appetite for the fairer sex is insatiable. In short, when you next find yourself alone in a forest, do your best to avoid him."

We both laugh. Then I remember that the woodwose has killed a lion.

"What about the lion, Master?"

"Ah well, the lion, you see, symbolises loyalty and strength and fortitude, all attributes which the woodwose has made his own by killing the lion."

"I understand strength and fortitude but what exactly do you mean by loyalty, Master?"

"Well loyalty is really a synonym for amorous intentions. If you look carefully at the front of Giovanna's green robe, about half way down, can you see another little lion?"

"I can, Master."

"You probably know that the lion is a common symbol of the Resurrection. The story goes according to the bestiaries (and I have one in my library) that a lioness gave birth to still-born cubs who lay dead for three days until their father brought them to life by breathing in their faces. So I have placed a lion beside Giovanna's womb to signify that although she is not yet great with child, she will become so and bring forth a firstborn, the fruit of the marriage. The lion is wishing her strength and

275

immortality, or at least a long and happy married life.

Giovanna is in very good company. Many famous men and women have taken the lion as their personal emblem – St Mark of course and St Jerome who always had one in his library. And there are others. Then there are those strong men famed for their virility and ability to wrestle with lions, I mean Samson, David and Hercules."

"When you explain it, it all becomes clear."

"I am glad. Do you have any other problems with the lion?"

"Yes, Master. What about the lion at the foot of the chandelier? The one you said was part of the Burgundian coat of arms. Does he have any further significance?"

"Yes, of course. I'm glad you asked. Everything in this picture is capable of two interpretations, remember. The lion is breathing life into the couple below him, just like the lion in the bestiary. And he is also Leo who is associated in the Zodiac with July. So he is both animating the couple and telling us that this wedding took place in the month of July, July 20th to be precise, St Margaret's Day, as we can see from the statuette on top of the bed."

I manage to restrain myself from confessing that I thought it was St Mark with his winged lion. How wrong I have been all along.

Suddenly van Eyck jumps up.

"Talking of St Margaret, come and meet my wife," he says as he walks out of the room. He is already on the stairs when an afterthought strikes him.

"You must meet my son too."

Chapter 35

20th July, 1434

An Experience
(continued)

We are back again after a break of what I would judge to be an hour (remember, I have no watch) or an hour and a half. I have met Margaretha and the van Eyck's son, Philip. He is an enchanting, chubby, gurgling baby, not yet three months old. It is clear that his parents dote on him. He was very much the centre of attention whilst we stood around. Indeed Jan could not take his eyes off him and played with him constantly. Margaretha was equally solicitous.

While the fond parents cooed over Philip, I could observe Margaretha. Strange woman, certainly no beauty, but obviously highly intelligent. I can see her now as I write this 'Experience' – sharp, pinched features, bright eyes, a tight little mouth, somewhat small in stature with a high pitched, rather nasal voice. But all in all, I thought she was nice and she made me feel welcome and at home.

Talking of home and looking back on this extraordinary 'experience', to me the greatest surprise has been that I was not more worried than I was about getting back to the twentieth century and Beaminster. I can assure you that I felt very relaxed and untroubled throughout my stay in Bruges where I have been for a number of hours, as far as I can judge.

So we stayed downstairs some time, played with Philip, talked with Margaretha and partook of some refreshment. Then it was back to work in the studio. Now where have we got to? Ah yes, we have been considering the central axis and have reached the lion half way down Giovanna's dress. We settle down in our chairs once more and look at the painting. After a few moments van Eyck prompts me.

"What about her slippers?"

"Well, I can see them there plain enough at the foot of the back wall, Master, sitting prettily beneath the prie-dieu. I think they are hers, they look too small to fit his feet. Silk, I presume. Why she is not wearing them I have not the faintest idea."

"Well, there is one very simple explanation and two complex ones. The simple answer is that she left them there when she unrobed to have her pre-nuptial bath here earlier in the day."

"She had a bath here, in this very room?"

"She did indeed, assisted by my wife."

"Was she dirty?"

"No, of course not, but it is a tradition in my country that a bride-to-be always takes a pre-nuptial bath on the day of her wedding."

Van Eyck gives me one of his warm little smiles.

"Now for the complex reasons. Let me try to explain."

He gets up and fetches a book from a little bookcase. I can see that it is hand-written and richly illuminated. He searches through it for a few minutes, then makes a soft clucking noise when he finds the right page.

"This book is the Pentateuch. I read from the Second Book of Moses, commonly called Exodus. Chapter 3, verse 5."

He begins to read aloud.

"'Draw not nigh hither: Put off thy shoes from off thy feet, for the place whereon thou standest is holy ground.' You will remember that this is what an Angel said to Moses in the midst of a burning bush which was not consumed by the fire. So it was a miracle, just as the sacrament of marriage is a miracle. That is why the couple have removed their shoes. The floor has been sprinkled from an aspergillum by my servant Pieter with holy water consecrated by the priest. So while Giovanna comes all clean and fresh from her world indoors, Giovanni arrives shod with pattens filthy from the bustling, dirty streets of busy Bruges."

"I see."

278

"But there is a second reason why they are barefoot. You may well think that Arnolfini who has discarded his pattens is barefoot. He isn't. Actually he is wearing little dark purple bootees, made of silk. As for her, I don't think I am giving away any secrets when I tell you that under that immense gown she is barefoot. The reason that I know that for a fact is that my wife who helped to dress her told me so. Therefore, Arnolfini with his little silk bootees is as near as matters barefoot and Giovanna certainly is. Why? Well, not to beat about the bush, what is taking place is a marriage and in normal circumstances such as these what is required of the couple, indeed wished upon them by one and all, is fertility. He must be fertile and she must respond to the fertility. Now it is widely believed at this time that when a woman's feet touch the ground or floor that action will help to ensure her fertility. And even men can be helped by removing their shoes."

I must have registered incredulity on my face for van Eyck quickly assures me that there is some evidence that what he has just said is true. I feel it is prudent to let the subject drop and create a diversion.

"Master, what about the carpet? Is that significant?"

"Of course! Nothing in this picture is left to chance. The carpet which is oriental, not Turkish, as I think you said, is probably from Kurdistan or Khorasan. It is part of Giovanna's dowry and her father bought it in Paris. Now it is an unusual carpet in that it has no fringe. It is embellished with a pattern of lilies and other flowers, all associated with the Blessed Virgin Mary and her properties of fertility, purity, beauty, fragrance and innocence."

"Are you saying then, Master, that Giovanna is the Blessed Virgin Mary?"

For the first time in our interview van Eyck looks annoyed at my stupidity and answers brusquely.

"Good heavens, no! Of course not! Giovanna is Giovanna Cenami from Lucca. She is a virgin, as I have made abundantly clear from the blue undergarment which she is wearing. But I have given her a pose which we Flemish artists like to think is suggestive of the Virgin. As you probably know, the Marian cult

279

was begun by Bernard of Clairvaux three hundred years ago. When I was living in Tournai in 1427, I met Robert Campin and Rogier van der Weyden, both great painters like me. Of course we discussed ideas and influenced each other. But the one thing which we had in common was a new naturalistic approach and an obsession with painting the Madonna. So you could say that Giovanna is posing like the Madonna of Humility. But I am merely alluding to her meekness and saintliness, I am in no sense being blasphemous."

"May I raise a delicate matter? Would you say a word, Master, about her appearance? To put it bluntly, there are some who might say she looks as if she were pregnant."

Van Eyck looks shocked.

"Of course she is not great with child. How can you possibly think that?"

"Not me, Master, I do assure you," I splutter.

"Very well. Then all I will say on the subject is that her pose which exaggerates the child-bearing part of her body is at the moment extremely fashionable, especially in Paris whence she comes. In painting her the way I have I am both following the fashion and hinting at her impending confinement."

"I see. To change the subject, what about the rings on her fingers which don't seem to fit, what about those?"

"Ah, they are unfortunate. Her husband purchased them from a leading goldsmith here in Bruges, one Jean Peutin, an excellent craftsman and a very good fellow. I know him well. He has often done commissions for me. Unfortunately for Arnolfini though, there is a wedding tradition in Italy that husbands buy two rings for their brides, one to represent the husband, the other the wife, and that they do not let the bride wear the rings until the actual moment of marriage when rings are exchanged. So poor old Arnolfini has bought two rings which do not fit his bride's fingers, whilst the single ring which she has ordered from Jan de Leeuw, Master Goldsmith of Bruges, fits the middle finger of his right hand perfectly, as you can see."

"Are you saying then, Master, that, despite appearance, Giovanna is a lot more practical than her husband?"

"Well, that's one theory, one possibility. I prefer to reserve my ammunition. Others can fire off their ideas about my pictures, often very plausible, very soundly argued, most convincing. Just as you have been, my dear friend. But in the long run, my pictures have an inscrutable and enigmatic quality which like the riddle of the Sphinx is not meant to be solved."

"So Thebes must remain inviolate?"

"Precisely. Too much knowledge about a picture can destroy its integrity. The citadel must repel the barbarians, the painting retain some mystery."

"Tell me, Master, if you would be so kind, how will a lady like Giovanna, once she is married, spend her days while her husband is busy making all that money? I imagine she will have plenty of occupations."

"Oh yes, plenty. Let me see. If she is anything like my wife, she will frequently call on and receive ladies of her acquaintance whom she deems her friends. They will spend their time conversing while exercising their fingers with needles. Giovanna will almost certainly be expert in lace-making, embroidering, caulwork, the spinning of silk, sewing and dress-making. She will read Holy Scripture continually, or the histories of her own or foreign countries. She will write poetry in Latin and translate from it. She can probably play the lute and the cittern; she can do pricksong and dance gracefully. She will be practised in surgery, the distillation of waters and other artificial practices pertaining to the ornature and commendation of her body. She will be a skilful cook, cunning in supplying the wants of the kitchen with a number of delicate dishes of her own devising. She is particularly adept at Portuguese and of course Italian cooking. She can dress another lady's hair. She can speak four languages fluently, though her Flemish is execrable. She will learn how to run a household and she is by no means as meek as she looks."

We both laugh.

There is silence for a few moments while we reassess Giovanna's beauty. Then suddenly van Eyck swivels in his chair and looks hard at me.

"Come on, sir, the axis, you've almost completed it. What have we at the bottom of the picture?"

"The dog."

281

"Yes, the dog, the long-haired Belgian Griffon to be precise. He's a wedding present from him to her. Dogs represent fidelity. This particular dog, who I think goes by the absurd name of Hendrik, is the faithful companion of Giovanna. But he is also the guardian, the watchdog who sees us coming into the room and who challenges our right to be there. We have dogs in our country for four reasons – they are used for shepherding, retrieving, hunting or as pets. Hendrik is of course a pet but I have chosen to represent him in this painting as a guard-dog and as I have explained already he poses in front of Arnolfini as Melancholy. Actually he's a jolly little fellow though I don't mind admitting that I had the devil of a job painting him. He simply would not stand still. He was always barking and wagging his tail and jumping up at me. I don't like animals in my paintings, they are too unpredictable. and eye-catching. But there he is. I think I have caught his expression rather well, don't you?"

"You have, Master, brilliantly. You can see every hair on his body. And that glorious wet nose! He seems to be looking directly at us, the two witnesses in the mirror. To enter the castle, so to speak, we must first solve the riddle of the painting and pass the sphinx-like animal at its gates. Am I right?"

Van Eyck laughs again.

"I like the analogy but I must admit that I had not thought of it like that. So how is the foot of the picture defined?"

"By Hendrik standing foursquare on the floor, anchoring the picture."

"Yes, but what about the shoes?"

"What about them, Master?"

"The shoes define the bottom left-hand corner. They are the work tools of Arnolfini and point outwards to the business world of Bruges. They are hard, dirty, unfashionable, probably uncomfortable, but must be worn to enable him to do his business.

And on the other side of the painting at the bottom, I have painted the sinuous, sumptuous, feminine curves and folds of Giovanna's gown Do you see?"

"Yes, Master, I see it all when you explain it."

"Good. Now let's move to the cassone by the window with its fruit. What do you make of them?"

"Well, Master, I see one apple on the window sill. I presume you are alluding to the fruit of the Tree of Knowledge which Adam was forbidden to eat and which he did eat when tempted by Eve."

"Yes, and what happened then?"

"They were both expelled from the garden of Eden."

"Exactly. They committed the original sin for which Christ had to come down on earth and sacrifice Himself for our redemption. Without the Apple we would not have had the Cross. Man's Fall produces the Redeemer."

"So the apple on the sill represents Arnolfini's fallibility?"

"That's putting it rather crudely but you are on the right lines. What about the golden oranges on the cassone?"

"Well, golden oranges or Adam's apples as I think they are sometimes called suggest to me the Judgment of Paris. Am I getting warm?"

"Very good. I applaud your intuition. You will recall that Paris voted with a golden apple not for land and riches as promised by June, not for military victories as offered by Minerva, but for the love of any woman he chose as given by Venus."

"So these golden fruit on the cassone suggest that Arnolfini has found his Helen of Troy?"

"Of course. Golden apples are also the attributes of the Three Graces, the handmaidens of Venus. I think it was Seneca who described them as smiling maidens who stood for the threefold aspect of generosity: the giving, receiving and returning of gifts. That is one aspect of Giovanna. But I have also tried to show Giovanna as the epitome of the three phases of Love: Beauty arousing Desire which leads to Fulfilment. So she represents *Castitas*, *Pulchritudo* and *Amor* – Chastity, Beauty and Love. Now whether I have succeeded in my aims, posterity must judge."

"May I say, Master, that I think you have succeeded marvellously."

"It is easy for you to hand me gratuitous compliments. But

let me tell you that no artist is ever wholly satisfied with his finished work. It does not matter what the medium is – literature, architecture, sculpture or painting. The craftsman always feels inadequate, however superficially brilliant his work may be. Of course I am grateful for your enthusiasm and intelligent perception of some of the merits in my painting. You have been very kind to me and spotted some subtleties. But the real merits and mysteries of the picture lie hidden behind the somewhat superficial naturalism and symbolism prevalent therein. The body must remain partially clothed; I do not choose to remove all the veils."

"And I am enormously grateful for your courtesy, your scholarship and your patience with an ignoramus like me."

"Nonsense. It has been an amusing diversion for me from the rigours of painting all day. Do you have any other questions before we call it a day?"

"The trees outside the window with fruit on them, what are they, Master?"

"They are the tops of cherry trees, thus telling us that we are on the first floor of the house. Cherries, as you probably know, are called the Fruit of Paradise. They are given as a reward for virtuousness and symbolise Heaven. Heaven lies outside the window, not here in this room. Whether it will be attainable for this couple is entirely another matter."

"And the colours. Do the red and green have any financial significance?"

Van Eyck laughs again.

"None whatsoever. The red stands for Passion, either the divine Passion of the prie-dieu with Christ's Passion in the ten Rondels immediately above it as one prays, or for human passion in the bed. Green is fertility, blue virginity, brown business. It's quite simple really."

"It is when you explain it."

"Do you know what is the most difficult thing to paint?"

I think hard for a moment before replying. When I do, my suggestion is tentative, as I am pretty sure that it is the wrong answer.

"The human face?"

"That is difficult, I admit, but there is something harder."

"Hands?"

"Also hard, certainly. But the greatest problem is light. I always tell people who ask me about painting that the light comes first. If you cannot paint light, you cannot paint. It is as simple as that. If you want an example of what I can do with light when there is a challenge, I invite you to examine the fur on the right sleeve of Arnolfini. If you look closely, you will see that the intensity of the light on the fur varies considerably from a very dark brown just below his elbow to a very light terra cotta colour further up his arm. Then again look at the chandelier or the dog or the mirror to see how I have made the light flow in and out like the tide. I find that painting light accurately is the most rewarding aspect of all my art."

"Certainly the light in your painting is extraordinary, it is so subtle. It seems to emanate from so many sources. What is the secret, Master?"

Again that warm smile, again the twinkle in his eyes.

"That is a secret which shall remain a secret. All I will say is that specific light means specific space and specific space equals specific time."

"I think I need specific time to think about that last remark, Master."

Van Eyck smiles again, amused by my tiny witticism. I am looking hard at the painting, searching for its secrets, engrossed in its fascination and magic.

"Everything and everyone in your painting is so monumentally still; it is almost as though it is carved in stone. The mirror hangs on the wall, two men stand in the doorway watching, the couple in the room are poised in their stillness with Giovanna looking up at her husband in that timeless fashion while Arnolfini holds his right hand up and gazes into space; the little dog – Hendrik, did you say? – gazes at us, the cherries glitter on the tree, the fruit on the cassone tempt us with their still life propensities; the slippers remain where they have been kicked off on the floor; the woodwose grins at us, St Margaret stares at your signature, the candle gleams in the shining chandelier; the beads reflect the light, the brush hangs from the

285

bed waiting to be used domestically; the whole tableau is reflected in the mirror, clothes sit elegantly on the couple's bodies, the shutter is half open; the couple stand on very solid floor boards. There is a permanence and fixity about everything."

Van Eyck who is listening intently remains silent, inviting me to go on.

"And yet, and yet, there is movement implicit everywhere. In a few moments, as we have seen, Arnolfini's hand will descend onto hers, Hendrik will wag his tail, jump up and bark, the candle will flicker and be extinguished, shoes will be placed more tidily or even put on, oranges will be eaten, cherries will rustle in the wind, witnesses will return to your studio to be royally entertained and this night the bed will be occupied by two people."

"Go on. Anything else?"

"Yes, and in the rondels there is implicit movement – in the Garden, before Pilate, at the Column, on the way to Calvary, even on the Cross."

"An admirable summary, I congratulate you, most succinct and pertinent."

Van Eyck rises and places a cloth over the painting on the easel. It is clear that the lesson is over.

At this moment the tankard of bitter beer starts to make its presence known in my bladder. I stir uneasily in my seat.

"Master, may I pay another visit to your garderobe?"

"Of course, my dear sir. You know where it is. Forgive me if I do not accompany you."

With a gracious wave of his hand he turns back to a table where he busies himself with some brushes.

Thus I leave Jan van Eyck. Briskly I walk down the corridor, impelled by a certain physical urgency. The last door on the right yields the garderobe. I hurry in, beginning to adjust my dress. It is as I move towards the large hole in the ground that it happens. Perhaps I am careless; perhaps I am preoccupied with undoing the lower portions of my costume. I shall never know.

Suddenly I slip and feel myself falling down that hole. I

286

remember thinking that van Eyck will be worried about me when I fail to return and will consider it rude of me to depart without a formal leave-taking and thanks; that my mother will not understand my predicament; that Heather Hepton may even find the situation funny and let rip one of her braying laughs. And then I am falling, falling, falling.

Chapter 36

June, 1995

John Arnold M.A. Esq.,
Weybridge
Surrey

From the Chairman of West Dorset
Decorative & Fine Arts Society

Dear John,

Well, I have read your so-called "Experience" from cover to cover. I found it so extraordinary that I promptly read it through again very carefully. It was equally fascinating the second time. You ask me not to divulge its contents to anyone. I am afraid I cannot comply. I have shown it to my husband, to a psychiatrist whom I happen to know and to all of my committee.

We are unanimous in our opinion. The document is, in the minds of all of us, absolute twaddle. I repeat, twaddle, twaddle and I say again twaddle. Or let me put it another way, what you have written is a figment of your imagination, could not have happened and indeed could never have happened. I find myself groping for words because this event is so extra-perceptory that I do not possess the necessary vocabulary.

Let's go back four weeks to that moment in your lecture when you were examining the enlargement of the mirror. You were taking a last look at the couple standing in the doorway, the backview of Arnolfini and his wife and all the other ingredients of that room. We were all at that moment fascinated and we could see and hear that you were too. You left the rostrum and took a step towards the screen. You paused. You took another step. I think you paused again if I remember rightly. Then when you took a third step, you seemed to trip and immediately you fell full length on the stage. Of course we were all concerned that you had hurt yourself. Various scenarios flashed through our minds – a blackout, a faint, even a stroke or a heart-attack.

At any rate, everyone sprang splendidly into action. I dashed onto the stage, so did Francis, so did my husband. We helped you to your feet. You were clearly a bit groggy and not quite sure where you were. But you were fully conscious. I remember asking, "Is there a doctor in the house?" and immediately regretting my words because I knew full well that were at least four retired doctors in the audience, all of whose names I knew well because I had been the Membership Secretary before I became Chairman and anyway I had seen them all enter the Hall before the meeting.

You professed yourself quite all right and offered to accept questions which we then had.

The point is, John, that you were 'out' on the stage for a matter of thirty seconds, say forty-five at the most. Yet you assert that during that period you spent ages with Jan van Eyck discussing his picture. Van Eyck lived in the 15th century, we are in the 20th; you were unconscious for less than a minute; in your account you spent many hours in the company of van Eyck. These are irreconcilable contradictions. Neither I nor my committee can accept your account of what happened. Unless you are lying or have a very fertile imagination, I can find no logical explanation. That is what I meant by twaddle.

Of course this is an enormous pity because up to the point when you fell, we were enjoying your talk hugely. Then I am afraid it all went to pieces.

You ask if you might return on another occasion to give us another talk. I am sorry. My committee are unanimous that you should not be invited back again. I fully endorse their decision. Sorry, but there it is.

In the meantime, I remain,
Yours sincerely,
Heather Hepton
Chairman

P.S. The one person who really does seem to miss you is Mr Chips with whom you seem to have scored a notable victory!!

Chapter 37

May, 1995

"Is there a doctor in the house?"

John never thought that he would hear those words spoken in earnest during his life. Surely they existed only in some farce. He recalls Ralph Richardson telling a very funny story in a television programme. He was standing on the stage of Wyndham's Theatre reminiscing about his theatrical career. Richardson remembered that in the middle of a play that he was in at Wyndham's which was not going very well a member of the audience in the stalls suddenly stood up and called out, "Is there a doctor in the house?" The play had ground to a halt and a man in the dress circle had responded by saying, "Yes, I am a doctor." Whereupon the man in the stalls had replied, "Are you? I'm so glad. Isn't this a wretched play, doctor?"

But this is no time for theatrical reminiscences. John thinks he can recognise the dulcet tones of Heather Hepton appealing for medical assistance. What on earth is she doing? Vaguely he wonders who it is for. Has someone fainted perhaps? Could it be van Eyck? Jan was all right when John left him a few minutes ago.

Then it begins to dawn upon John that he is in the Beaminster Arts Centre, giving a lecture. What is he doing on his hands and knees on the platform? Why are people helping him to his feet? Then it slowly comes back to him; he remembers falling, falling, falling.

Like him you must have fallen great distances and enjoyed the experience. It is so exhilarating to plunge through the air. Like free fall parachuting without that ghastly moment when you have to leap out of the aeroplane.

Dreams of course. When you fall in your dreams, there is

no sensation of wind or of danger, merely triumph over adversity and one's environment. You feel absolutely terrific, full of joy and barely restrained excitement.

Yet here he is, being helped to his feet by Heather and another person. The fact is he feels perfectly all right, merely disorientated. But he finds he is returning to the Beaminster ambience and his interrupted lecture with alacrity. He explains to Heather that he is perfectly all right, that he merely tripped on some wire on the stage and that he would like to answer questions, that is if there are any.

"Are you sure?" Heather is breathing solicitously in his face. He can smell her perfume. Her right hand is held out in supplication towards him. "It would be perfectly easy for me to close the meeting and let you rest."

"No, no, Heather,' he protests, taking her right hand with his left and waving his right hand in the air. "I am quite all right. Please ask the audience if they would like to ask any questions." And as if to emphasise his point, he brings his right hand firmly down on Heather's right. For a moment their three hands are interlocked. The action worries John, there is something wrong, he doesn't know what. Then they part and Heather puts on her chairman's voice as she addresses the audience.

"Ladies and gentlemen, Mr Arnold tells me that he is perfectly all right. That he merely tripped on some wretched wire lying about on the stage. Can we have the lights on, please, Francis?"

Lights flicker on all around the hall. John thinks the audience appear as if they have just seen a B-movie in a pre-war cinema and are looking forward to the electric organ recital and the ice creams. They stir in their seats, aware that they will shortly be released from this cultural ordeal to face the bright sunlight of South street.

Heather continues.

"John Arnold has very sportingly agreed to answer questions on his fascinating talk. But first perhaps we should show our appreciation for his scholarship and courage."

The ripple of applause is just long enough not to be labelled perfunctory. John becomes aware that he is sitting on a chair

291

midway between the screen and the podium. Some sixth sense tells him that his flies are undone. Very slowly, very discreetly and very surreptitiously he slides his zip up towards the decency zone.

There is a pause while Heather gazes expectantly around the audience. A hand goes up in the third row. John acknowledges the presence of a tweedy lady by standing up.

"Mr Arnold, in the course of your delightful talk, you kept mentioning Flanders. Where exactly is Flanders?"

"Ah. Good question. I should have made that clear. Thank you. Well, the short answer is that in the 15th century Flanders was what today we call Belgium, Luxembourg and most of the Netherlands. But I could give you a more detailed answer in which I would mention places like Holland – that's a region in the south of the Netherlands – Brabant, Liège, Utrecht, Artois, Hainault, Guelders and Luxembourg.

In mediaeval rhetoric, you know, there is a device called *Occupatio* whereby the speaker makes brief reference to a subject under cover of passing it over. You know the sort of thing, "Ladies and gentlemen, I have no time to tell you about." And then he tells you all about it. Well, I've just used *Occupatio*. I do hope you don't mind."

There is a gentle, sympathetic laugh. John feels that he has answered that question rather well. He waits for the next ball; it is sure to be a bouncer, you always get one.

"Any more questions?" This from Heather, hovering on the side of the stage, microphone in hand.

Another hand, another voice. Male this time, blue blazer, regimental tie, moustache, retired colonel almost certainly. They are not usually as stupid as they look and can ask devilishly difficult questions.

"You have made us aware, Sir, in your talk, a talk which I may say I very much enjoyed – I never realised that one could look at one picture for over an hour and not be bored. I – er – intend that last remark as a compliment, don't you know."

Laughter in house.

"As I was saying, you have made us aware that this painting is a national treasure. I believe you said that this van Eyck

Johnnie painted the picture in 1434. Can you tell us briefly the history of the painting since then? How did we get to acquire it for the National Gallery, if you take my meaning?"

"I do indeed," says John, grateful to receive these easy long hops which he can despatch without difficulty to the boundary, "well, as you say, van Eyck painted this picture in 1434. Presumably it was then owned by the Arnolfinis. A hundred years later Don Diego de Guevara who died in 1520 had purchased it. He gave it to Margaret of Austria who was Regent of the Netherlands in the 16th century. Her great niece, Mary of Hungary, acquired it. She went to Spain so that by 1558, when she died, it finished up in the Spanish Royal collections in Madrid. Not the Prado because that did not exist at that time. Then it found its way into the Alcazar in the eighteenth century where it is recorded as having verses from Ovid on the frame. If you are interested, I can tell you what they were."

"Yes, please."

"They are, so my notes tell me,
promittas facito, quid enim promittere laedit?
Pollicitis dives quilibet esse potest
I hope you won't feel insulted if I translate this for you. It is just possible that your Latin may be a trifle rusty."

"Yes, Sir, it has long since failed its M.O.T. test."

More laughter in the hall.

"Very well. My translation of the Ovid goes something like this. 'See that you promise. What harm is there in promises? In promises anyone can be rich.' And that comes from Book One of Ovid's *Ars Amatoria* which was an immensely popular and rather naughty book by Ovid on how men should woo women of easy virtue and how women should seduce men. Despite its success it got Ovid banished to Tomi on the Black Sea!

And so after that stay in Spain, the picture found its way to Brussels, we don't know how. In that city Major-General James Hay, who fought at the battle of Vitoria in 1813 and was wounded at Waterloo, was taken to a room in Brussels where he convalesced, gazing at the Arnolfini Wedding portrait which had somehow found its way to that room. Lucky man, I say, to be wounded and to find such a masterpiece! Anyway, he bought the painting and brought it back to England where it was first exhibited in the Prince Regent's collection in Carlton House. The National Gallery purchased it from Major-General Hay in 1842 for I believe 600 guineas, quite a large sum at that date. It was numbered one hundred and eighty-six in the National Gallery catalogue and accorded six lines of description. In the latest catalogue entitled *The 15th Century Netherlandish Schools* by Lorne Campbell no less than thirty-seven pages are devoted to this single picture. Does that answer your question?"

"Indeed, Sir, most comprehensively, I am extremely grateful."

Silence from the military.

"Any more questions?" from Heather.

A shy hand at the back.

"Yes?" asks John.

"May I ask you to kindly explain,' says a timid voice from the darkness of the back rows, timidly splitting her infinitives, "what exactly you mean by tempera which you mentioned van Eyck used?"

"Are you a painter yourself?" John asks.

"Well, yes, I must admit that I do try to modestly indulge. But I'm very bad." Here a little timid laugh. John thinks of the Dormouse and longs to stuff this questioner into a teapot.

"It's another good question. Let me try to explain. Tempera is the Italian word for any form of binding which will serve to 'temper' powder colour and make it workable. But in practice we confine the word to egg tempera which is what van Eyck used as an underpainting – that is to say powder colour, raw egg and water. He prepared oils which made them far more suitable for use with egg tempera. His transparent films of oil colour served in effect as a protective surface. His paintings are still radiant today because he understood about how to mix his oils and fix them on top of his underpaintings.

By the way there is a myth that van Eyck was the inventor of oil painting. Quite untrue. But van Eyck was certainly one of the most important pioneers and early masters of painting techniques. Does that answer your question?"

"Oh, yes, thank you very much,' says the Dormouse.

"Anyone else?"

A lady in the front row (always a dangerous place, usually it's the committee members who pinch the best seats and ask difficult questions).

"It may be just my imagination but I got the clear impression from your excellent slides that there was a split in the wooden panel on which van Eyck painted his lovely picture. Am I right?"

"You are, Madam. The panel is made up of three oak boards joined together. There is a split of about ten inches in the central panel which runs down from the top through the chandelier and behind the left-hand side of the mirror. I'm afraid I don't know how old the split is but it is certainly several centuries old."

"Thank you. May I ask a second question?"

"Of course."

"Then it's this. I can't quite work out how everything fits into the room. Is there more than one scale?"

"I'm very glad you asked me that and congratulations on your perspicacity. Yes, there is indeed more than one scale. Just to mention a few obvious factors – if Giovanni and Giovanna were to turn round and walk to the back of the room, they would bump their heads on the chandelier. The mirror is impossibly big, the bed too short. Then just look at Arnolfini once more. He has a very large head, huge hands but extremely narrow shoulders. Again, the upper part of his body has been deliberately diminished by the artist.

"I see. Yes, that's quite plain. Thank you."

A cultured voice from the tip-up seats at the back.

"Mr Arnold, I found your talk very interesting and most convincing. You have taken us through all the details in the picture and shown us that there is innate symbolism everywhere. I concede that you have made a very convincing case. But what I would like to ask is, how can you really prove it? She may be pregnant, the mirror on the wall may be just a painting of a mirror on a wall, if you follow me. The single candle may be lit merely because they wanted a bit of light in the room or to show how stinking rich they were. Perhaps they have kicked their shoes off because they felt more comfortable that way. Eyck uses lots of red and green because he likes red and green. Or maybe that is what he had lots of in his studio and needed to get rid of. Do you see what I am saying? I mean, it is just possible that we are being too clever by half with this painting, that van Eyck merely wished to record a scene with two people in a room containing a number of interesting objects. And though you made it plausible at the time, I cannot accept that he is divorcing her. Nobody has their divorce commemorated in a painting. Do you take my meaning? I'm not trying to be offensive but are you, in short, being too clever?"

The audience stirs, its interest renewed.

For a moment John is nonplussed and says nothing. It is Heather who comes to his rescue.

"I think you have bowled what I believe is called in cricket parlance a googly, possibly on a sticky wicket, though I must confess that I do not know what either term means."

The audience laughs.

"John?"

John gathers himself up for a final effort to repel boarders.

"Neither do I, Heather. That's a very good question, sir. Have I been talking nonsense? Have I found more in the painting than van Eyck intended? Is it really a divorce that is going on? Well, to deal with the last question first, I must now confess something which you may find extraordinary. For reasons which I cannot divulge, during the course of this lecture I have changed my mind. I do not now believe that it is a divorce at all. The picture commemorates, in my judgment, a betrothal and I don't think I want to say more than that.

Have I been talking nonsense? Probably! All my theories have been in effect uncorroborated and entirely hypothetical. I freely admit it. Suppose, just suppose for a moment that Magritte, the surrealist, had painted this picture. What would we deduce? That nothing can be taken for granted – as you say, the mirror on the back wall could be a painting of a mirror on the back wall (as in fact it is), the chandelier could turn out to be another painting, the couple holding hands are mere cut-outs, the window on the left an illusion of a window, the dog a cat in

296

disguise. And so on. *Ad absurdam*. You're right, absolutely right, I freely admit that I have been talking nonsense, unmitigated rubbish, and that if I were to give this lecture again right now (heaven forbid!), it would be entirely different from the one that I have just given. Scepticism is the name of the game in art criticism and I am grateful to you for pointing it out. Are you happy with that answer?"

"More than happy, Mr. Arnold, I am devastated by your candour."

There was more laughter from all sides followed by an expectant hush.

Heather gave the silence three seconds before launching herself into her final peroration.

"Then it only remains, ladies and gentlemen, on your behalf, to thank John Arnold for his intriguing and I almost said astonishing lecture. Personally, I have often stood in front of this double portrait and gazed at the couple with the little dog at their feet and wondered just what was going on. But I never realised that there was so much to learn about the picture.

Someone once said, 'I don't know much about art, but I knows what I like.' What I say to that person is, 'Piffle! Balderdash! More fool you!' A knowledge of art enormously enhances one's appreciation and enjoyment of the pictures in a gallery. I thought John brought much scholarship and insight to a wonderful picture which we shall all rush off to see again in the National Gallery. Thank you, John, very much indeed."

Heather makes a futile attempt to lead the clapping while clutching a microphone. The audience gives a polite burst.

"Ladies and gentlemen, one last word."

Heather is fighting for their attention as they start to look for lost umbrellas and scarves under their seats.

"Please, ladies, thank you. I just wanted to say that tea is now being served in the back room. Just down the corridor. Thank you."

Chapter 38

May, 1995

John disconnects himself from his throat microphone and starts to collect his notes together. He can see that Brian the projectionist is unloading the carousel and putting his precious slides into his cartridge. A quick cup of tea and he can be on his way.

He still feels disorientated. Where is he at the moment, in mediaeval Bruges or 20th century Beaminster? His 'dream' has been so vivid, so sharply etched on his memory. He longs to get home and write it all down before he forgets it. Quick, grab the slides, gulp the tea down and head for home. That is the end of everything he can remember about that extraordinary 'Experience'.

A small, chubby, impossibly cheerful man bounds up the three steps onto the platform and collars him. John is reminded of a cheeky little terrier behaving incorrigibly. What is that Devon parson called who invented a breed of dog? Jack Russell, that's it. The terrier starts to address him.

"Mr Arnold, you don't know me, Simpson is my name, Bill Simpson, peripatetic schoolmaster. Found your talk fascinating, deeply stimulating, immensely privileged to have heard it."

John wonders why on earth the man is talking like Mr Jingle. Is there something in the Beaminster air that breeds such eccentrics? He makes a great show of gathering up his papers and stuffing them into his briefcase. He very much hopes that Bill Simpson will notice that he is busy and make himself scarce.

No such luck.

"Liked it, liked it very much indeed. Do a bit of art lecturing myself. Never tackled that period. Bit dodgy. Stick to the eighteenth century myself. Gainsborough and all that, don't you know? Oh, and the good old Impressionists too of course."

He lets out a short sharp bray of a laugh, just past the jackass variety, well short of the hyena. But definitely nothing like a Jack Russell, thinks John. His hands are firmly stuck in the pockets of his baggy brown suit. He appears to be massaging his thighs compulsively. Or masturbating.

John finds himself wondering as he collects his slides from Brian who has brought them up to the stage if this Simpson fellow has missed one or two vital lessons at school, those on etiquette and the proper use of the personal pronoun, for example.

"Was there something which you wanted to ask me?" he asks.

"John, dear, tea in the back room. Follow me, leave your brief case, we can pick it up later."

Sergeant-Major Heather Hepton has appeared as if by magic to rescue John. With a quick 'excuse me', he follows Heather out of the Hall, past the myriad notices of impending shows in the neighbourhood (clearly, bags of culture in the west) and an exhibition of photographs of stone walls on Dartmoor (very black, very grainy), down a short corridor into a room with tables and plates of biscuits thereon. Heather brings him a cup of tea and then goes off in search of the biscuits. John stirs his tea and sips. No sugar. What the hell! It's not worth the hassle. Then the vultures close in.

Two ladies sidle up to him, both well dressed, plenty of flesh on them, not yet gone to seed, the one silver-haired, the other blonde.

"That was very nice, we did enjoy it, most interesting, wasn't it, Hilary?" This from silver-haired.

"Yes, very nice, most interesting."

John is rescued from these banalities by Heather who heaves alongside like a 64-gun frigate about to unleash a broadside. Curiously, her first words seem to corroborate the simile.

"Everything shipshape and Bristol fashion, John?"

"Yes, thank you, Heather, everything's fine. Lovely audience, good questions."

"Yes, weren't they good? I told you we had the finest NADFAS in this neck of the woods. The best in the west. Never at rest, full of zest."

She lets out another bray.

Mr Jingle elbows his way into the party.

"Here we are again." He makes it sound like the opening chorus of pierrots on the end of the pier. "Just a few questions. If you don't mind."

"Don't mind,' says John, unconsciously lapsing into Mr Jingle's style of speech. He takes a grip on himself.

"What can I do for you?"

Heather has drifted off with silver-hair and blondie. John must fight this battle on his own. He takes another sip of the lukewarm, unsugared and disgusting tea as a defensive barrier against what he is sure to be a difficult broadside.

"Found your talk fascinating. Just puzzled by a couple of points. Mind if I ask you two questions?"

John stared at his teacup.

"Go ahead."

"Talked about colours – red for lust, green for commerce. Don't agree. Think that red is for the Passion of Christ, not just earthly lust. Green for fertility. Possible?"

"It's possible,' John says, stirring his non-existent tea uncomfortably.

"Second point. This Giovanna bird. Where on earth are her parents and relatives and servants? I don't see much trace of them. Why is she on her own in a foreign city?"

John is overcome with acute lassitude and a longing to be rid of Jingle.

"I've no idea,' he says lamely. He is suddenly aware that he is profoundly bored with Arnolfini.

"All right. Here's another point. The mirror. You say the mirror is the priest. But I've got a completely different theory. What I think about the mirror is.."

But fortunately for John he never hears what the irritating little man's theory is. At that moment Heather comes to his rescue. He is swept off to receive his cheque from Dick the Treasurer ("I do hope I've got your initials right, Mr Arnold'), to

300

collect his slides and briefcase and to be driven back to Heather's house where his car is parked.

The greeting from Mr Chips is effusive and salivary. John surreptitiously wipes with his handkerchief a large globule from his trousers. Farewells are perfunctory. All the platitudes seem to have been expended. Suddenly Heather seems tired of the whole business.

"Goodbye, John. It was super. Thank you so much. Drive carefully. Safe journey home. Farewell."

John edges his car out into the back streets of Beaminster, past the deserted cattle market and onto the A30. With his head in a whirl and half his mind still back in mediaeval Bruges, he hardly notices the glorious landscape of West Dorset. Pretty thatched cottages, Eggardon Hill, Maiden Castle, a line of huge electricity pylons marching imperiously across the green sward, everything slips past him, unobserved. He by-passes Dorchester and thinks of turning on the radio for some music. At Tolpuddle he switches on Classic FM. Schumann's violin concerto played by some Japanese prodigy with an unpronounceable name exactly matches his sombre mood.

It occurs to him that maybe, just maybe, Jan van Eyck would like this music. Smiling to himself, he drives on across Egdon Heath, far from the madding crowd.

Chapter 39

July 1434

In that room at the top of his house in Sint Gillis Nieuw Straat, Jan van Eyck is busy painting a portrait. Both the street and the house are places with which we should by now be familiar. Certainly we have been in the room before. Littering the room here are all the impedimenta, tools and bric-à-brac of a great painter.

In one corner stand three stone slabs for grinding colours. Around the room are five easels (what van Eyck calls his 'wooden tripods'), all with panels of wood thereon. On the trestle tables stands a quantity of jars packed with brushes of different lengths and quality. The larger brushes are made of bristle (what van Eyck calls in Flemish *borstelen*); the smaller ones or pinceaux are much finer and are known as *pinselen*. Amongst his many pigments are lapis lazuli, natural ultra-marine and various quality azurites, which give him all those wonderful blues he so cherishes. There is a particularly vibrant crimson lake for his reds. Once his assistants have ground these pigments, they are presented, ready for use, in scallop shells. Another table is covered with pots of charcoal, chalk, quill pens and silverpoint styli or *pinceaux d'argent*. There are two vats of oil in a corner, one of linseed, the other walnut. Five or six finished paintings are stacked neatly in one corner. In another, a polychromed statue of the Duke, evidently a commission, stands on a small dais.

But all this clutter is incidental to what is happening in the centre of the studio. Van Eyck is painting another picture. It is to be as exciting, original and sensational as the Arnolfini Wedding portrait.

Nicolas Rolin, Chancellor of Burgundy, has commissioned

this picture from the great Jan van Eyck. He wishes to present a sacred painting to the Cathedral City of Autun in Burgundy where his son is Bishop. It will hang in the Sacristy. It is to show a Nativity scene, the Virgin with the Holy Child on her lap and perhaps a flying angel hovering overhead holding a crown. Long discussions have taken place between sitter and artist. The donor must be present in the scene but not too obtrusively. The Christ Child is all-important.

"He will be the focal point," explained van Eyck to Nicolas Rolin on a previous visit. "What I propose, having given the matter much thought and rejected several ideas, is that the Virgin and Child should be in an open Loggia of your Palace. You will be kneeling on the left, worshipping the Christ Child. A flying angel with rainbow-coloured wings will hover miraculously over the Holy Family, holding a golden crown."

"Good, maestro, very good. I like the concept. It is original, it is daring, it is the work of a genius which is only what I would expect from a master-painter such as he in whose presence I am privileged to be."

The Chancellor inclines his head graciously towards van Eyck who permits himself a small smile and slight nod.

What shall I be wearing?" asks Rolin, his mind already excited by the thought of his presence in the painting.

"A fur-trimmed brown cloak lavishly embellished with gold motifs. I see you kneeling at a simple desk covered with a green cloth on which sits an illuminated Gospel. You will be staring across, not at the Christ Child, but at the Chapel where the picture is to hang."

"Excellent. And what is at the back of the room where I am praying?"

"A Romanesque loggia with three central arches."

"Is that the whole picture?"

"Oh no, through the arches, we shall look down on a little garden, full of birds and flowers, especially lilies for the Virgin. The garden will of course be enclosed, a hortus conclusus."

"Ah yes, I see, a symbol of the Virgin."

"Precisely."

"And that is all?"

"By no means. Beyond the garden there will be a small stone parapet with a castellated wall. I might put two figures there, with their backs to Christ, looking down from a great height at the view."

"What will they be looking at?"

"At a river which divides two towns and a cultivated landscape with mountains in the background.

"Real towns?"

"No, imaginary, but I shall put in architectural elements of various buildings I have studied in my travels. You know, bits of Maastricht, Liège, Utrecht, Lyon, Geneva and of course Autun. I am a well-travelled man, you know,' says van Eyck laughing.

Chancellor Rolin permits himself the smallest of smiles. He is enchanted with van Eyck's dazzling concept and excited to think that one day soon he will be permanently hanging in the Sacristy at Autun cathedral, for ever adoring the Christ Child on the Virgin's lap. If that doesn't get him into heaven, nothing else will!

Thus it is, on this late day in July, 1434, the great Chancellor of Burgundy is kneeling at a prie-dieu for his picture and holding a difficult pose. For a while, neither man says anything. The silence is neither oppressive nor embarrassing. Both men are preoccupied with their thoughts. Rolin is contemplating how much the picture is going to cost. Van Eyck is concentrating on his sitter's hands, which Rolin holds in the prayer position. They are long, slender and powerful, exuding strength and authority but also beginning to reflect their owner's age. Rolin is no longer in his youth or even middle age. In fact he is fifty-eight years old which in 1434 means that he is an old man.

Van Eyck's silverpoint pen is hard at work. A look, a scratch, another look, a scratch, a look, a scratch and then another. Van Eyck is totally absorbed in his work. Rolin sighs deeply. He is beginning to find holding the pose very tiring. But he says nothing and grits his teeth. The only sound in the room is sporadic scratching, like a very timid mouse exploring the wainscot.

***

In his Palace over on the west side of Bruges, Duke Philip is dictating a letter to his Scribe. The Duke is of course literate but prefers to leave the tedium of inscribing his words onto vellum to others. The subject of his correspondence is the financial affairs of his renowned painter, Jan van Eyck, one of the principal treasures of the Duke's court in Flanders. He has been so impressed with van Eyck's prowess and the great reflected glory that van Eyck has bestowed upon his court that he has taken the exceptional step of raising his salary from 100 *livres* to 360 *livres per annum*, a huge sum in those days.

Graciously has the Duke informed the painter of his intentions; gratefully has van Eyck replied to the benevolent Duke. But for some inexplicable reason the Duke's accountants in Lille, who control his treasury, have refused to pay the painter. Last Tuesday Jan complained (in his mildest tone) to Duke Philip who was instantly outraged at his accountants' behaviour. Here is part of his stinging letter to his recalcitrant financiers:-

He is telling them that if Jan is not paid his salary, *'le conviendra, à cette cause, laisser nostre service, en quoy prendrions très grant desplaisir, car nous le voulons entretenir pour certains grans ouvraiges, en quoy l'entendons occuper cy après et que nous trouverions point le pareil à nostre gré ni si excellent en son art et science...'*

Once the Duke has finished dictating in French his rebuke, he dismisses his Scribe and applies himself to the improvement of his mind. He is in his Library, a exquisitely panelled small room with no less than sixty books in it, a very large library for the time. Philip selects a book with care and walks up and down the long corridor outside as he reads.

Regiæ moles jam reliquent pauca juera
Aratro; stagna latius extenta
Lucrino lacu visentur undique; cœlebs
Platanusque evincet ulmos.

His translation of the Horace (his favourite Latin author, by the way) owes more to accuracy than poetic felicity:-

> *The palatial structures will soon leave only a few acres*
> *for the ploughshare; fishponds of wider extent than the*
> *Lucrine lake will be seen everywhere; and the barren*
> *Plane tree shall supplant the elms.*

He glances out of a window in the corridor, high up on the third floor of his palace. The view is extensive. Below him an army of workmen are labouring to construct another wing to his palace. The project has involved swallowing up several acres of arable land. Even as he watches, a large elm comes crashing to the ground, felled by one of his foresters. The relevance and irony of what he is reading at that moment does not escape him. He continues his perusal.

> *Tum violaria et myrtus, et omnis copia*
> *Narium spargent odorem olivetis*
> *Fertilibus priori domino.*

***

A marriage has been consummated in a scarlet bed (with that curious smudge on the counterpane). On the prie-dieu at the back of the thalamus or reception room has been placed an immense green woollen gown, trimmed with white fur. On top of it are laid a blue underdress edged with fur, a chemise and a linen veil, all neatly folded.

Over on the cassone underneath the window whose shutters have all been closed lie higgledy-piggledy a brown tabard or *heuque*, a satin damask doublet, dark purple hose and boots and on top of all, an immense black straw hat. A pair of mud-stained pattens still litter the floor where they have been carelessly discarded.

The room is in semi-darkness, the candles in the brass chandelier having long since gone out or been extinguished. Through the six shutters on both of the windows, the light from a July dawn in Bruges filters through, allowing Giovanni to gaze enraptured at his bride. They have made love four or was it five times during the night? It doesn't matter. Both are blissfully happy. A thought strikes Giovanni as he holds his beloved in his arms.

"Would you like an orange, darling?"

Giovanna giggles and gives her brand new husband an affectionate squeeze. He takes that as an affirmative and scrambles out of bed. He walks across the carpet to the cassone for two oranges and returns to the bed. The mirror on the back wall watches the stark naked figure impassively.

In bed there is much furtive mirth and murmurs of delight as oranges are peeled (by Giovanni) and luscious segments placed in the mouth (of Giovanna). Inevitably pips escape and elude capture. A furious hunt begins accompanied by much laughter. Giovanni's hands are sticky; Giovanna obligingly licks them clean.

The two oranges have been demolished, their remains thrown carelessly on the floor. Are they a mild aphrodisiac? At any rate, both occupants suddenly feel the need for further activity. It is time to draw a discreet veil over the proceedings. If this were a Hollywood film shot in the thirties, the camera would pan politely away from the bed and start examining with prolonged interest a brand new double wedding portrait of the couple which now hangs proudly on the far wall beside the door.

***

Outside on a corner of the Burg, Pieter is chatting up Anna and Joop whom he has encountered by chance on their day off. There is much gossip to be exchanged. Pieter allows them to do most of the talking whilst he wonders which one he is going to pull tonight. Anna is the more phsical, Joop the more intelligent. It's a toss-up really, not much difference. 'Maybe I'll 'ave both of 'em,' he thinks as he idly holds a rope.

"What's that 'ere bit of string you've got in yer 'ands, Pieter?" asks Joop during a lull in the conversation. The bit of string in question is a fine length of cord which goes from Pieter's left hand for about ten yards to the south-west corner of the Burg where it disappears from sight round the corner.

"Blimey, Hendrik!' yells Pieter, rushing anxiously round the corner followed by a gale of laughter from the two girls. Hendrik is indeed round the corner where he has been making friends with an accommodating bitch. When Pieter arrives, they have finished whatever they have been doing. Hendrik is hard at work licking himself with what appears to be a satisfied smile on his face; his companion is barking excitedly. Pieter gives a sharp pull on the rope.

"Come 'ere, you 'orrible 'ound, you ought to ashamed of yerself, behaving like that. Come on, heel, let's get on with our walk. You can walk, can't yer, or are you too flippin' tired?"

Hendrik does not reply as he falls in at Pieter's heels. Maybe he really is rather exhausted.

***

Over on the west side of the city a few days later the wife of a celebrated goldsmith is giving him some stick.

"Jean Peutin, I told you those rings wouldn't fit that poor lady. If you remember, you tried them on my fingers and they were far too small."

Jean Peutin grumbles into his tankard of ale. He can tell a customer where he gets off, his wife is another kettle of fish. He has to tread warily.

"Don't blame me, my dear! I warned him. I remember saying at the time, I said, 'Signor Arnolfini, they won't fit, I do know what I'm talking about. I have made a few rings in my time. Many a fine lady in this city is wearing my products. Just you go and ask them if they are satisfied. They'll tell you in very plain language, I can assure you.' But, oh no, he wouldn't listen. Bloody foreigner!"

"Jean Peutin, I won't tolerate language like that in my parlour. You take yourself off at once to your workshop and start altering those rings."

Jean Peutin is not one to argue with his wife. The huge man levers himself out of his chair and lumbers off to his little workshop in Noordzandstraat. As he settles down at his workbench, he notices with disgust but resignation that a particularly offensive little boy is making rude faces at him through the window. He considers reciprocating the gesture but decides it would only exacerbate the situation.

As Jean Peutin breaks and enlarges the two rings so that they will fit Giovanna's fingers, he thinks it has been one of those days. He cannot decide whether the wrath of Arnolfini or his own wife is worse. There is not much to choose between them. Arnolfini had stormed into his workshop yesterday and made a very big scene whereas his wife had given him all that stick just now.

He sighs and picks up one of the offensive rings and a file from his bench and bends to his work. The small boy soon tires of his sport and wanders off down the street looking for further victims.

Chapter 40

May 1995

"Hello, mother."

"John, darling, how lovely to hear your voice. I haven't heard from you for at least a week. Where have you been?"

"Sorry, mother, I've been extremely busy. I've been…"

"Yes, but all the same you could have given me a telephone call. I mean it's not as though you were that busy."

"Sorry, mother, but I was going to tell you that…"

"I know, you've told me, you've been very busy."

"Yes.'"

"So have I as a matter of fact."

"What have you been doing, mother?"

"I've been going to hospital out-patients all last week. Dr Barnes says I need heat treatment for my beastly ulcers."

"How are your ulcers, mother? I should have asked sooner."

"Not much better, thank you, dear. But the heat does give some relief, I'm glad to say. Actually, I think if the truth be told, it does my rheumatism more good than the ulcers. But I mustn't go on talking about myself. What have you been doing?"

"I've been lecturing, mother."

"Lecturing? Where?"

"In the west country. Place called Beaminster. You won't know it."

"Beaminster? Never heard of it. Did you have a good audience?"

"A lot of nice old dears, mostly ladies, half of whom went to sleep. You know how it is."

"Oh dear, I'm sure I wouldn't have if I'd been there. I bet your talk was very good and they all loved it."

"It went quite well, apart from one curious mishap."

"What happened?"

"I'd rather not talk about it if you don't mind."

"Oh, very well, if you insist and want to shut up like a clam. I'm not nosey. What was the talk about, incidentally? Did you give them your Bayeux Tapestry lecture? That always goes down well."

"No, I talked about van Eyck and the Arnolfini portrait."

"Ah, yes, of course, that's always been your favourite, hasn't it?

"Always. Ever since I was at school. I can remember quite plainly the moment when I first saw it and became fascinated by it."

"Really?"

"Yes, I was in a classroom at my prep school and had to write an essay on something and I chose that picture because it was hanging on the wall and because I thought it was interesting. I remember I wrote the most awful twaddle but still got a prize."

"That's something that you have always been good at, isn't it, dear? I mean writing essays and talking about art."

"Well, I try."

"I'm sure your lecture was very good and they all thought you were the cat's whiskers. Where are you, by the way? Are you at home?"

"No, mother, I'm in my car. On the mobile."

"On your mobile? Goodness, don't try to explain it. I don't even begin to understand modern science. Just tell me exactly where you are."

"Well, mother, I'm on the A31 at this moment being passed by a Jaguar that must be doing a cool hundred miles per hour. Idiot! Sorry, mother, not you, but that really was very dangerous driving. As I was saying, I'm on the A31. I'm – erm – in the New Forest at this very moment, stopping to feed the ponies, you know."

"I thought you weren't allowed to feed them."

"That was a joke, mother."

"Sorry, dear, I'm getting slow in my old age."

"Doesn't matter. Oh, now I know precisely where I am. I am just passing the Rufus Stone at this very moment."

"That's nice, dear. Hang on, there's a ring at the doorbell. I'm expecting Mrs Rushton round. She's bringing some gladioli for my garden. I'd better go."

"All right, mother, nice talking to you. Take care and I'll come and see you very soon."

"Goodbye, darling. I'll see you soon. Drive carefully."

"Bye, mother."

John clicks the 'off' button on his mobile and settles down to listen to Classic FM while he drives at a steady seventy. Henry Kelly is playing Puccini's Nessun dorma for Jim Jones of Colchester who is in hospital for a hernia operation. John turns the volume up. As always, the bit where the choir comes in softly after the tenor has belted out the tune makes the hairs on the back of his neck tingle. He lets José Carreras work his magic on Jim Jones's hernia as he accompanies the Puccini with his fingers on the steering wheel and drives steadily north east. But his mind is still in Bruges.

**

Three, two, one, winking turning left, John slows down as he turns off the M3 into the Fleet Service Station. Getting out of his car stiffly, for he has been driving for the past two hours, he walks past the R.A.C. man touting for customers, up to the restaurant and shops. First stop, the Gents, to empty all that West Dorset tea slopping around inside. Filling station? thinks John. More like an Emptying station.

Relieved, he saunters back to the restaurant where he picks up a tray and loads it with a plate of shepherd's pie, chips and peas, a roll and butter, a chocolate meringue and a cafetière of coffee. He pays, collects his cutlery and looks for an empty table.

As he has been driving down the M3, his mind has been in a turmoil. He cannot make up his mind whether he is in twentieth century Britain or 15th century Bruges. If anything, Bruges seems the more real. Everything about the English countryside in the late 20th century seems to him phoney. The cows stand around in impossibly staged postures, the half-timbered houses are all Mock Tudor, even the cars on the M3 all look the same, all go at the same speed, all lack any character or personality. As for that audience in Beaminster, they were completely bogus. None of them really cared one jot or tittle for van Eyck or the Wedding Portrait, despite his impassioned lecture. And Heather, what a fake! She was all false eyelashes and hogwash. Not a real emotion in the whole of her corsetted body.

No, the real place had been Bruges and that charming van Eyck where he had been, when was it? Yesterday? Today? Five hundred and sixty-one years ago? He starts to recall some of the conversation he had with Jan as he takes his food off the tray and shovels in the first forkful of shepherd's pie and peas. Gosh! He suddenly realises that he is very hungry. When did he last eat? Lunch with Heather in Beaminster? Supper with van Eyck in Bruges? But when was that? How long ago? He finds he is hopelessly muddled.

The food is curiously tasteless. What the shepherd's pie needs is some piquancy. Worcester sauce, yes, that is what is required. He looks around for a bottle, spots one on an adjacent table where a customer is sitting. He gets up to ask for the sauce and is about to approach the table when he suddenly notices something extraordinary. As he approaches, he thinks he recognises the man who is looking at him.

"Yes?"

John stares at the face of the speaker, at the hooded almond-shaped eyes, the long Roman nose, the cleft chin, the almost total lack of eyebrows, the strange ears.

The man has had to repeat his question as John remains transfixed, completely disorientated. He has left mediaeval Bruges, he is now back in the 20th century, in England. But where has he seen that face before? It can't be! And yet there is an uncanny resemblance.

"Did you want something?"

For a moment John almost loses the power of speech as he stares at the man.

"Um...Yes. Er, erm, that is, yes, I would like something. I do hope you don't mind. But do you think I might borrow your

313

Worcester sauce?"

"Of course, old man, help yourself."

"Thanks. I say, I do apologise for staring at you like that. But we haven't met somewhere, by any chance, have we? I mean, do I know you?"

For a brief moment the man at the table hoods his eyes with a curious blink. Then he raises his right hand and makes a small gesture of dissent.

"Sorry, old man, I think not. In fact, I'm quite sure. No can do."

John stumbles back to his chair, clutching his Worcester sauce, utterly confused. That blink, that gesture, those features, all belonged to Arnolfini. He remembers so clearly in that room he had just entered when he had fallen through the mirror the invitation from van Eyck to Arnolfini to make his wedding vows. Standing as John was only a few feet in front of Arnolfini, he could observe him perfectly. Just before Arnolfini had intoned his vows, he had hooded his eyes in a curiously prolonged blink before raising his long elegant fingers in that gesture of affirmation. Just like this bloke at the next table. John shakes his head in disbelief as he stares at his shepherd's pie. He unscrews the top of the bottle and pours himself some sauce. As he puts the lid back on, he makes up his mind to tackle the man once more. He simply can't go on living in this agony of indecision. He picks up the bottle and gets up to take it back to the man at the next table. But he has gone.

Somehow the pie is peculiarly tasteless after that, *pace* the Worcester sauce. John wastes little time in half finishing his meal. As he saunters out of the building, he is accosted by the R.A.C. man.

"Good afternoon, sir. Can I interest you in a very good offer which the R.A.C. are making this month?"

"Tell me more."

"Well, sir, for a very reasonable charge, we can guarantee to come and fetch you immediately if you break down anywhere, at any time, at any place."

"Anywhere?"

"Anywhere, sir."

"At any time, in any place?"

"Absolutely, sir."

"Would you fetch me from Bruges, for example?"

"Bruges? That's in Holland, isn't it, sir?"

"Belgium actually."

"Belgium, of course, sir, how stupid of me! Yes, we would certainly rescue you from Bruges if that is where you had a breakdown."

"Good. In any year?"

"I don't quite follow you, sir"

"Supposing, just supposing I had broken down in Bruges a few years ago, would you have been able to help me?"

"Of course, sir. We would have been out there like a shot."

"Even if it was a very long time ago?"

"How long ago, sir?"

"Well, let's say just for the sake of argument, five hundred and sixty-one years ago. What were my chances of being rescued by your organisation from Bruges five hundred and sixty-one years ago?"

"Ha, ha, ha, sir. I would say, without consulting my books and speaking off the top of my head, that your chances would have been fairly slender. Not to put too fine a point on it, minimal. Sorry I can't be of more help. Does that satisfy you, sir?"

"It certainly does. Thank you very much."

"Thank you, sir."

John walks back to his car. As he adjusts his safety belt, struggling slightly with the straps that have become twisted, he remembers a similar incident earlier today (was it really only today?) when he had found himself in trouble unbuckling his clothing. He smiles as he slides out onto the M3 and heads east. He puts the gear into fifth and accelerates smoothly up to seventy.

It has been a long day.

GLOSSARY

acolyte	minor church official
apocalyptic	the Revelation of St John on the island of Patmos
aspergillum	brush for sprinkling holy water
battage brush	used in the manufacture of silk
bestiary	mediaeval book of beasts
borstelen	bristle paint brush
boss	carved projection of wood at intersecting point of stone ribs in a church
braggadocio	empty boasting
Brobdingnagian	immensely large, imaginary kingdom of giants in *Gulliver's Travels*
cadel	calligraphic flourish
campanile	Italian bell tower
capriccio	an invented or fantastic landscape
cartoon	preparatory drawing
cassone	painted wooden chest, containing dowry
caulwork	embroidering
censer	one who incenses or the vessel in which incense is burnt
chandelle éteinte	extinguished candle = adjudication of legal claims
chantry	chapel endowed for the singing of masses
chaperon	a turban-like hat

317

chasuble	sleeveless vestment of celebrant at the Eucharist
chaudwyn	pudding
chrisom-cloth	christening robe or shroud
chronogram	phrase in which the Roman numeral letters give the date
citole	wire-stringed lute-like instrument
cornette	long piece of cloth
crozier	bishop's crook
dagging	elaborate embroidery
dextrarum junctio	joining of hands, act of submission
diptych	two paintings hinged together
dowcet	pudding
duomo	Italian cathedral
eschatological	to do with the Day of Judgment
finial	topmost part of a pinnacle
flacherie	disease attacking silkworms
garderobe	mediaeval toilet
geans	Mazzard or Mahaleb cherries
gesso grosso	plaster of Paris or gypsum used as a base on a canvas
gittern	type of early guitar
gonfaloniere	Italian civic official
grasserie	disease attacking silkworms
griffon	coarse-haired terrier-like breed of dog
guttine	disease attacking silkworms
heuque	tabard of silk velvet
hortus conclusus	enclosed garden, symbol of the Virgin
huvé	horned hair style
Infanta	daughter of the King of Spain or Portugal
	female of an insect which feeds on

318

	an evergreen oak
kleerbezem	clothes brush
kroon	chandelier
kroonluchter	chandelier
leche	pudding
lichtkroon	chandelier
Lucchese	citizen of Lucca
Lucullan	profusely luxurious, named after Lucullus, a Roman general of 1st century BC, famous for his lavish banquets
lunette	semi-circular space or picture
maul stick	stick used by painter to steady his hand
miniver	belly fur of squirrels
missal	prayer book
monochrome	one colour
morus alba	mulberry tree
muller	stone used for grinding pigments
napery	fine table linen
negenoog	mirror
paternoster	beads in a rosary for saying the Lord's Prayer
pattens	wooden shoes
pébrine	disease attacking silkworms
pentateuch	the first five books of the Bible
perron	double set of steps
petycote	male under-garment
pinceaux d'argent	silverpoint styli
pinselen	fine paint brush
polychroming	painting in several colours
polyptych	many paintings joined together
poursuivant	herald
prie-dieu	prayer desk

pricksong	written vocal music
pyx	vessel in which consecrated bread is kept (in *Henry V* Bardolph is hanged by the king for stealing a pyx from a French church before the battle of Agincourt)
retable	the exterior of a closed polyptych
rijder	Flemish coin
rochet	surplice-like vestment worn by bishops
Romanesque	style of architecture between the Classical and Gothic periods, 1050-1200
rondel	tiny round painting, protected by glass
Sapphic	Sappho was a poetess of Lesbos c.600 BC who invented a four-line stanza imitated by Horace, a Roman poet who died in 8 BC
shawm	type of oboe
shock	sheaf of corn
sibyl	pagan prophetess
soltelte	pudding
stomacher vampys	male under-garment
tenebrae	darkness in church
thalamus	inner room
theorbo	two-necked lute
thurible	censer
tierce	canonical hour of prayer @ 9 am
timbrel	tambourine
virge	staff of office used by a virger/verger
Volto Santo	Holy Face
woodwose/woodhouse	wild man of the woods
ypocras	pudding

Selected Bibliography

Early Netherlandish School, *Martin Davis*. National Gallery.
Splendours of Flanders, *Alain Arnould*. C.U.P.
Jan van Eyck. *L.J.Bol*. Blandford Press.
The Secret Life of Paintings. *Pamela Tudor-Craig*. Boydell.
The van Eycks and their Art. *W.H.James Weale*. Bodley Head.
Hubert & Jan van Eyck. *Leo van Puyvelde*. Hamish Hamilton.
The Revolutionary Manifesto. *Michael Levy*. The Observer.
Flemish Verve. *Richard Cork*. The Times.
Angels from the realms of glory. *Enoch Powell*. The Times.
Know the Gallery. *W.R.Dalzell*. E.P. Publishing.
Flemish Art 1300-1700. *Catalogue*. Royal Academy.
The Embarrassment of Riches. *Simon Schama*. Collins.
The Arnolfini Marriage. National Gallery.
Focus on the Arnolfini Marriage. *Paul Overy*. The Times.
City Map of Bruges. *Leonard Allen*. The Times.
Early Dutch painting. *Albert Châtelet*. Wellfleet Press.
Les Très Riches Heures. *Jean Longnon*. Thames & Hudson.
Jan van Eyck's Arnolfini Portrait. *Linda Seidel*. C.U.P.
Meals and Manners. *Frederick Furnivall*. Kegan Paul.
Van Eyck and the Founders of Early Netherlandish Painting.
Otto Pacht. John Murray.
Subjects & Symbols in Art. *Hall James*. John Murray.
Penguin Dictionary of Saints. *Donald Attwater*. Penguin.
Age of Chivalry. *Jonathan Alexander*. Royal Academy.
The Paston Letters. *Ed. John Fenn*. Everyman.
The 15th Century Netherlandish Schools. *Lorne Campbell*.
National Gallery.
Handbook of Dates. *C.R. Cheney*.
The Mystic Lamb. *Alfons Dierick*. Hofstraat 301, Gent.
The van Eycks. *Giorgio T.Faggin*. Penguin Classics.

Making Masterpieces. *Neil MacGregor*. BBC.

Jan van Eyck. *Craig Harbison*. Reaktion Books.

The Arnolfini Betrothal. *Edwin Hall*. University of California Press.

On Reflection. *Jonathan Miller*. National Gallery.

Jan van Eyck. *Symposium*. National Gallery.

The Civilization of Europe in the Renaissance. *John Hale*. HarperCollins.

The Ghent Altarpiece. *Elisabeth Dhanens*. Allen Lane.

Hubert and Jan van Eyck. *Léo van Puyvelde*. Hamish Hamilton.

The Story of Art. *E.H. Gombrich*. Phaidon.

The National Gallery Companion Guide. *Erika Langmuir*. National Gallery.

15th Century Paintings. *Rose-Marie & Rainer Hagen*. Taschen.

Giotto to Dürer. *Jill Dunkerton*. National Gallery.

Northern Renaissance Art. *James Snyder*. Harry N. Abrams.

Jan van Eyck's Amolfini Portrait. *Erwin Panofsky.* Burlington Magazine (1934)